Carnegie Learning Analytic Geometry

Student Edition
Volume 1

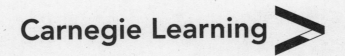

Carnegie Learning >

437 Grant St., Suite 918
Pittsburgh, PA 15219
Phone 412.690.2442
Customer Service Phone 877.401.2527
Fax 412.690.2444

www.carnegielearning.com

ISBN: 978-1-60972-240-1
Student Edition, Analytic Geometry, Volume 1

Printed in the United States of America
1-07/2013 B&B

Dear Student,

You are about to begin an exciting endeavor using mathematics! To be successful, you will need the right tools. This book is one of the most important tools you will use this year. Throughout this book there is space for note-taking, sketching, and calculating. You will be given opportunities to think and reason about various mathematical concepts and use tools such as tables, graphs, and graphing calculators.

This year you will face many new challenges both in and outside of the classroom. While some challenges may seem difficult, it is important to remember that effort matters. You must realize that it may take hard work and perseverance to succeed—and your hard work will pay off!

Connections in mathematics are important. Throughout this text, you will build new knowledge based upon your prior knowledge. It is our goal that you see mathematics as relevant because it provides a common and useful language for discussing and solving real-world problems.

I bet the folks at home would like to know what we're going to do this year!

Don't worry—you will not be working alone. Working with others is a skill that you will need throughout your life. When you begin your career, you will most likely work with all sorts of people, from shy to outgoing, from leaders to supporters, from innovators to problem solvers—and many more types of people! Throughout this book, you will have many opportunities to work with your classmates. You will be able to discuss your ideas and predictions to different problem situations; present your calculations and solutions to questions; and analyze, critique and suggest, or support your classmates' answers to problem situations.

Today's workplace demands teamwork and self-confidence. At Carnegie Learning, our goal is to provide you with opportunities to be successful in your math course. Enjoy the year and have fun Learning by Doing ™!

—The Carnegie Learning Curriculum Development Team

Acknowledgments

Carnegie Learning Authoring Team

- **Sandy Bartle**
  Senior Academic Officer
- **David Dengler**
  Sr. Director, Curriculum Development
- **Joshua Fisher**
  Math Editor
- **John Fitsioris**
  Curriculum Developer
- **Beth Karambelkar**
  Curriculum Developer
- **David "Augie" Rivera**
  Math Editor
- **Lezlee Ross**
  Curriculum Developer

Contributing Authors

- Jaclyn Snyder
- Dr. Mary Lou Metz

Vendors

- Cenveo® Publisher Services
- Mathematical Expressions
- Bookmasters, Inc.
- Hess Print Solutions
- Bradford & Bigelow
- Mind Over Media
- Lapiz
- eInstruction

Special Thanks

- Carnegie Learning Managers of School Partnerships for their content review.
- Teacher reviewers and students for their input and review of lesson content.
- Carnegie Learning Software Development Team for their contributions to research and content.
- William S. Hadley for being a mentor to the development team, his leadership, and his pedagogical pioneering in mathematics education.
- Amy Jones Lewis for her review of content.

Table of Contents

3 Properties of Triangles 209

4 Similarity Through Transformations 257

Congruence Through Transformations 333

5.1 We Like to Move It!
Translating, Rotating, and Reflecting Geometric Figures 335

5.2 Hey, Haven't I Seen You Before?
Congruent Triangles 357

5.3 It's All About the Sides
Side-Side-Side Congruence Theorem 365

5.4 Make Sure the Angle Is Included
Side-Angle-Side Congruence Theorem 373

5.5 Angle to the Left of Me, Angle to the Right of Me
Angle-Side-Angle Congruence Theorem 383

5.6 Sides Not Included
Angle-Angle-Side Congruence Theorem 389

5.7 Any Other Theorems You Forgot to Mention?
Using Congruent Triangles 401

Chapter 5 Summary 411

Using Congruence Theorems 419

6.1 Time to Get Right
Right Triangle Congruence Theorems 421

6.2 CPCTC
Corresponding Parts of Congruent Triangles are Congruent 439

6.3 Congruence Theorems in Action
Isosceles Triangle Theorems 447

6.4 Making Some Assumptions
Inverse, Contrapositive, Direct Proof, and Indirect Proof 455

Chapter 6 Summary 469

viii ■ Table of Contents

Table of Contents

Properties of Quadrilaterals   477

Table of Contents

Arcs and Sectors of Circles   721

Table of Contents

The Crew

The Crew is here to help you throughout the text. Sometimes they will remind you about things you have already learned. Sometimes they will ask you questions to help you think about different strategies. Sometimes they will share fun facts. They are members of your group—someone you can rely on!

Teacher aides will guide you along your way. They will help you make connections and remind you to think about the details.

Mathematical Representations

Introduction

During this course, you will solve problems and work with many different representations of mathematical concepts, ideas, and processes to better understand the world. Each lesson will provide you with opportunities to discuss your ideas, work within groups, and share your solutions and methods with your class. These process icons are placed throughout the text.

Discuss to Understand

- Read the problem carefully.
- What is the context of the problem? Do we understand it?
- What is the question that we are being asked? Does it make sense?
- Is this problem similar to some other problem we know?

Think for Yourself

- Do I need any additional information to answer the question?
- Is this problem similar to some other problem that I know?
- How can I represent the problem using a picture, a diagram, symbols, or some other representation?

Work with Your Partner

- How did you do the problem?
- Show me your representation.
- This is the way I thought about the problem—how did you think about it?
- What else do we need to solve the problem?
- Does our reasoning and our answer make sense to each other?
- How will we explain our solution to the class?

Share with the Class

- Here is our solution and the methods we used.
- Are we communicating our strategies clearly?
- We could only get this far with our solution. How can we finish?
- Could we have used a different strategy to solve the problem?

Academic Glossary

Key Terms of the Course

There are important terms you will encounter throughout this book. It is important that you have an understanding of these words as you get started through the mathematical concepts. Knowing what is meant by these terms and using these terms will help you think, reason, and communicate your ideas. The Graphic Organizers shown display a definition for a key term, related words, sample questions, and examples.

You will see these terms throughout each lesson.

Definition

To study or look closely for patterns.

Analyzing can involve examining or breaking a concept down into smaller parts to gain a better understanding of it.

Related Words

- examine
- evaluate
- determine
- observe
- consider
- investigate
- what do you notice?
- what do you think?
- sort and match
- identify

Ask Yourself

- Do I see any patterns?
- Have I seen something like this before?
- What happens if the shape, representation, or numbers change?
- What is the question asking me to accomplish?
- What is the context?
- What does the solution mean in terms of this problem situation?

Analyze

Example

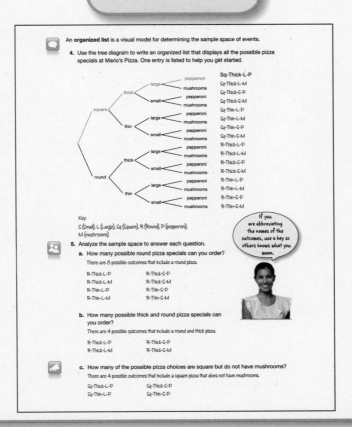

Definition

To give details or describe how to determine an answer or solution.

Explaining your reasoning helps justify conclusions.

Related Words

- show your work
- explain your calculation
- justify
- why or why not?

Ask Yourself

- How should I organize my thoughts?
- Is my explanation logical?
- Does my reasoning make sense?
- How can I justify my answer to others?
- Did I use complete sentences in my answer?

Don't forget to check your answers!

Explain Your Reasoning

Example

3. The high school pep squad is preparing a halftime performance for the next basketball game. Six students will hold banners to form a regular hexagon as shown with the school mascot in the very center. Each of the banners is exactly 4 feet long.

a. What angle does each student form with his or her banners? Explain your reasoning.

The banners each student holds form an interior angle of the hexagon.

$$\frac{180(6-2)}{6} = 120$$

Each student forms a 120° angle with his or her banners.

b. What is the distance from each student on the regular hexagon to the school mascot in the center? Show your work and explain your reasoning.

I can draw two line segments from the center of the hexagon to two adjacent vertices, bisecting two 120° angles. This creates an equilateral triangle, because the measures of all three angles are 60° (180 − 120 = 60).

So, every side of the triangle is 4 feet long. Thus, the distance from the school mascot at the center to two of the students on the hexagon is 4 feet. This will be the same for all the other vertices of the hexagon, so the distance from the school mascot to any student on the hexagon is 4 feet.

Definition

To display information in various ways.

Representing mathematics can be done using words, tables, graphs, or symbols.

Related Words

- show
- sketch
- draw
- create
- plot
- graph
- write an equation
- complete the table

Ask Yourself

- How should I organize my thoughts?
- How do I use this model to show a concept or idea?
- What does this representation tell me?
- Is my representation accurate?
- What units or labels should I include?
- Are there other ways to model this concept?

Represent

Example

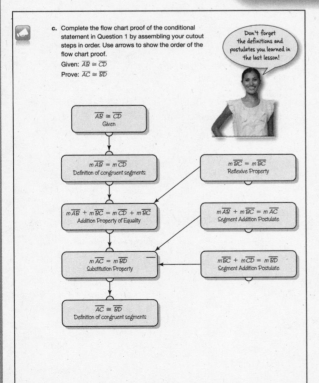

c. Complete the flow chart proof of the conditional statement in Question 1 by assembling your cutout steps in order. Use arrows to show the order of the flow chart proof.

Given: $\overline{AB} \cong \overline{CD}$

Prove: $\overline{AC} \cong \overline{BD}$

Don't forget the definitions and postulates you learned in the last lesson!

$\overline{AB} \cong \overline{CD}$
Given

$m\,\overline{AB} = m\,\overline{CD}$
Definition of congruent segments

$m\,\overline{BC} = m\,\overline{BC}$
Reflexive Property

$m\,\overline{AB} + m\,\overline{BC} = m\,\overline{CD} + m\,\overline{BC}$
Addition Property of Equality

$m\,\overline{AB} + m\,\overline{BC} = m\,\overline{AC}$
Segment Addition Postulate

$m\,\overline{AC} = m\,\overline{BD}$
Substitution Property

$m\,\overline{BC} + m\,\overline{CD} = m\,\overline{BD}$
Segment Addition Postulate

$\overline{AC} \cong \overline{BD}$
Definition of congruent segments

A **two-column proof** is a proof in which the steps are written in the left column and the corresponding reasons are written in the right column. Each step and corresponding reason are numbered.

d. Create a two-column proof of the conditional statement in Question 1. Each box of the flow chart proof in Question 1, part (c) should appear as a row in the two-column proof.

Given: $\overline{AB} \cong \overline{CD}$

Prove: $\overline{AC} \cong \overline{BD}$

Statements	Reasons
1. $\overline{AB} \cong \overline{CD}$	1. Given
2. $m\overline{AB} = m\overline{CD}$	2. Definition of congruent segments
3. $m\overline{BC} = m\overline{BC}$	3. Reflexive Property
4. $m\overline{AB} + m\overline{BC} = m\overline{CD} = m\overline{BC}$	4. Addition Property of Equality
5. $m\overline{AB} + m\overline{BC} = m\overline{AC}$	5. Segment Addition Postulate
6. $m\overline{CD} + m\overline{BC} = m\overline{BD}$	6. Segment Addition Postulate
7. $m\overline{AC} = m\overline{BD}$	7. Substitution Property
8. $\overline{AC} \cong \overline{BD}$	8. Definition of congruent segments

A **paragraph proof** is a proof in which the steps and corresponding reasons are written in complete sentences.

e. Write a paragraph proof of the conditional statement in Question 1. Each row of the two-column proof in Question 1, part (d) should appear as a sentence in the paragraph proof.

If $AB \cong CD$, then $m\overline{AB} = m\overline{CD}$ by the definition of congruent segments. Add the same line segment measure, $m\overline{BC}$, to both segments. By the Addition Property of Equality, $m\overline{AB} + m\overline{BC} = m\overline{CD} + m\overline{BC}$. By segment addition, the segments can be renamed such that $m\overline{AB} + m\overline{BC} = m\overline{AC}$ and $m\overline{BC} + m\overline{CD} = m\overline{BD}$. Then $m\overline{AC} = m\overline{BD}$ because if you add the same segment ($\overline{BC}$) to two segments of equal measure, the resulting segments remain equal in measure. Therefore, $\overline{AC} \cong \overline{BD}$.

Academic Glossary

Definition

To declare or tell in advance based on the analysis of given data.

Predicting first helps inform reasoning.

Related Words

- estimate
- approximate
- expect
- about how much?

Ask Yourself

- What do I know about this problem situation?
- What predictions can I make from this problem situation?
- Does my reasoning make sense?
- Is my solution close to my estimation?

Predict

Example

PROBLEM 1 On a Roll

1. A standard sized sheet of paper measures 8.5 inches by 11 inches. Use two standard sized sheets of paper to create two cylinders. One cylinder should have a height of 11 inches and the other cylinder should have a height of 8.5 inches.

2. Carol predicts that the cylinder with a height of 11 inches has a greater volume. Lois predicts that the cylinder with a height of 8.5 inches has a greater volume. Stu predicts that the two cylinders have the same volume.

   Predict which cylinder has the greatest volume.

   Student response may include:
   I predict both cylinders will have the same volume because the same sized paper was used to create both cylinders.

3. Determine the radius and the height of each cylinder without using a measuring tool.

   Radius of cylinder with height of 8.5 inches:
   $$C = 2\pi r$$
   $$11 = 2\pi r$$
   $$\frac{11}{2\pi} = r$$
   $$r \approx 1.75$$
   The cylinder with a height of 8.5 inches has a radius of approximately 1.75 inches.

   Radius of cylinder with height of 11 inches:
   $$C = 2\pi r$$
   $$8.5 = 2\pi r$$
   $$\frac{8.5}{2\pi} = r$$
   $$r \approx 1.35$$
   The cylinder with a height of 11 inches has a radius of approximately 1.35 inches.

4. Calculate the volume of each cylinder to prove or disprove your prediction and determine who was correct.

   Volume of the cylinder with height of 8.5 inches:
   $$V = \pi r^2 h$$
   $$= \pi (1.75)^2 (8.5)$$
   $$\approx 81.74$$

   Volume of the cylinder with height of 11 inches:
   $$V = \pi r^2 h$$
   $$= \pi (1.35)^2 (11)$$
   $$\approx 62.95$$

   Lois is correct. The cylinder with a height of 8.5 inches has a greater volume.

5. Does the radius or the height have a greater impact on the magnitude of the volume? Explain your reasoning.

   The radius has a greater impact on the volume than the height because the radius is squared, whereas the height is not squared. The height would have to have been substantially longer to create a larger volume.

Definition

To represent or give an account of in words. Describing communicates mathematical ideas to others.

Related Words

- demonstrate
- label
- display
- compare
- define
- determine
- what are the advantages?
- what are the disadvantages?
- what is similar?
- what is different?

Ask Yourself

- How should I organize my thoughts?
- Is my explanation logical?
- Did I consider the context of this situation?
- Does my reasoning make sense?
- Did I use complete sentences in my answer?
- Did I include appropriate units and labels?
- Will my classmates understand my reasoning?

Describe

Example

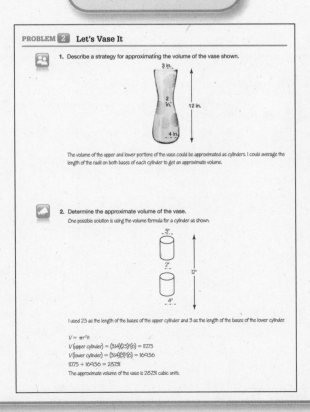

Definition

To mark a figure or diagram to indicate measurements, relationships, or characteristics.

Related words

- mark
- identify
- name

Ask yourself

- What information is given about the diagram?
- What is unknown in the diagram?
- What am I trying to determine or calculate?
- Can I classify the figure?
- What are the components that make up the diagram?
- What is the relationship between the components?
- What definitions, postulates, or theorems can I use?
- What units are appropriate?
- What symbols or marks can I use in the diagram?

Label

Example

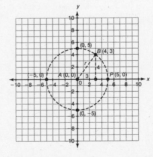

PROBLEM 1 **Identifying Points on a Circle**

In this problem, you will continue to explore the connection between the Pythagorean Theorem and circles.

Consider circle A with its center point located at the origin and point P (5, 0) on the circle as shown.

1. Use the axes to plot three additional points on circle A and label the coordinates for each point.

Three additional points on circle A on the axes are (0, 5), (−5, 0), and (0, −5).

Definition

To verify the truth of a statement through a sequence of steps and corresponding reasons.

Related words

- confirm
- convince
- demonstrate
- explain
- justify
- show
- validate
- verify

Ask yourself

- What is the given information?
- What am I trying to prove?
- What additional information follows from each step?
- Can I create an outline of the proof?
- What form of proof can I use?
- Can I work backwards?
- What definitions, postulates, or theorems can I use?

Prove

Example

b. Complete the flow chart proof of the Alternate Interior Angle Conjecture by writing the reason for each statement in the boxes provided.

$w \parallel x$
Given

$\angle 2 \cong \angle 6$
Corresponding Angle Postulate

$\angle 2 \cong \angle 3$
Vertical angles are congruent

$\angle 3 \cong \angle 6$
Transitive Property

c. Create a two-column proof of the Alternate Interior Angle Theorem.

Statements	Reasons
1. $w \parallel x$	1. Given
2. $\angle 1 \cong \angle 5$	2. Corresponding Angle Postulate
3. $\angle 1 \cong \angle 4$	3. Vertical angles are congruent
4. $\angle 4 \cong \angle 5$	4. Transitive Property

Congratulations! You can now use this theorem as a valid reason in proofs.

You have just proven the Alternate Interior Angle Conjecture. It is now known as the **Alternate Interior Angle Theorem**.

Problem Types You Will See

Worked Example

All of the proofs up to this point were *direct proofs*. A **direct proof** begins with the given information and works to the desired conclusion directly through the use of givens, definitions, properties, postulates, and theorems.

An **indirect proof**, or **proof by contradiction**, uses the contrapositive. If you prove the contrapositive true, then the original conditional statement is true. Begin by assuming the conclusion is false, and use this assumption to show one of the given statements is false, thereby creating a contradiction.

Let's look at an example of an indirect proof.

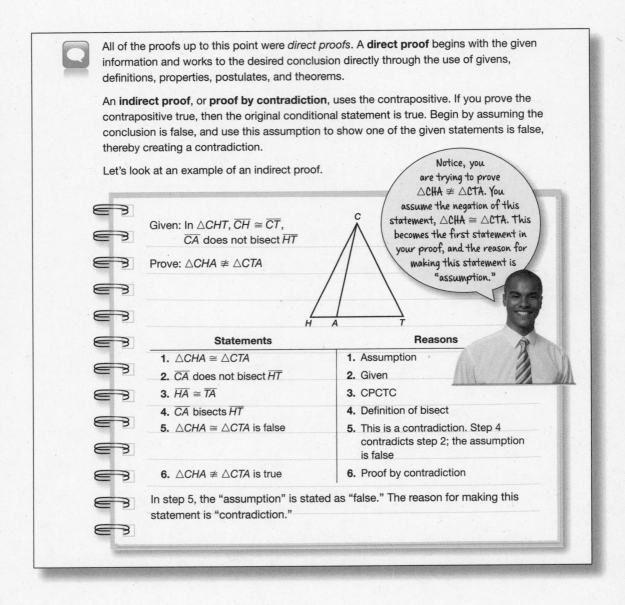

Given: In $\triangle CHT$, $\overline{CH} \cong \overline{CT}$,
$\overline{CA}$ does not bisect $\overline{HT}$

Prove: $\triangle CHA \not\cong \triangle CTA$

> Notice, you are trying to prove $\triangle CHA \not\cong \triangle CTA$. You assume the negation of this statement, $\triangle CHA \cong \triangle CTA$. This becomes the first statement in your proof, and the reason for making this statement is "assumption."

Statements	Reasons
1. $\triangle CHA \cong \triangle CTA$	1. Assumption
2. $\overline{CA}$ does not bisect $\overline{HT}$	2. Given
3. $\overline{HA} \cong \overline{TA}$	3. CPCTC
4. $\overline{CA}$ bisects $\overline{HT}$	4. Definition of bisect
5. $\triangle CHA \cong \triangle CTA$ is false	5. This is a contradiction. Step 4 contradicts step 2; the assumption is false
6. $\triangle CHA \not\cong \triangle CTA$ is true	6. Proof by contradiction

In step 5, the "assumption" is stated as "false." The reason for making this statement is "contradiction."

Thumbs Down

7. Explain why Alicia is incorrect.

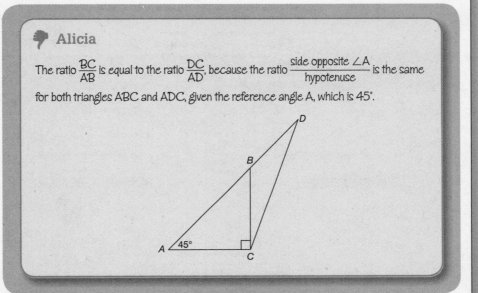

> **Alicia**
>
> The ratio $\frac{BC}{AB}$ is equal to the ratio $\frac{DC}{AD}$, because the ratio $\frac{\text{side opposite } \angle A}{\text{hypotenuse}}$ is the same for both triangles ABC and ADC, given the reference angle A, which is 45°.

Alicia is incorrect because triangles *ABC* and *ADC* are not similar triangles and they are not both right triangles. Each of the three ratios $\frac{\text{side opposite } \angle A}{\text{hypotenuse}}$, $\frac{\text{side adjacent to } \angle A}{\text{hypotenuse}}$, and $\frac{\text{side opposite } \angle A}{\text{side adjacent to } \angle A}$ are only equal in similar right triangles with a given reference angle.

Problem Types

Thumbs Up

- Take your time to read through the *correct* solution.
- Think about the connections between steps.

ASK YOURSELF

- Why is this method correct?
- Have I used this method before?

PROBLEM 3 One Sock, Two Sock, Red Sock, Blue Sock

You have 2 red, 1 blue, and 3 green socks in a drawer.

Suppose you reach into the drawer without looking and choose a sock, replace it, and then choose another sock. You choose a total of 2 socks.

1. Use this information to answer each question.

   a. Does the action "choosing the first sock" affect the outcomes of "choosing the second sock"? If so, how? Explain your reasoning.

   No. After I choose the first sock and replace it, there are still the same number of possible outcomes for the second sock.

   b. Use a tree diagram or organized list to represent the sample space for this situation.

R_1R_1	R_2R_1	BR_1	G_1R_1	G_2R_1	G_3R_1
R_1R_2	R_2R_2	BR_2	G_1R_2	G_2R_2	G_3R_2
R_1B	R_2B	BB	G_1B	G_2B	G_3B
R_1G_1	R_2G_1	BG_1	G_1G_1	G_2G_1	G_3G_1
R_1G_2	R_2G_2	BG_2	G_1G_2	G_2G_2	G_3G_2
R_1G_3	R_2G_3	BG_3	G_1G_3	G_2G_3	G_3G_3

   Key: R = red, B = blue, G = green

   You can use small numbers called subscripts to indicate the different red or green socks. For example, R_1 and R_2 can represent the two red socks.

   c. How can you use the Counting Principle to determine the total number of possible outcomes? Explain your reasoning.

   I can multiply the number of outcomes for each sock choice. There are 6 possible outcomes for choosing the first sock and 6 possible outcomes for choosing the second sock. So, there are 6×6, or 36, total possible outcomes for choosing both socks.

   I can use my tree diagram or organized list to check my answers—as long as I made them correctly!

---

d. Calculate the probability of choosing:

- a blue sock and then a red sock

$P(\text{blue 1st}) = \frac{1}{6}$

$P(\text{red 2nd}) = \frac{2}{6}$, or $\frac{1}{3}$

$P(\text{blue 1st and red 2nd}) = \frac{1}{6} \times \frac{1}{3} = \frac{1}{18}$

- a red sock and then a sock that is not blue

$P(\text{red 1st}) = \frac{2}{6}$, or $\frac{1}{3}$

$P(\text{not blue 2nd}) = 1 - \frac{1}{6} = \frac{5}{6}$

$P(\text{red 1st and not blue 2nd}) = \frac{1}{3} \times \frac{5}{6} = \frac{5}{18}$

- two socks with the 1st sock being green

$P(\text{green 1st}) = \frac{3}{6}$, or $\frac{1}{2}$

$P(\text{any color 2nd}) = \frac{6}{6}$, or 1

$P(\text{green 1st and any color 2nd}) = \frac{1}{2} \times 1 = \frac{1}{2}$

Who's Correct?

WHEN YOU SEE A WHO'S CORRECT? ICON

- Take your time to read through the situation.
- Question the strategy or reason given.
- Determine which solution is correct and which is not correct.

ASK YOURSELF

- Does the reasoning make sense?
- If the reasoning makes sense, what is the justification?
- If the reasoning does not make sense, what error was made?

3. Simone says that since triangle *ABC* and triangle *DCB* have two pairs of congruent corresponding sides and congruent corresponding angles, then the triangles are congruent by SAS. Is Simone correct? Explain your reasoning.

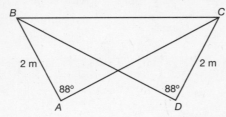

Simone is not correct. The congruent angles are not formed by two pairs of congruent sides, so they are not the included angles. There is not enough information to determine if the triangles are congruent by SAS or SSS.

Problem Types

The Standards for Mathematical Practice

Effective communication and collaboration are essential skills of a successful learner. With practice, you can develop the habits of mind of a productive mathematical thinker.

Make sense of problems and persevere in solving them.

I can:
- explain what a problem "means" in my own words.
- analyze and organize information.
- keep track of my plan and change it if necessary
- always ask myself, "does this make sense?"

Attend to precision.

I can:
- calculate accurately and efficiently.
- use clear definitions when I talk with my classmates, my teacher, and others.
- specify units of measure and label diagrams and other figures appropriately to clarify the meaning of different representations.

Reasoning and Explaining

Reason abstractly and quantitatively.

I can:
- create an understandable representation of a problem situation.
- consider the units of measure involved in a problem.
- understand and use properties of operations.

Construct viable arguments and critique the reasoning of others.

I can:
- use definitions and previously established results in constructing arguments.
- communicate and defend my own mathematical reasoning using examples, drawings, or diagrams.
- distinguish correct reasoning from reasoning that is flawed.
- listen to or read the conclusions of others and decide whether they make sense.
- ask useful questions in an attempt to understand other ideas and conclusions.

Modeling and Using Tools

Model with mathematics.

I can:

- identify important relationships in a problem situation and represent them using tools such as, diagrams, tables, graphs, and formulas.
- apply mathematics to solve problems that occur in everyday life.
- interpret mathematical results in the contexts of a variety of problem situations.
- reflect on whether my results make sense, improving the model I used if it is not appropriate for the situation.

Use appropriate tools strategically.

I can:

- use a variety of different tools that I have to solve problems.
- use a graphing calculator to explore mathematical concepts.
- recognize when a tool that I have to solve problems might be helpful and also when it has limitations.

Seeing Structure and Generalizing

Look for and make use of structure.

I can:

- look closely to see a pattern or a structure in a mathematical argument.
- can see complicated things as single objects or as being composed of several objects.
- can step back for an overview and can shift my perspective.

Look for and express regularity in repeated reasoning.

I can:

- notice if calculations are repeated.
- look for general methods and more efficient methods to solve problems.
- evaluate the reasonableness of intermediate results.
- make generalizations based on results.

Each lesson provides opportunities for you to think, reason, and communicate mathematical understanding. Here are a few examples of how you will develop expertise using the Standards for Mathematical Practice throughout this text.

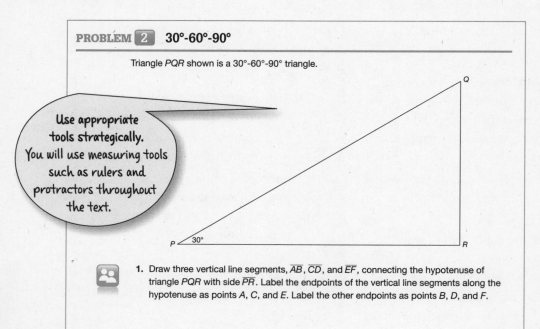

PROBLEM 2   30°-60°-90°

Triangle *PQR* shown is a 30°-60°-90° triangle.

> **Use appropriate tools strategically.**
> You will use measuring tools such as rulers and protractors throughout the text.

1. Draw three vertical line segments, $\overline{AB}$, $\overline{CD}$, and $\overline{EF}$, connecting the hypotenuse of triangle *PQR* with side $\overline{PR}$. Label the endpoints of the vertical line segments along the hypotenuse as points *A*, *C*, and *E*. Label the other endpoints as points *B*, *D*, and *F*.

2. Measure each of the sides of the four similar right triangles in millimeters. Record the side length measurements in the table.

Triangle Name	Length of Side Opposite Angle *P*	Length of Side Adjacent to Angle *P*	Length of Hypotenuse
Triangle *PQR*			
Triangle *PEF*			
Triangle *PCD*			
Triangle *PAB*			

> **Attend to precision.**
> You will specify units of measure and express answers with a degree of precision appropriate for the problem context.

Habits of Mind

3. Determine each side length ratio for all four triangles using angle P as the reference angle.

Triangle Name	$\dfrac{\text{side opposite } \angle P}{\text{hypotenuse}}$	$\dfrac{\text{side adjacent to } \angle P}{\text{hypotenuse}}$	$\dfrac{\text{side opposite } \angle P}{\text{side adjacent to } \angle P}$
Triangle PQR			
Triangle PEF			
Triangle PCD			
Triangle PAB			

Model with mathematics.
You will identify relationships and represent them using diagrams, tables, graphs, and formulas.

4. Compare the side length ratios of all four triangles in the table. What do you notice?

Look for and make use of structure.
You will look for patterns in your calculations and use those to make conclusions.

5. What conclusions can you draw from Problem 1 and Problem 2 about the three ratios you studied in 45°-45°-90° triangles and 30°-60°-90° triangles?

Construct viable arguments and critique the reasoning of others.
You will share your answers with your classmates and listen to their responses to decide whether they make sense.

Tools of Geometry

1

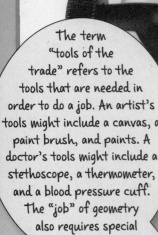

The term "tools of the trade" refers to the tools that are needed in order to do a job. An artist's tools might include a canvas, a paint brush, and paints. A doctor's tools might include a stethoscope, a thermometer, and a blood pressure cuff. The "job" of geometry also requires special tools.

Let's Get This Started!

Points, Lines, Planes, Rays, and Line Segments

Do you have techno-joy or techno-fear? For people who have techno-fear, learning about a new technology—whether it's a smart phone, new computer, or new TV—can be a nervous endeavor. For people in the techno-joy category, it's, "get out of the way, I can handle this new device! I don't need to read the directions!"

Technical writers are the kind of people who bridge the gap between techno-joy and techno-fear. Technical writers are people who write and edit the manuals for all kinds of devices—from cars to airplanes, from electronic tablets to blenders, from industrial ventilation fans to electronic medical devices, from vacuums to whatever device you can think of! Most technical writers take the technological language and specifications and convert them into language that is more comprehensible to the average user. Some technical writers will also translate manuals into different languages.

Have you ever had trouble building something by reading the instructions? It's a tough job to write instructions, especially when you don't really know the audience.

PROBLEM 1 Point, Line, Plane

There are three essential building blocks of geometry—the point, the line, and the plane. These three terms are called undefined terms; we can only describe and create mathematical models to represent them.

A **point** is described simply as a location. A point in geometry has no size or shape, but it is often represented using a dot. In a diagram, a point can be labeled using a capital letter.

A **line** is described as a straight, continuous arrangement of an infinite number of points. A line has an infinite length, but no width. Arrowheads are used to indicate that a line extends infinitely in opposite directions. In a diagram, a line can be labeled with a lowercase letter positioned next to the arrowhead.

A mathematical model of several points and lines is shown.

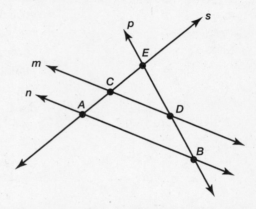

1. Does the name "line C" describe a unique line? Explain why or why not.

2. Does the name "line CD" describe a unique line? Explain why or why not.

3. Does the name "line m" describe a unique line? Explain why or why not.

Lines have names just like people. Many people may have the same first name. Many lines may pass through the same point.

4. How many points are needed to name a specific line?

5. What is another name for line AB?

Line AB can be written using symbols as $\overleftrightarrow{AB}$ and is read as "line AB."

6. Analyze each model and explanation.

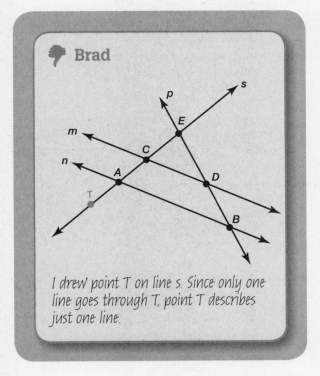

Brad

I drew point T on line s. Since only one line goes through T, point T describes just one line.

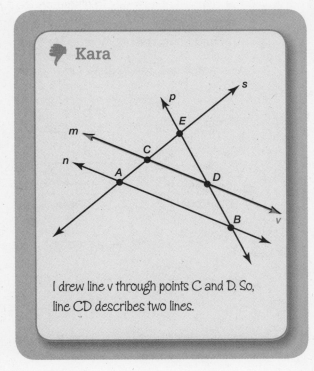

Kara

I drew line v through points C and D. So, line CD describes two lines.

Describe the inaccuracy in each students' reasoning.

7. How many lines can be drawn through a single point?

Collinear points are points that are located on the same line.

8. Use the diagram shown prior to Question 1.

  a. Name three points that are collinear.

  b. Name three points that are not collinear.

1

A **plane** is described as a flat surface. A plane has an infinite length and width, but no depth, and extends infinitely in all directions. One real-world model of a plane is the surface of a still body of water. Three non-collinear points describe a unique plane, but planes are usually named using one italic letter located near a corner of the plane as drawn.

Three planes can intersect in a variety of ways or may not intersect at all.

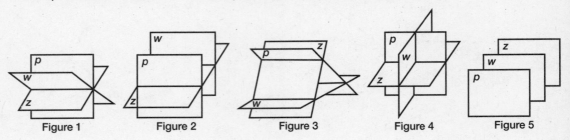

Figure 1   Figure 2   Figure 3   Figure 4   Figure 5

9. Describe the intersection of planes *p*, *w*, and *z* in each figure.

   a. Figure 1

   b. Figure 2

   c. Figure 3

   d. Figure 4

   e. Figure 5

10. List all of the possible ways that three planes can intersect.

11. Sketch and describe all possible ways that a line and a plane can intersect.

PROBLEM 2 Creating Geometric Figures

You can use many tools to create geometric figures. Some tools, such as a ruler or a protractor, are classified as measuring tools. A **compass** is a tool used to create arcs and circles. A **straightedge** is a ruler with no numbers. It is important to know when to use each tool.

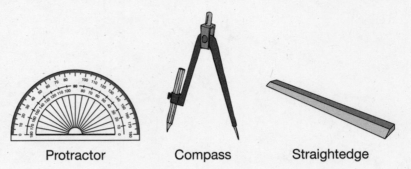

Protractor   Compass   Straightedge

● When you **sketch** a geometric figure, the figure is created without the use of tools.

● When you **draw** a geometric figure, the figure is created with the use of tools such as a ruler, straightedge, compass, or protractor. A drawing is more accurate than a sketch.

● When you **construct** a geometric figure, the figure is created using only a compass and a straightedge.

1. Sketch and then draw each figure. Describe the steps that you performed to complete your sketch and your drawing.

   a. square

   b. isosceles triangle

Coplanar lines are two or more lines that are located in the same plane. **Skew lines** are two or more lines that do not intersect and are not parallel. Skew lines do not lie in the same plane.

2. Draw and label three coplanar lines.

3. Look around your classroom. Describe the location of two skew lines.

PROBLEM **3** **Using Undefined Terms to Define New Terms**

A **ray** is a part of a line that begins with a single point and extends infinitely in one direction. The **endpoint of a ray** is the single point where the ray begins.

A ray is named using two capital letters, the first representing the endpoint and the second representing any other point on the ray. Ray *AB* can be written using symbols as $\overrightarrow{AB}$, which is read as "ray *AB*."

1. Sketch and label $\overrightarrow{AB}$.

●   ●
A   *B*

The endpoint is where the ray *begins*? Shouldn't it be called the "begin-point" instead?

2. Sketch and label $\overrightarrow{BA}$.

●   ●
A   *B*

3. Are $\overrightarrow{AB}$ and $\overrightarrow{BA}$ names for the same ray? Explain why or why not.

4. Use symbols to name the geometric figure shown.

A **line segment** is a part of a line that includes two points and all of the collinear points between the two points. The **endpoints of a line segment** are the points where the line segment begins and ends.

A line segment is named using two capital letters representing the two endpoints of the line segment. Line segment AB can be written using symbols as $\overline{AB}$, which is read as "line segment AB."

5. Draw and label $\overline{AB}$.

$\bullet$ $\bullet$
A B

6. Draw and label $\overline{BA}$.

$\bullet$ $\bullet$
A B

7. Are $\overline{AB}$ and $\overline{BA}$ names for the same line segment? Explain why or why not.

8. Use a ruler to measure $\overline{AB}$ in Question 5.

Don't forget the unit of measure!

9. The measure of $\overline{AB}$ can be expressed in two different ways. Complete each statement:

a. "AB = _____ inches" is read as "the distance from point A to point B is equal to _____ inches."

b. "$m\overline{AB}$ = _____ inches" is read as "the measure of line segment AB is equal to _____ inches."

c. How do you read "$m\overline{CF}$ = 3 inches"?

d. How do you read "SP = 8 inches"?

10. Use symbols to name each geometric figure.

a.

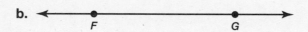

F   G

b. ← ●—————————————● →
F   G

c. ● ————————————— ● →
F   G

If two line segments have equal measure, then the line segments have the same length. **Congruent line segments** are two or more line segments of equal measure.

If $m\overline{AB} = m\overline{CD}$, then line segment AB is congruent to line segment CD by the definition of congruent line segments. This statement can be written using symbols as $\overline{AB} \cong \overline{CD}$ and is read as "line segment AB is congruent to line segment CD."

Use the congruence symbol, $\cong$, between references to congruent geometric figures; and the equal symbol, $=$, between references to equal lengths or distances.

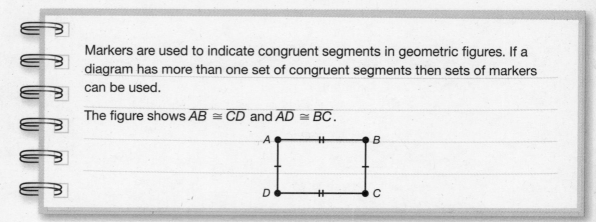

Markers are used to indicate congruent segments in geometric figures. If a diagram has more than one set of congruent segments then sets of markers can be used.

The figure shows $\overline{AB} \cong \overline{CD}$ and $\overline{AD} \cong \overline{BC}$.

11. Draw and label two congruent line segments. Then, use symbols to write a statement that describes their relationship.

12. Ms. Snyder drew the triangle shown and asked her students to classify it.

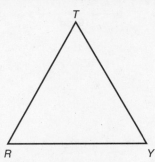

a. Mariah says the triangle is an equilateral triangle.

Is she correct?

b. Ms. Snyder then drew markers and asked her students to classify the triangle.

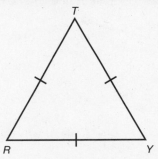

Mariah says the triangle is an isosceles triangle. Justin says the triangle is an equilateral triangle.

Who is correct?

c. Ms. Snyder also asked her students to write a statement that best describes the congruency of the line segments forming the triangle.

Mariah	Justin
TR = RY = YR	$\overline{TR} \cong \overline{RY} \cong \overline{YR}$

Who is correct?

13. Use symbols to write three valid conclusions based on the figure shown. How do you read each conclusion?

F ———10 cm——— G   H ———10 cm——— I

14. Use symbols to name all lines, rays, or segments shown.

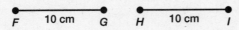

15. Explain when it is appropriate to use the statement $JK = MN$ and when it is appropriate to use the statement $\overline{JK} \cong \overline{MN}$.

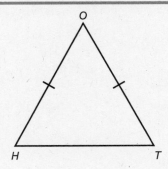

Circle each statement that is valid about triangle HOT.

$\overline{HO} = \overline{TO}$ $m\overline{HO} = m\overline{TO}$

$\overline{HO} \cong \overline{TO}$ $m\overline{HO} \cong m\overline{TO}$

$HO = TO$ $mHO = mTO$

$HO \cong TO$ $mHO \cong mTO$

Be prepared to share your solutions and methods.

1

Attack of the Clones

Translating and Constructing Line Segments

LEARNING GOALS

In this lesson, you will:

- Determine the distance between two points.
- Use the Pythagorean Theorem to derive the Distance Formula.
- Apply the Distance Formula on the coordinate plane.
- Translate a line segment on the coordinate plane.
- Copy or duplicate a line segment by construction.

KEY TERMS

- Distance Formula
- transformation
- rigid motion
- translation
- pre-image
- image
- arc

CONSTRUCTIONS

- copying a line segment
- duplicating a line segment

Are you better at geometry or algebra? Many students have a preference for one subject or the other; however, geometry and algebra are very closely related. While there are some branches of geometry that do not use much algebra, analytic geometry applies methods of algebra to geometric questions. Analytic geometry is also known as the study of geometry using a coordinate system. So anytime you are performing geometric calculations and it involves a coordinate system, you are studying analytic geometry. Be sure to thank Descartes and his discovery of the coordinate plane for this!

What might be the pros and cons of analytic geometry compared to other branches of geometry? Does knowing about analytic geometry change how you feel about your own abilities in geometry or algebra?

PROBLEM **1** **Where Do You Live?**

Don, Freda, and Bert live in a town where the streets are laid out in a grid system.

1. Don lives 3 blocks east of Descartes Avenue and 5 blocks north of Elm Street. Freda lives 7 blocks east of Descartes Avenue and 2 blocks north of Elm Street. Plot points to show the locations of Don's house and Freda's house on the coordinate plane. Label each location with the student's name and the coordinates of the point.

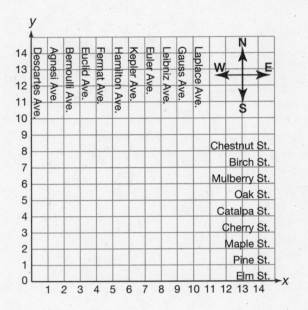

a. Name the intersection of streets that Don lives on.

b. Name the intersection of streets that Freda lives on.

2. Bert lives at the intersection of the avenue that Don lives on, and the street that Freda lives on. Plot and label the location of Bert's house on the coordinate plane. Describe the location of Bert's house with respect to Descartes Avenue and Elm Street.

3. How do the x- and y-coordinates of Bert's house compare to the x- and y-coordinates of Don's house and Freda's house?

4. Use Don's and Bert's house coordinates to write and simplify an expression that represents the distance between their houses. Explain what this means in terms of the problem situation.

5. Use Bert's and Freda's house coordinates to write and simplify an expression that represents the distance between their houses. Explain what this means in terms of the problem situation.

6. All three friends are planning to meet at Don's house to hang out. Freda walks to Bert's house, and then Freda and Bert walk together to Don's house.

   a. Use the coordinates to write and simplify an expression that represents the total distance from Freda's house to Bert's house to Don's house.

   b. How far, in blocks, does Freda walk altogether?

7. Draw the direct path from Don's house to Freda's house on the coordinate plane. If Freda walks to Don's house on this path, how far, in blocks, does she walk? Explain how you determined your answer.

What shape do you see? How can that help you determine the distance of the direct path?

8. Complete the summary of the steps that you took to determine the direct distance between Freda's house and Don's house. Let d be the direct distance between Don's house and Freda's house.

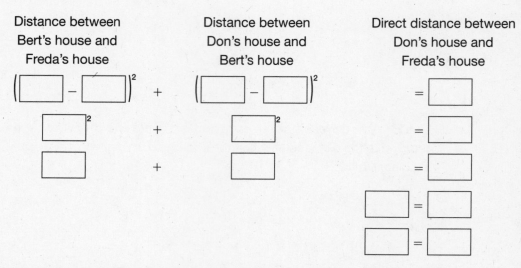

Distance between Bert's house and Freda's house

Distance between Don's house and Bert's house

Direct distance between Don's house and Freda's house

$$\left(\boxed{} - \boxed{}\right)^2 + \left(\boxed{} - \boxed{}\right)^2 \quad = \boxed{}$$

$$\boxed{}^2 + \boxed{}^2 \quad = \boxed{}$$

$$\boxed{} + \boxed{} \quad = \boxed{}$$

$$\boxed{} = \boxed{}$$

$$\boxed{} = \boxed{}$$

Suppose Freda's, Bert's, and Don's houses were at different locations but oriented in a similar manner. You can generalize their locations by using x_1, x_2, y_1, and y_2 and still solve for the distances between their houses using variables. Let point F represent Freda's house, point B represent Bert's house, and point D represent Don's house.

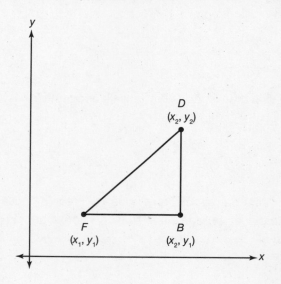

9. Use the graph to write an expression for each distance.

a. Don's house to Bert's house (DB)

b. Bert's house to Freda's house (BF)

Sure, they can live in different locations, but the points must still form a right triangle in order for us to generalize this, right?

10. Use the Pythagorean Theorem to determine the distance from Don's house to Freda's house (*DF*).

You used the Pythagorean Theorem to calculate the distance between two points on the coordinate plane. Your method can be written as the *Distance Formula*.

The **Distance Formula** states that if (x_1, y_1) and (x_2, y_2) are two points on the coordinate plane, then the distance d between (x_1, y_1) and (x_2, y_2) is $d = \sqrt{(x_2 - x_1)^2 + (y_2 - y_1)^2}$.

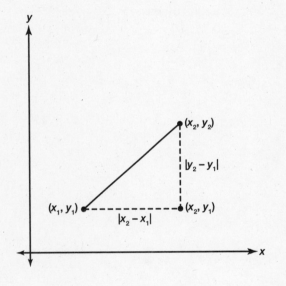

The absolute value symbols are used to indicate that the distance is always positive.

11. Do you think that it matters which point you identify as (x_1, y_1) and which point you identify as (x_2, y_2) when you use the Distance Formula? Use an example to justify your answer.

12. Calculate the distance between each pair of points. Round your answer to the nearest tenth if necessary. Show all your work.

a. (1, 2) and (3, 7)

b. (−6, 4) and (2, −8)

c. (−5, 2) and (−6, 10)

d. (−1, −3) and (−5, −2)

13. Carlos and Mandy just completed Question 12 parts (a) through (c). Now, they need to calculate the distance between the points $(-4, 2)$ and $(-2, 7)$. They notice the similarity between this problem and part (a).

Mandy

$d = \sqrt{(-4--2)^2 + (2-7)^2}$

$d = \sqrt{(-2)^2 + (-5)^2}$

$d = \sqrt{4+25}$

$d = \sqrt{29}$

$d \approx 5.4$

Carlos

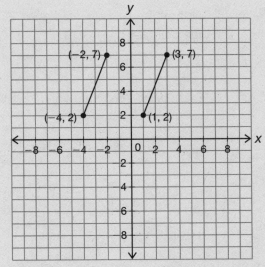

$(1, 2) \rightarrow (-4, 2)$ The point moved 5 units to the left

$(3, 7) \rightarrow (-2, 7)$ The point moved 5 units to the left

Since both points moved 5 units to the left, this did not alter the distance between the points, so the distance between points $(-4, 2)$ and $(-2, 7)$ is approximately 5.4.

Who used correct reasoning?

14. The distance between $(x, 2)$ and $(0, 6)$ is 5 units. Use the Distance Formula to determine the value of x. Show all your work.

PROBLEM 2 **Translating a Line Segment**

1. Pedro's house is located at (6, 10). Graph this location on the coordinate plane and label the point *P*.

2. Jethro's house is located at (2, 3). Graph this location on the coordinate plane and label the point *J*.

3. Draw a line segment connecting the two houses to create line segment *PJ*.

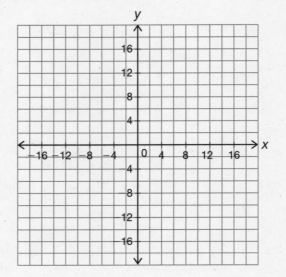

4. Determine the length of line segment *PJ*.

Length is the same as distance on the coordinate plane!

A **transformation** is the mapping, or movement, of all the points of a figure in a plane according to a common operation.

A **rigid motion** is a transformation of points in space.

A **translation** is a rigid motion that "slides" each point of a figure the same distance and direction. Sliding a figure left or right is a horizontal translation, and sliding it up or down is a vertical translation.

The original figure is called the **pre-image**. The new figure created from the translation is called the **image**.

5. Line segment PJ is horizontally translated 10 units to the left.

   a. Graph the image of pre-image $\overline{PJ}$. Label the new points P' and J'.

   b. Identify the coordinates of P' and J'.

> A line, or even a point, can be considered a figure.

6. Line segment $P'J'$ is vertically translated 14 units down.

   a. Graph the image of pre-image $\overline{P'J'}$. Label the new points P'' and J''.

   b. Identify the coordinates of P'' and J''.

> The prime symbol, like on P' or P'', indicates that this point is related to the original point P. P' is read as "P prime" and P'' is read as "P double prime."

7. Line segment $P''J''$ is horizontally translated 10 units to the right.

   a. Without graphing, predict the coordinates of P''' and J'''.

   b. Graph the image of pre-image $\overline{P''J''}$. Label the new points P''' and J'''.

8. Describe the translation necessary on $\overline{P'''J'''}$ so that it returns to the location of $\overline{PJ}$.

9. How do the lengths of the images compare to the lengths of the pre-images? Explain how you could verify your answer.

10. Analyze the coordinates of the endpoints of each line segment.

   a. Identify the coordinates of each line segment in the table.

Line Segments	$\overline{PJ}$	$\overline{P'J'}$	$\overline{P''J''}$	$\overline{P'''J'''}$
Coordinates of Endpoints				

   b. Describe how a horizontal translation changes the x- and y-coordinates of the endpoints.

   c. Describe how a vertical translation changes the x- and y-coordinates of the endpoints.

11. Describe a sequence of two translations that will result in the image and the pre-image being the same.

12. Describe a sequence of four translations that will result in the image and the pre-image being the same.

In the previous problem, you translated line segments on the coordinate plane. The lengths of the line segments on the coordinate plane are measurable.

In this problem, you will translate line segments when measuring is not possible. This basic geometric construction is called **copying a line segment** or **duplicating a line segment.** You will perform the construction using a compass and a straightedge.

One method for copying a line segment is to use circles. But before you can get to that, let's review how to draw perfect circles with a compass.

Remember that a compass is an instrument used to draw circles and arcs. A compass can have two legs connected at one end.

One leg has a point, and the other holds a pencil. Some newer compasses may be different, but all of them are made to construct circles by placing a point firmly into the paper and then spinning the top of the compass around, with the pencil point just touching the paper.

1. Use your compass to construct a number of circles of different sizes.

Take your time. It may take a while for you to be able to construct a clean, exact circle without doubled or smudged lines.

2. Point *C* is the center of a circle and $\overline{CD}$ is a radius.

a. Construct circle *C*.

Remember a circle is a set of all points in a plane that are the same distance from a given point called the center of the circle. A radius is a segment drawn from the center to a point on the circle.

b. Draw and label points *A*, *B*, *E*, and *F* anywhere on the circle.

c. Construct $\overline{AC}$, $\overline{BC}$, $\overline{EC}$, and $\overline{FC}$.

d. Shawna makes the following statement about radii of a circle.

👍 **Shawna**

All radii are the same length, because all of the points of a circle are equidistant from the circle's center.

Explain how Shawna knows that all radii are the same length? Does this mean the line segments you constructed are also radii?

An **arc** is a part of a circle. You can also think of an arc as the curve between two points on the circle.

3. Point *C* is the center of a circle and $\overline{AC}$ is the radius.

a. Construct an arc of circle *C*. Make your arc about one-half inch long. Construct the arc so that it does not pass through point *A*.

b. Draw and label two points *B* and *E* on the arc and construct $\overline{CE}$ and $\overline{CB}$.

c. What conclusion can you make about the constructed line segments?

Recall that congruent line segments are line segments that have the same length. The radii of a circle are congruent line segments because any line segment drawn from the center to a point on the circle has the same length.

4. Construct a circle with the center *A* and a radius of about 1 inch.

   a. Without changing the width of your compass, place the compass point on any point on the circle you constructed and then construct another circle.

   b. Draw a dot on a point where the two circles intersect. Place the compass point on that point of intersection of the two circles, and then construct another circle.

   c. Repeat this process until no new circles can be constructed.

   d. Connect the points of the circles' intersections with each other.

● *A*

   e. Describe the figure formed by the line segments.

Now let's use these circle-drawing skills to duplicate a line segment.

5. Circle A is congruent to Circle A'.

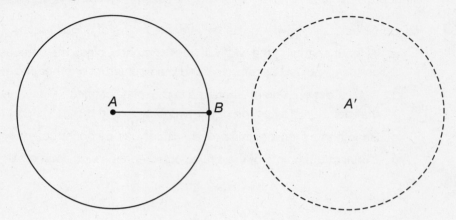

a. Duplicate $\overline{AB}$ in Circle A'. Use point A' as the center of the circle, then label the endpoint of the duplicated segment as point B'.

b. Describe the location of point B'.

c. If possible, construct a second line segment in Circle A' that is a duplicate of $\overline{AB}$. Label the duplicate segment $\overline{A'C'}$. If it is not possible, explain why.

To duplicate a line segment, you don't have to draw a full circle.

You can duplicate a line segment by constructing an exact copy of the original line segment.

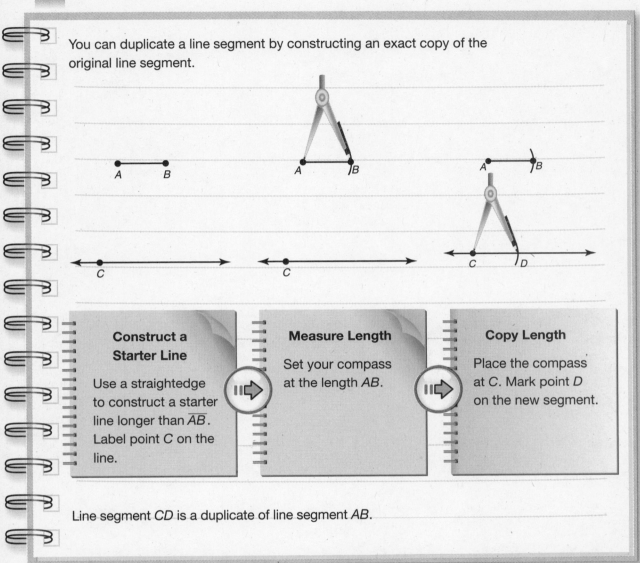

Construct a Starter Line	**Measure Length**	**Copy Length**
Use a straightedge to construct a starter line longer than $\overline{AB}$. Label point C on the line.	Set your compass at the length AB.	Place the compass at C. Mark point D on the new segment.

Line segment CD is a duplicate of line segment AB.

1. Construct a line segment that is twice the length of $\overline{AB}$.

Make sure to construct a starter line first.

2. Duplicate each line segment using a compass and a straightedge.

 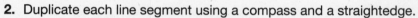

U   V   W   X

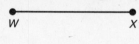

Y   Z

3. Dave and Sandy are duplicating $\overline{AB}$. Their methods are shown.

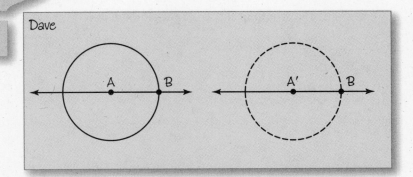

Dave

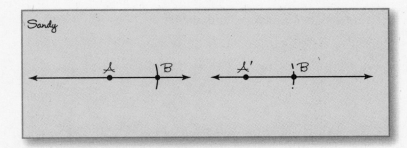

Sandy

Which method is correct? Explain your reasoning.

4. Which method do you prefer? Why?

Talk the Talk

1. You translate a line segment vertically or horizontally. Is the length of the image the same as the length of the pre-image? Explain why or why not.

2. If both endpoints of a line segment were not moved the same distance or direction, would the length of the line segment change? Would this still be considered a translation? Explain your reasoning.

3. What can you conclude about the length of a line segment and the length of its translated image that results from moving points on a coordinate plane the same distance and the same direction?

4. What can you conclude about the length of a line segment and the length of its translated image that results from construction?

Be prepared to share your solutions and methods.

Stuck in the Middle
Midpoints and Bisectors

When you hear the phrase "treasure hunt," you may think of pirates, buried treasure, and treasure maps. However, there are very few documented cases of pirates actually burying treasure, and there are no historical pirate treasure maps! So where did this idea come from?

Robert Louis Stevenson's book *Treasure Island* is a story all about pirates and their buried gold, and this book greatly influenced public knowledge of pirates. In fact, it is Stevenson who is often credited with coming up with the concept of the treasure map and using an X to mark where a treasure is located.

Have you ever used a map to determine your location or the location of another object? Did you find it difficult or easy to use? How does the idea of a treasure map relate to a familiar mathematical concept you are very familiar with?

PROBLEM 1 Locating the Treasure

Ms. Lopez is planning a treasure hunt for her kindergarten students. She drew a model of the playground on a coordinate plane as shown. She used this model to decide where to place items for the treasure hunt, and to determine how to write the treasure hunt instructions. Each grid square represents one square yard on the playground.

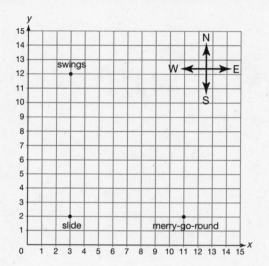

Remember to include units when describing distances.

1. Ms. Lopez wants to place some beads in the grass halfway between the merry-go-round and the slide.

   a. Determine the distance between the merry-go-round and the slide. Show all your work.

   b. How far should the beads be placed from the merry-go-round and the slide?

   c. Write the coordinates for the location exactly halfway between the merry-go-round and the slide. Graph a point representing the location of the beads on the coordinate plane.

   d. How do the *x*- and *y*-coordinates of the point representing the location of the beads compare to the coordinates of the points representing the locations of the slide and the merry-go-round?

2. Ms. Lopez wants to place some kazoos in the grass halfway between the slide and the swings.

    a. Write the coordinates for the location of the kazoos. Graph the location of the kazoos on the coordinate plane.

    b. How do the x- and y-coordinates of the point representing the location of the kazoos compare to the coordinates of the points representing the locations of the slide and the swings?

3. Ms. Lopez wants to place some buttons in the grass halfway between the swings and the merry-go-round.

    a. Determine the distance between the swings and the merry-go-round.

    b. How far should the buttons be placed from the swings and the merry-go-round?

    c. How is determining the coordinates for the location of the buttons different than determining the coordinates for the locations of the beads or the kazoos?

d. Write the coordinates for the location of the kazoos. Graph the location of the buttons on the coordinate plane.

You can draw right triangles on the coordinate plane to figure out the exact location of the buttons. Do you see how?

Suppose the slide, the swings, and the merry-go-round were at different locations but oriented in a similar manner. You can generalize their locations by using x_1, x_2, y_1, and y_2, and then solve for the distances between each using variables.

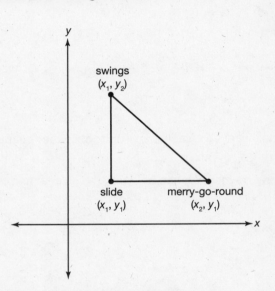

4. Use the diagram to describe each distance algebraically.

a. the vertical distance from the x-axis to the slide

b. the distance from the slide to the swings

c. half the distance from the slide to the swings

d. the vertical distance from the x-axis to the slide plus half the distance from the slide to the swings

5. Simplify your expression from Question 4, part (d).

6. Use the diagram to describe each distance algebraically.

    a. the horizontal distance from the y-axis to the slide

    b. the distance from the slide to the merry-go-round

    c. half the distance from the slide to the merry-go-round

    d. the horizontal distance from the y-axis to the slide plus half the distance from the slide to the merry-go-round

7. Simplify your expression from Question 6, part (d).

The coordinates of the points that you determined in Questions 5 and 7 are *midpoints*. A **midpoint** is a point that is exactly halfway between two given points. The calculations you performed can be summarized by the *Midpoint Formula*.

The **Midpoint Formula** states that if (x_1, y_1) and (x_2, y_2) are two points on the coordinate plane, then the midpoint of the line segment that joins these two points is
$$\left(\frac{x_1 + x_2}{2}, \frac{y_1 + y_2}{2} \right).$$

8. Use the Midpoint Formula to determine the location of the buttons from Question 3.

9. Do you think it matters which point you identify as (x_1, y_1) and which point you identify as (x_2, y_2) when you use the Midpoint Formula? Explain why or why not.

10. Determine the midpoint of each line segment from the given endpoints. Show all of your work.

a. (0, 5) and (4, 3)

b. (8, 2) and (6, 0)

c. (−3, 1) and (9, −7)

d. (−10, 7) and (−4, −7)

1. Jack buried a spare key to his house in the backyard in case of an emergency. He remembers burying the key halfway between the back door and an oak tree. The location of the back door is point $B(2, 3)$, and the location of the oak tree is point $T(12, 3)$.

   a. Determine the location of the key. Show all of your work. Then graph the location of the key as point M.

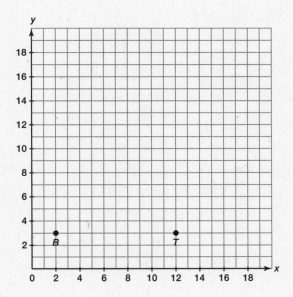

   b. Suppose Jack buried his spare key $\frac{1}{3}$ of the way between the back door and the oak tree. Determine the location of the key. Show all of your work.

2. Jean also buried her house key. She remembers burying the key between the front porch and a rose bush. The location of the front porch is point $P(1, 2)$ and the location of the rose bush is point $B(16, 14)$.

   a. Suppose Jean buried her key $\frac{1}{2}$ of the way between the front porch and the rose bush. Determine the location of the key. Show all your work.

   b. Suppose Jean buried her key $\frac{1}{4}$ of the way between the front porch and the rose bush. Determine the location of the key. Show all your work.

   c. Suppose Jean buried her key $\frac{1}{3}$ of the way between the front porch and the rose bush. Explain why the Midpoint Formula is not helpful in determining the location of Jean's spare key.

3. Rick and Courtney used different methods to determine the location that is $\frac{1}{3}$ of the way between the front porch and the rose bush.

 Rick

I drew a vertical line from point B and a horizontal line from point P and determined the coordinates of point Z where they intersected. I divided the horizontal line and the vertical line into 3 equal parts and wrote the coordinates. I used those coordinates to divide segment BP into three parts. Then, I calculated the coordinates along BP.

 Courtney

I thought about the slope of segment BP. If I want to divide segment BP into three parts then I need to start at point P and perform three vertical and horizontal shifts to get to point B. So I can just divide the total horizontal and vertical shifts by three to calculate each vertical and horizontal shift. After that, determining the coordinates is a snap!

Calculate the location of the point that is $\frac{1}{3}$ of the way between the front porch and the rose bush using Rick's method and Courtney's method. Use a graph to support your work.

a. Rick's Method

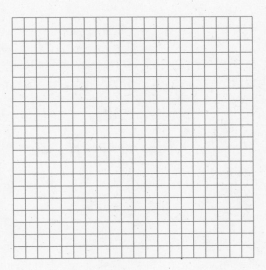

b. Courtney's Method

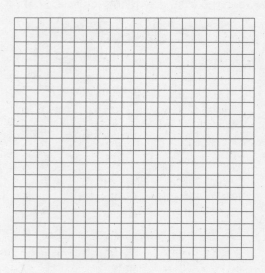

4. Suppose Jean buried her key $\frac{1}{5}$ of the way between the front porch and the rose bush. Determine the location of the key. Show all your work.

In the previous problem, you located the midpoint of a line segment on the coordinate plane. The lengths of the line segments on the plane are measurable.

In this problem, you will locate the midpoint of a line segment when measurement is not possible. This basic geometric construction used to locate a midpoint of a line segment is called **bisecting a line segment**. When bisecting a line segment, you create a *segment bisector*. A **segment bisector** is a line, line segment, or ray that divides a line segment into two line segments of equal measure, or two congruent line segments.

Just as with duplicating a line segment, there are a number of methods to bisect a line segment.

You can use tracing paper—also known as patty paper—to bisect a line.

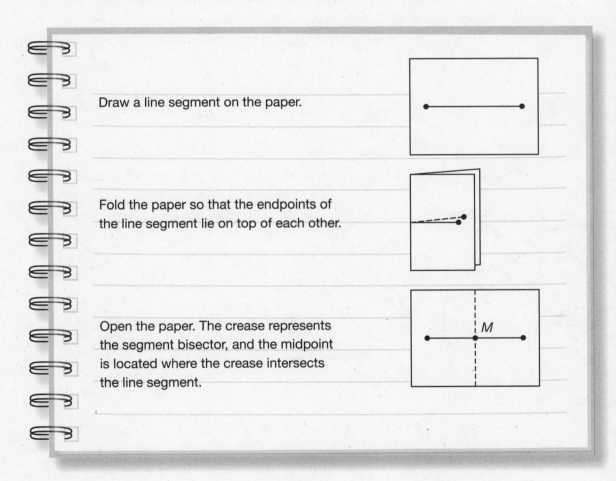

Draw a line segment on the paper.

Fold the paper so that the endpoints of the line segment lie on top of each other.

Open the paper. The crease represents the segment bisector, and the midpoint is located where the crease intersects the line segment.

1. Use tracing paper to duplicate a line segment. How do you know your bisector and midpoint are accurate?

2. Thomas determined the midpoint of $\overline{AB}$ incorrectly.

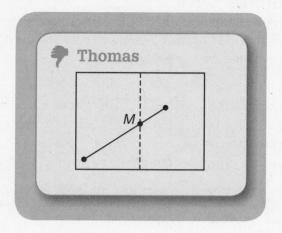

Explain what Thomas did incorrectly and how you can tell he is incorrect. Explain how he can correctly determine the midpoint of $\overline{AB}$.

You can use a compass and straightedge to construct a segment bisector.

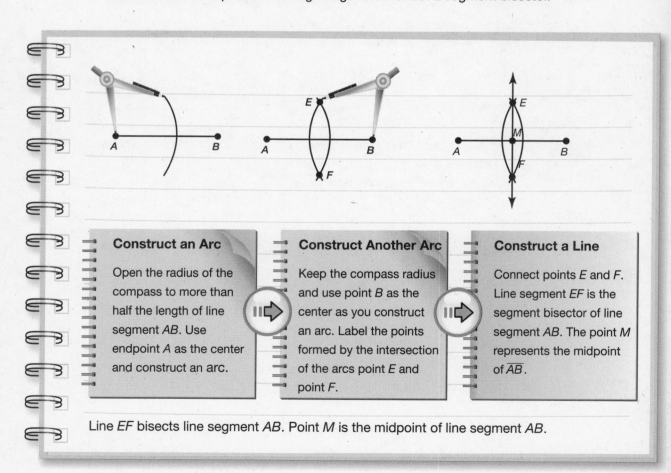

Construct an Arc

Open the radius of the compass to more than half the length of line segment AB. Use endpoint A as the center and construct an arc.

Construct Another Arc

Keep the compass radius and use point B as the center as you construct an arc. Label the points formed by the intersection of the arcs point E and point F.

Construct a Line

Connect points E and F. Line segment EF is the segment bisector of line segment AB. The point M represents the midpoint of $\overline{AB}$.

Line EF bisects line segment AB. Point M is the midpoint of line segment AB.

3. Aaron is determining the midpoint of line segment *RS*. His work is shown.

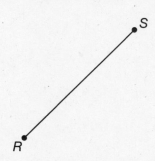

He states that because the arcs do not intersect, this line segment does not have a midpoint. Kate disagrees and tells him he drew his arcs incorrectly and that he must redraw his arcs to determine the midpoint. Who is correct? Explain your reasoning.

4. Use construction tools to locate the midpoint of each given line segment. Label each midpoint as *M*.

a.

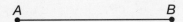

b.

c.

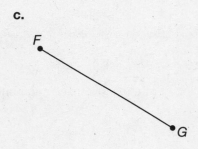

5. Perform each construction shown. Then explain how you performed each construction.

  a. Locate a point one-fourth the distance between point *A* and point *B*.

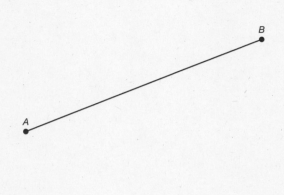

How does your point compare to your classmates' points?

  b. Locate a point one-third the distance between point *A* and point *B*.

6. Explain how you can duplicate a line segment to verify that the midpoint resulting from bisecting the line segment is truly the midpoint of the segment.

Talk the Talk

1. When bisecting a line segment using construction tools, does it make a difference which endpoint you use to draw the first arc?

2. When locating the midpoint of a line segment on a coordinate plane using the Midpoint Formula, does it make a difference which endpoint you use as x_1 and y_1?

3. How will you decide if you should use the Midpoint Formula or construction tools to locate a midpoint?

Be prepared to share your solutions and methods.

What's Your Angle?
Translating and Constructing Angles and Angle Bisectors

LEARNING GOALS

In this lesson, you will:

- Translate an angle on the coordinate plane.
- Copy or duplicate an angle by construction.
- Bisect an angle by construction.

KEY TERMS

- angle
- angle bisector

CONSTRUCTIONS

- copying an angle
- duplicating an angle
- bisecting an angle

You may have never thought of it this way, but drawing and geometry are closely linked. Drawing is the process of deliberately arranging lines and curves to create an image. Most drawings have a number of different angles that are created through the intersection of these lines and curves. However, an art movement known as De Stijl (pronounced duh SHTEEL) limits drawings to using only horizontal and vertical lines. They also limit the colors used to the primary colors. While you may think this sounds restricting, many artists have created many works of art in this style. In fact, an architect even designed a house adhering to the De Stijl principles!

If De Stijl limits the artists to only using horizontal and vertical lines, what types of angles can be created in their art work? What types of angles cannot be created? What might be some challenges with drawing or painting in this style?

PROBLEM 1 Translating an Angle

Previously, you practiced translating a line segment on the coordinate plane horizontally or vertically.

1. Describe how to translate a line segment on a coordinate plane.

An **angle** is formed by two rays or line segments that share a common endpoint. The sides of the angle are represented by the two rays or segments. Each ray of an angle contains an infinite number of line segments. The ∠ symbol represents "angle." Angle *DMB* can be written as ∠*DMB*.

2. Analyze ∠*DBM* shown on the coordinate plane. Describe how you would translate this angle on the coordinate plane.

> Remember that a ray has one endpoint and extends forever in one direction.

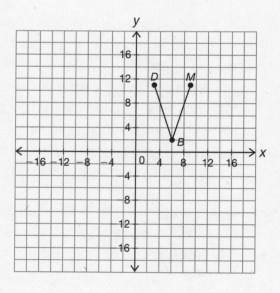

3. Complete each translation.

   a. Horizontally translate ∠DBM 13 units left. Label the image ∠D'B'M'.

   b. Vertically translate ∠D'B'M' 15 units down. Label the image ∠D''B''M''.

   c. Horizontally translate ∠D''B''M'' 13 units right. Label the image ∠D'''B'''M'''.

   d. Use the graph to complete the tables by determining the endpoints of each line segment.

Line Segments	$\overline{MB}$	$\overline{M'B'}$	$\overline{M''B''}$	$\overline{M'''B'''}$
Coordinates of Endpoints				

Line Segments	$\overline{DB}$	$\overline{D'B'}$	$\overline{D''B''}$	$\overline{D'''B'''}$
Coordinates of Endpoints				

4. Describe how a horizontal translation changes the x- and y-coordinates of the endpoints of each side of an angle.

5. Describe how a vertical translation changes the x- and y-coordinates of the angle endpoints of each side of an angle.

6. Describe a sequence of two translations that will result in the image and the pre-image of an angle being the same.

7. Describe a sequence of four translations that will result in the image and the pre-image of an angle being the same.

8. Measure each angle on the coordinate plane. How do the measures of each image compare to its corresponding pre-image?

> An angle is measured using a protractor. The measure of an angle is expressed in units called degrees.

9. What is the result of moving only one angle endpoint a specified distance or direction? How does this affect the measure of the angle? Is this still considered a translation?

PROBLEM 2 Constructing an Angle

Previously, you translated an angle on the coordinate plane using line segments that were associated with units of measure. You can also translate an angle not associated with units of measure.

This basic geometric construction to translate an angle not associated with units of measure is called **copying an angle** or **duplicating an angle**. The construction is performed using a compass and a straightedge.

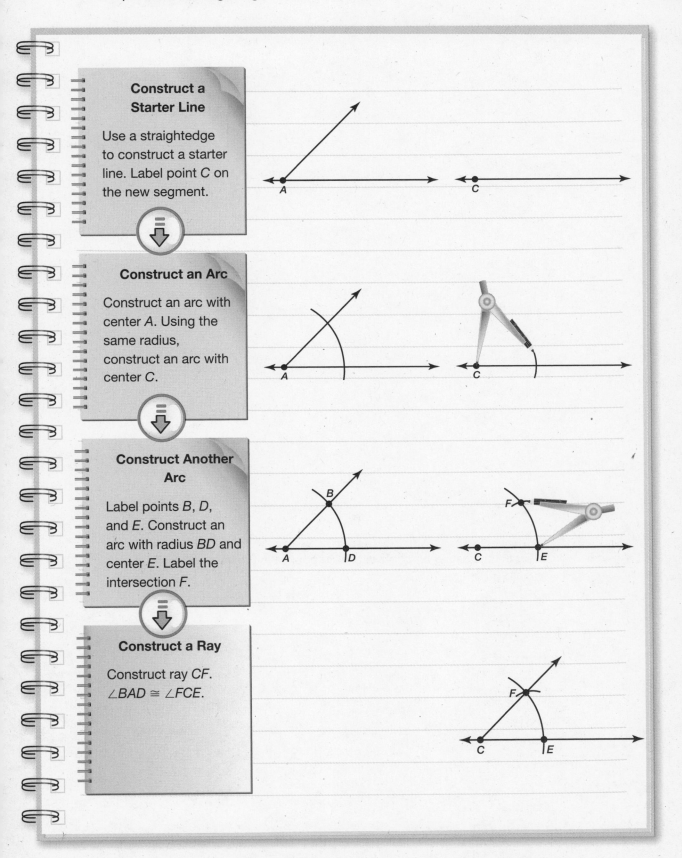

Construct a Starter Line

Use a straightedge to construct a starter line. Label point C on the new segment.

Construct an Arc

Construct an arc with center A. Using the same radius, construct an arc with center C.

Construct Another Arc

Label points B, D, and E. Construct an arc with radius BD and center E. Label the intersection F.

Construct a Ray

Construct ray CF. ∠BAD ≅ ∠FCE.

1. Construct an angle that is twice the measure of ∠A. Then explain how you performed the construction.

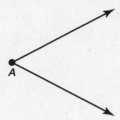

 2. How is duplicating an angle similar to duplicating a line segment? How is it different?

PROBLEM 3 Bisecting an Angle

Just as line segments can be bisected, angles can be bisected too. If a ray is drawn through the vertex of an angle and divides the angle into two angles of equal measure, or two congruent angles, this ray is called an **angle bisector**. The construction used to create an angle bisector is called **bisecting an angle**.

One way to bisect an angle is using tracing paper.

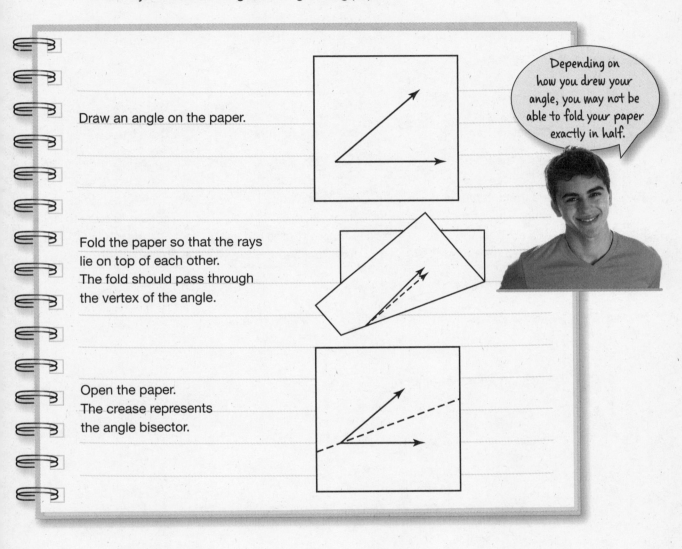

Draw an angle on the paper.

Fold the paper so that the rays lie on top of each other. The fold should pass through the vertex of the angle.

Open the paper. The crease represents the angle bisector.

Depending on how you drew your angle, you may not be able to fold your paper exactly in half.

1. Angela states that as long as the crease goes through the vertex, it is an angle bisector. Is she correct? Why or why not?

You can also bisect an angle using a compass and a straightedge.

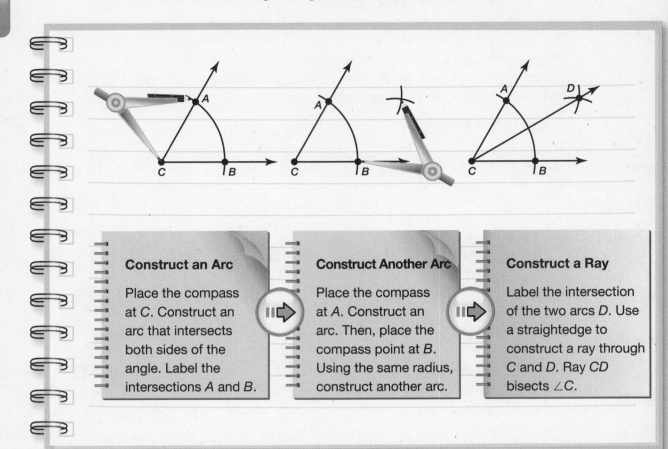

Construct an Arc

Place the compass at C. Construct an arc that intersects both sides of the angle. Label the intersections A and B.

Construct Another Arc

Place the compass at A. Construct an arc. Then, place the compass point at B. Using the same radius, construct another arc.

Construct a Ray

Label the intersection of the two arcs D. Use a straightedge to construct a ray through C and D. Ray CD bisects ∠C.

2. Construct the bisector of ∠A.

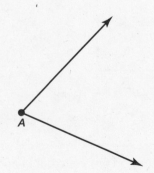

3. Construct an angle that is one-fourth the measure of ∠H. Explain how you performed the construction.

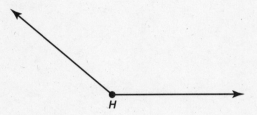

4. Describe how to construct an angle that is one-eighth the measure of ∠H from Question 3.

5. Use a compass and straightedge to show that the two angles formed by the angle bisector of angle A are congruent. Explain how you performed the construction.

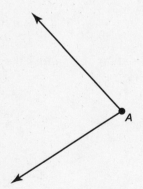

Talk the Talk

Translating an angle on the coordinate plane using coordinates and translating an angle by construction using construction tools both preserve the measure of the angle.

1. How are the two methods of translation similar?

2. How are the two methods of translation different?

3. Does either a vertical or a horizontal translation of an angle alter the measure of the angle? Explain why or why not.

Be prepared to share your solutions and methods.

If You Build It . . .

Constructing Perpendicular Lines, Parallel Lines, and Polygons

LEARNING GOALS

In this lesson, you will:

- Construct a perpendicular line to a given line.
- Construct a parallel line to a given line through a point not on the line.
- Construct an equilateral triangle given the length of one side of the triangle.
- Construct an isosceles triangle given the length of one side of the triangle.
- Construct a square given the perimeter (as the length of a given line segment).
- Construct a rectangle that is not a square given the perimeter (as the length of a given line segment).

KEY TERM

- perpendicular bisector

CONSTRUCTIONS

- a perpendicular line to a given line through a point on the line
- a perpendicular line to a given line through a point not on the line

There's an old saying that you might have heard before: "They broke the mold when they made me!" A person says this to imply that they are unique. Of course, humans do not come from molds, but there are plenty of things that do.

For example, take a look at a dime if you have one handy. Besides some tarnish on the coin and the year the coin was produced, it is identical to just about every other dime out there. Creating and duplicating a coin a few billion times is quite a process involving designing the coin, creating multiple molds (and negatives of the molds), cutting the design onto metal, and on and on.

Can you think of any times when the "original" might be more important than a duplicate? Can you think of any examples where the "original" product might be more expensive than a generic brand of the same product?

PROBLEM **1** **Constructing Perpendicular Lines**

Previously, you practiced bisecting a line segment and locating the midpoint of a line segment by construction. In fact, you were also constructing a line segment perpendicular to the original line segment.

A **perpendicular bisector** is a line, line segment, or ray that bisects a line segment and is also perpendicular to the line segment.

Follow the steps to construct a perpendicular line through a point on the line.

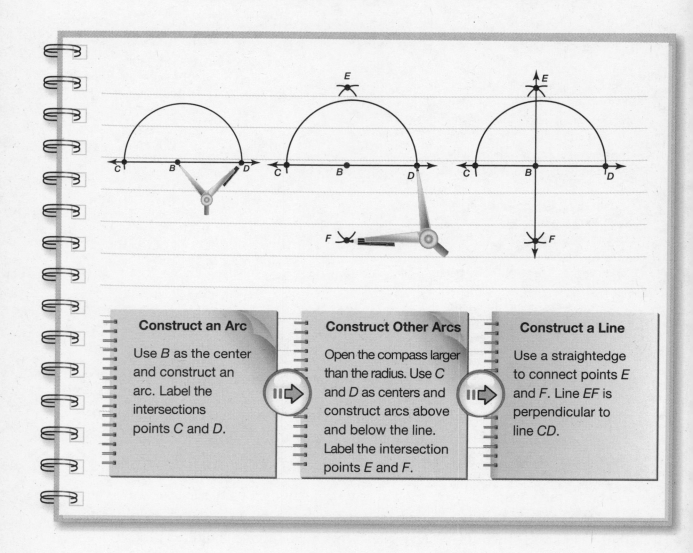

Construct an Arc

Use *B* as the center and construct an arc. Label the intersections points *C* and *D*.

Construct Other Arcs

Open the compass larger than the radius. Use *C* and *D* as centers and construct arcs above and below the line. Label the intersection points *E* and *F*.

Construct a Line

Use a straightedge to connect points *E* and *F*. Line *EF* is perpendicular to line *CD*.

1. Construct a line perpendicular to the given line through point *P*.

P

2. How is constructing a segment bisector and constructing a perpendicular line through a point on a line different?

3. Do you think that you can only construct a perpendicular line through a point that is on a line? Why or why not?

Follow these steps to construct a perpendicular line through a point not on a line.

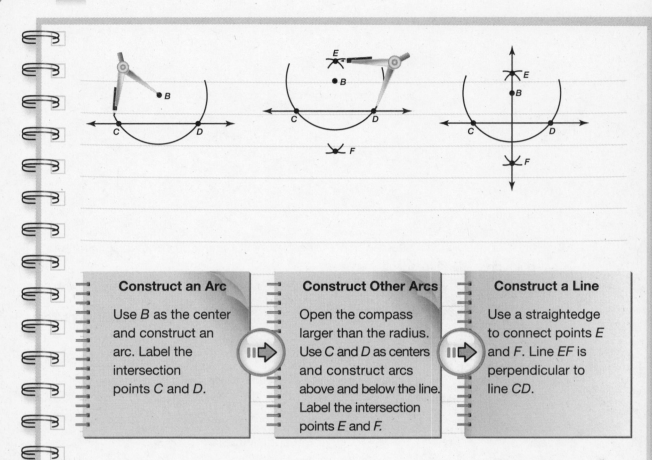

Construct an Arc		**Construct Other Arcs**		**Construct a Line**
Use B as the center and construct an arc. Label the intersection points C and D.	▐▶	Open the compass larger than the radius. Use C and D as centers and construct arcs above and below the line. Label the intersection points E and F.	▐▶	Use a straightedge to connect points E and F. Line EF is perpendicular to line CD.

4. Amos claims that it is only possible to construct a perpendicular line through horizontal and vertical lines because the intersection of the points must be right angles. Loren claims that a perpendicular line can be constructed through any line and any point on or not on the line. Who is correct? Correct the rationale of the student who is *not* correct.

5. Construct a line perpendicular to $\overleftrightarrow{AG}$ through point B.

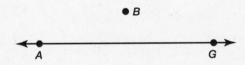

6. How is the construction of a perpendicular line through a point on a line different from the construction of a perpendicular line through a point not on the line?

7. Choose a point on the perpendicular bisector of $\overline{AG}$ and measure the distance from your point to point A and point G. Choose another point on the perpendicular bisector and measure the distance from this point to point A and point G. What do you notice.

8. Make a conjecture about the distance from any point on a perpendicular bisector to the endpoints of the original segment.

PROBLEM 2 Constructing Parallel Lines

To construct a line parallel to a given line, you must use a perpendicular line.

1. Analyze the figure shown.

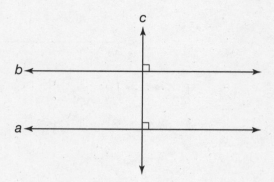

Describe the relationship between the lines given.

a. *a* and *c*

b. *b* and *c*

c. *a* and *b*

2. Construct line *e* parallel to line *d*. Then, describe the steps you performed for the construction.

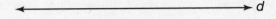 *d*

PROBLEM **3** **Constructing an Equilateral Triangle**

Remember, an equilateral triangle is a triangle that has three congruent sides.

In the rest of this lesson, you will construct an equilateral triangle, an isosceles triangle, a square, and a rectangle that is not a square. To perform the constructions, use only a compass and straightedge and rely on the basic geometric constructions you have learned such as duplicating a line segment, duplicating an angle, bisecting a line segment, bisecting an angle, constructing perpendicular lines, and constructing parallel lines.

1. The length of one side of an equilateral triangle is shown.

   a. What do you know about the other two sides of the equilateral triangle you will construct given the line segment shown?

   b. Construct an equilateral triangle using the given side length. Then, describe the steps you performed for the construction.

2. Sophie claims that she can construct an equilateral triangle by duplicating the line segment three times and having the endpoints of all three line segments intersect. Roberto thinks that Sophie's method will not result in an equilateral triangle. Who is correct? Explain why the incorrect student's rationale is not correct.

1. The length of one side of an isosceles triangle that is not an equilateral triangle is shown.

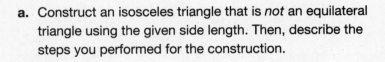

Remember, an isosceles triangle is a triangle that has at least two sides of equal length.

   a. Construct an isosceles triangle that is *not* an equilateral triangle using the given side length. Then, describe the steps you performed for the construction.

   b. Explain how you know your construction resulted in an isosceles triangle that is not an equilateral triangle.

   c. How does your construction compare to your classmates' constructions?

1

PROBLEM **5** **Constructing a Square Given the Perimeter**

Now you will construct a square using a given perimeter.

 1. The perimeter of a square is shown by $\overline{AB}$.

A   B

    a. Construct the square. Then, describe the steps that you performed for the construction.

    b. How does your construction compare to your classmates' constructions?

1. The perimeter of a rectangle is shown by $\overline{AB}$.

A   B

  a. Construct the rectangle that is not a square. Then, describe the steps you performed
  for the construction.

  b. How does this construction compare to your classmates' constructions?

   Be prepared to share your solutions and methods.

What's the Point?
Points of Concurrency

LEARNING GOALS

In this lesson, you will:

- Construct the incenter, circumcenter, centroid, and orthocenter.
- Locate points of concurrency using algebra.

KEY TERMS

- concurrent
- point of concurrency
- circumcenter
- incenter
- median
- centroid
- altitude
- orthocenter

Imagine playing a game of darts with a lot of people. You're all aiming for the bullseye, but of course it is the most difficult spot to hit on the dartboard. Therefore, it is probably the least hit spot on the board. Maybe you play a few hundred rounds, with each person having three throws on each turn, and each hit—no matter where it is—is recorded.

Now imagine that the dartboard is taken away, but all of the hits are shown as little dots on an empty wall. Could you determine the bullseye location using just the locations of those dots? How might you do it?

PROBLEM 1 **The New Zoo Review**

Josh and Lezlee have been given the task of building an information kiosk for the zoo. They want the kiosk to be easily accessible from each of the various exhibits. Three of the exhibits at the zoo are shown.

Elephantastic!
•

•
Primate Paradise

•
Girrafrica!

1. Josh suggests building the kiosk so that it is equal distance from Giraffrica! and Primate Paradise.

   a. Lezlee replies that the only location of the kiosk can be determined by determining the midpoint of the line segment between the two exhibits.

   Is Lezlee correct? Explain your reasoning.

   b. Use a construction to show all possible locations of the kiosk so that it is equal distance from Giraffrica! and Primate Paradise. Explain your reasoning.

2. Lezlee suggests building the kiosk so that it is equal distance from Elephantastic! and Primate Paradise. Use a construction to show all possible locations of the kiosk so that it is equal distance from Elephantastic! and Primate Paradise. Explain your reasoning.

3. Josh then wonders where the kiosk could be built so that it is equal distance from Elephantastic! and Giraffrica!. Use a construction to show all possible locations of the kiosk so that it is equal distance from Elephantastic! and Giraffrica!. Explain your reasoning.

4. Describe how to determine a location that is the same distance from all three exhibits. Is there more than one possible location that is equidistant from all three exhibits? Explain your reasoning.

5. Verify that the location you described in Question 4 is equidistant from each exhibit.

PROBLEM 2 Concurrence

Concurrent lines, rays, or line segments are three or more lines, rays, or line segments intersecting at a single point. The **point of concurrency** is the point at which concurrent lines, rays, or segments intersect.

1. Draw three concurrent lines and label C as the point of concurrency.

2. Draw three concurrent rays and label C as the point of concurrency.

3. Draw three concurrent line segments and label C as the point of concurrency.

1. Make a conjecture about the perpendicular bisectors of an acute triangle by performing the following steps.

   a. Draw an acute triangle that is not an equilateral triangle.

   b. Construct the three perpendicular bisectors of your acute triangle.

   c. Make a conjecture about the intersection of the three perpendicular bisectors of an acute triangle.

   d. Compare your conjecture to the conjectures of your classmates. What do you notice?

2. Make a conjecture about the perpendicular bisectors of an obtuse triangle by performing the following steps.

a. Draw an obtuse triangle.

b. Construct the three perpendicular bisectors of your obtuse triangle.

c. Make a conjecture about the intersection of the perpendicular angle bisectors of an obtuse triangle.

d. Compare your conjecture to the conjectures of your classmates. What do you notice?

3. Make a conjecture about the perpendicular bisectors of a right triangle by performing the following steps.

   a. Draw a right triangle.

   b. Construct the three perpendicular bisectors of your right triangle.

   c. Make a conjecture about the intersection of the three perpendicular bisectors of a right triangle.

   d. Compare your conjecture to the conjectures of your classmates. What do you notice?

4. Make a conjecture about the perpendicular bisectors of an equilateral triangle by performing the following steps.

    a. Construct an equilateral triangle.

    b. Construct the three perpendicular bisectors of your equilateral triangle.

    c. Make a conjecture about the intersection of the three perpendicular bisectors of an equilateral triangle.

    d. Compare your conjecture to the conjectures of your classmates. What do you notice?

5. Make a conjecture about the intersection of the three perpendicular bisectors of any triangle. Is the intersection on the interior, exterior, or on the triangle?

The **circumcenter** is the point of concurrency of the three perpendicular bisectors of a triangle.

6. Consider the four triangles that you drew in Questions 1 through 4.

   a. Measure the distance from the circumcenter to each vertex of the triangle.

   b. Is the circumcenter always, sometimes, or never equidistant from each vertex of the triangle? Explain your reasoning.

   c. Measure the distance from the circumcenter to each side of the triangle.

   d. Is the circumcenter always, sometimes, or never equidistant from each side of the triangle? Explain your reasoning.

PROBLEM 4   Investigating the Incenter

1. Make a conjecture about the angle bisectors of an acute triangle by performing the following steps.

   a. Draw an acute triangle that is not an equilateral triangle.

   b. Construct the three angle bisectors of your acute triangle.

   c. Make a conjecture about the intersection of the three angle bisectors of an acute triangle.

   d. Compare your conjecture to the conjectures of your classmates. What do you notice?

2. Make a conjecture about the angle bisectors of an obtuse triangle by performing the following steps.

   a. Draw an obtuse triangle.

   b. Construct the three angle bisectors of your obtuse triangle.

   c. Make a conjecture about the intersection of the three angle bisectors of an obtuse triangle.

   d. Compare your conjecture to the conjectures of your classmates. What do you notice?

3. Make a conjecture about the angle bisectors of a right triangle by performing the following steps.

   a. Draw a right triangle.

   b. Construct the three angle bisectors of your right triangle.

   c. Make a conjecture about the intersection of the three angle bisectors of a right triangle.

   d. Compare your conjecture to the conjectures of your classmates. What do you notice?

4. Make a conjecture about the angle bisectors of an equilateral triangle by performing the following steps.

    a. Construct an equilateral triangle.

    b. Construct the three angle bisectors of your equilateral triangle.

    c. Make a conjecture about the intersection of the three angle bisectors of an equilateral triangle.

    d. Compare your conjecture to the conjectures of your classmates. What do you notice?

5. Make a conjecture about the intersection of the three angle bisectors of any triangle. Is the intersection on the interior, exterior, or on the triangle?

The **incenter** is the point of concurrency of the three angle bisectors of a triangle.

6. Consider the four triangles that you drew in Questions 1 through 4.

   a. Measure the distance from the incenter to each vertex of the triangle.

   b. Is the incenter always, sometimes, or never equidistant from each vertex of the triangle? Explain your reasoning.

   c. Measure the distance from the incenter to each side of the triangle.

   d. Is the incenter always, sometimes, or never equidistant from each side of the triangle? Explain your reasoning.

A **median** of a triangle is a line segment that connects a vertex to the midpoint of the opposite side.

1. Make a conjecture about the medians of an acute triangle by performing the following steps.

  a. Draw an acute triangle that is not an equilateral triangle.

  b. Construct the three medians of your acute triangle.

  c. Make a conjecture about the intersection of the three medians of an acute triangle.

  d. Compare your conjecture to the conjectures of your classmates. What do you notice?

2. Make a conjecture about the medians of an obtuse triangle by performing the following steps.

   a. Draw an obtuse triangle.

   b. Construct the three medians of your obtuse triangle.

   c. Make a conjecture about the intersection of the three medians of an obtuse triangle.

   d. Compare your conjecture to the conjectures of your classmates. What do you notice?

3. Make a conjecture about the medians of a right triangle by performing the following steps.

    a. Draw a right triangle.

    b. Construct the three medians of your right triangle.

    c. Make a conjecture about the intersection of the three medians of a right triangle.

    d. Compare your conjecture to the conjectures of your classmates. What do you notice?

4. Make a conjecture about the medians of an equilateral triangle by performing the following steps.

    a. Construct an equilateral triangle.

    b. Construct the three medians of your equilateral triangle.

    c. Make a conjecture about the intersection of the three medians of an equilateral triangle.

    d. Compare your conjecture to the conjectures of your classmates. What do you notice?

5. Make a conjecture about the intersection of the three medians of any triangle. Is the intersection on the interior, exterior, or on the triangle?

The **centroid** is the point of concurrency of the three medians of a triangle.

6. Consider the four triangles that you drew in Questions 1 through 4.

   a. Measure the distance from the centroid to each vertex of the triangle.

   b. Is the centroid always, sometimes, or never equidistant from each vertex of the triangle? Explain your reasoning.

   c. Measure the distance from the centroid to each side of the triangle.

   d. Is the centroid always, sometimes, or never equidistant from each side of the triangle? Explain your reasoning.

7. The centroid divides each median into two segments. Compare the distance from the centroid to the vertex and the distance from the centroid to the midpoint of the opposite side in each of the triangles you created. What is the ratio?

PROBLEM 6 **Investigating the Orthocenter**

An **altitude** of a triangle is a line segment that is perpendicular to a side of the triangle and has one endpoint at the opposite vertex.

1. Make a conjecture about the altitudes of an acute triangle by performing the following steps.

   a. Draw an acute triangle that is not an equilateral triangle.

   b. Construct the three altitudes of your acute triangle.

   c. Make a conjecture about the intersection of the three altitudes of an acute triangle.

   d. Compare your conjecture to the conjectures of your classmates. What do you notice?

2. Make a conjecture about the altitudes of an obtuse triangle by performing the following steps.

    a. Draw an obtuse triangle.

    b. Construct the three altitudes of your obtuse triangle.

    c. Make a conjecture about the intersection of the three altitudes of an obtuse triangle.

    d. Compare your conjecture to the conjectures of your classmates. What do you notice?

3. Make a conjecture about the altitudes of a right triangle by performing the following steps.

   a. Draw a right triangle.

   b. Construct the three altitudes of your right triangle.

   c. Make a conjecture about the intersection of the three altitudes of a right triangle.

   d. Compare your conjecture to the conjectures of your classmates. What do you notice?

4. Make a conjecture about the altitudes of an equilateral triangle by performing the following steps.

  a. Construct an equilateral triangle.

  b. Construct the three altitudes of your equilateral triangle.

  c. Make a conjecture about the intersection of the three altitudes of an equilateral triangle.

  d. Compare your conjecture to the conjectures of your classmates. What do you notice?

5. Make a conjecture about the intersection of the three altitudes of any triangle. Is the intersection on the interior, exterior, or on the triangle?

The **orthocenter** is the point of concurrency of the three altitudes of a triangle.

6. Consider the four triangles that you drew in Questions 1 through 4.

    a. Measure the distance from the orthocenter to each vertex of the triangle.

    b. Is the orthocenter always, sometimes, or never equidistant from each vertex of the triangle? Explain your reasoning.

    c. Measure the distance from the orthocenter to each side of the triangle.

    d. Is the orthocenter always, sometimes, or never equidistant from each side of the triangle? Explain your reasoning.

PROBLEM 7 Points of Concurrency

1. Examine the incenter, circumcenter, centroid, and orthocenter for the equilateral triangles you created. What do you notice?

2. Complete the table to describe the location of each point of currency for acute, obtuse, and right triangles.

	Acute Triangle	Obtuse Triangle	Right Triangle
Incenter			
Circumcenter			
Centroid			
Orthocenter			

PROBLEM 8 **Using Algebra with Points of Concurrency**

1. Form a triangle on the grid by connecting the points $A(-6, -8)$, $B(6, -8)$, and $C(0, 10)$.

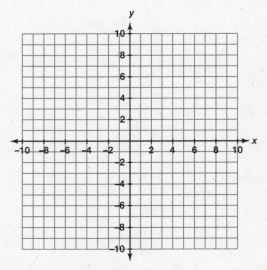

2. Classify triangle ABC by performing the following steps.

    a. Calculate the length of each side of the triangle using the Distance Formula.

    b. Use the side lengths to classify the triangle. Explain your reasoning.

3. Describe how you could use algebra to calculate the coordinates of each point of concurrency.

   a. centroid

   b. circumcenter

   c. orthocenter

   d. incenter

The prefix ortho- means "straight, or vertical."

4. Calculate the centroid of triangle *ABC*.

   a. Calculate the midpoint of each side of the triangle.

   b. Write an equation for each median.

   c. Calculate the coordinates of the centroid.

   d. Plot the centroid on the grid in Question 1.

5. Calculate the circumcenter of triangle *ABC*.

    a. Calculate the midpoint of each side of the triangle.

    b. Calculate the slope of each side of the triangle.

    c. Write an equation for each perpendicular bisector.

d. Calculate the coordinates of the circumcenter.

e. Plot the circumcenter on the grid in Question 1.

6. Calculate the orthocenter of triangle *ABC*.

   a. Calculate the slope of each side of the triangle.

   b. Write an equation for each altitude.

c. Calculate the coordinates of the orthocenter.

d. Plot the orthocenter on the grid in Question 1.

7. What do you notice about the location of the centroid, circumcenter, and orthocenter for isosceles triangle *ABC*?

8. Do you think the behavior that you described in Question 8 will also be true for the incenter? Explain your reasoning.

9. Do you think the behavior that you described in Questions 7 through 8 will be true for a triangle that is not isosceles? Explain how you could test your theory.

PROBLEM 9 The Mall

A construction company plans to build a large mall to serve three small towns as shown on the map below. They are considering a location that is equidistant from each of the three towns and agree to pay for building new roads connecting the mall to the three towns. Cost for building new roads is $150,000 per mile. Each unit on the graph represents one mile.

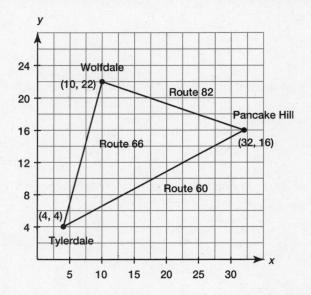

1. What point of concurrency is most useful in this situation? Explain your reasoning.

2. Determine the approximate coordinates of the location of the mall.

3. Determine the approximate distance from the mall location to each town. Round to the nearest mile.

4. How much money should be budgeted for road construction in this project?

Talk the Talk

1. Determine which point of concurrency would be most helpful in each situation.

   a. A flea market is situated on a triangular piece of land. Each entrance is located at one of the three vertices of triangle. Joanie wants to set up her merchandise at a location that is equidistant from all three entrances.

   b. An artist is building a mobile with several metal triangles of various sizes. The triangles are connected to each other using steel rods and the rods are welded onto each triangle at a point which would allow the triangle to balance horizontally.

   c. Jim's backyard is a triangular plot of land. He is using fencing to build a circular dog pen. He wants the dog pen to be as large as possible and needs to determine the location of the center of the circular dog pen.

2. The intersection of the three altitudes of any triangle is best described by this point.

3. The point of concurrency located two-thirds the way from the vertex to the midpoint of the opposite side and otherwise known as the center of gravity.

Be prepared to share your solutions and methods.

Chapter 1 Summary

KEY TERMS

- point (1.1)
- line (1.1)
- collinear points (1.1)
- plane (1.1)
- compass (1.1)
- straightedge (1.1)
- sketch (1.1)
- draw (1.1)
- construct (1.1)
- coplanar lines (1.1)
- skew lines (1.1)
- ray (1.1)
- endpoint of a ray (1.1)
- line segment (1.1)
- endpoints of a line segment (1.1)
- congruent line segments (1.1)
- Distance Formula (1.2)
- transformation (1.2)
- rigid motion (1.2)
- translation (1.2)
- pre-image (1.2)
- image (1.2)
- arc (1.2)
- midpoint (1.3)
- Midpoint Formula (1.3)
- segment bisector (1.3)
- angle (1.4)
- angle bisector (1.4)
- perpendicular bisector (1.5)
- concurrent (1.6)
- point of concurrency (1.6)
- circumcenter (1.6)
- incenter (1.6)
- median (1.6)
- centroid (1.6)
- altitude (1.6)
- orthocenter (1.6)

CONSTRUCTIONS

- copying a line segment (1.2)
- duplicating a line segment (1.2)
- bisecting a line segment (1.3)
- copying an angle (1.4)
- duplicating an angle (1.4)
- bisecting an angle (1.4)
- perpendicular line to a given line through a point on the line (1.5)
- perpendicular line to a given line through a point not on the line (1.5)

1.1 Identifying Points, Lines, and Planes

A point is a location in space that has no size or shape. A line is a straight continuous arrangement of an infinite number of points. A plane is a flat surface that has an infinite length and width, but no depth. Collinear points are points that are located on the same line. Coplanar lines are two or more lines that are located in the same plane. Skew lines are two or more lines that are not in the same plane.

Example

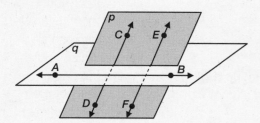

Points A and B lie on $\overleftrightarrow{AB}$, points C and D lie on $\overleftrightarrow{CD}$, and points E and F lie on $\overleftrightarrow{EF}$.

Line AB lies in plane q. Lines CD and EF lie in plane p.

Points A and B are collinear. Points C and D are collinear. Points E and F are collinear.

Lines CD and EF are coplanar.

Lines AB and CD are skew. Lines AB and EF are skew.

Planes p and q intersect.

1.2 Applying the Distance Formula

The Distance Formula can be used to calculate the distance between two points on the coordinate plane. The Distance Formula states that if (x_1, y_1) and (x_2, y_2) are two points on the coordinate plane, then the distance d between (x_1, y_1) and (x_2, y_2) is given by $d = \sqrt{(x_2 - x_1)^2 + (y_2 - y_1)^2}$.

Example

Calculate the distance between the points $(3, -2)$ and $(-5, 1)$.

$x_1 = 3, y_1 = -2, x_2 = -5, y_2 = 1$

$d = \sqrt{(x_2 - x_1)^2 + (y_2 - y_1)^2}$

$ = \sqrt{(-5 - 3)^2 + [1 - (-2)]^2}$

$ = \sqrt{(-8)^2 + (3)^2}$

$ = \sqrt{64 + 9}$

$ = \sqrt{73}$

$ \approx 8.5$

The distance between the points $(3, -2)$ and $(-5, 1)$ is $\sqrt{73}$ units, or approximately 8.5 units.

1.2 Translating Line Segments on the Coordinate Plane

A translation is a rigid motion that slides each point of a figure the same distance and direction. A horizontal translation of a line segment on the coordinate plane changes the x-coordinates of both endpoints while leaving the y-coordinates the same. A vertical translation changes the y-coordinates of both endpoints while leaving the x-coordinates the same.

Example

Line segment PQ is translated horizontally 10 units to the left to create $\overline{P'Q'}$. Line segment $P'Q'$ is translated vertically 8 units down to create line segment $\overline{P''Q''}$.

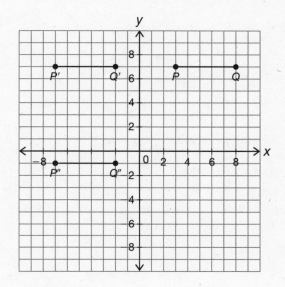

Line Segment	$\overline{PQ}$	$\overline{P'Q'}$	$\overline{P''Q''}$
Coordinates of Endpoints	(3, 7) (8, 7)	(−7, 7) (−2, 7)	(−7, −1) (−2, −1)

The lengths of the images and the pre-images remain the same after each translation.

1.2 Duplicating a Line Using Construction Tools

A straightedge and compass can be used to duplicate a line.

Example

Line segment JK can be duplicated using a straightedge and compass by drawing a starter line and then duplicating a line segment that is the same length as $\overline{JK}$.

1.3 Applying the Midpoint Formula

A midpoint is a point that is exactly halfway between two given points. The Midpoint Formula can be used to calculate the coordinates of a midpoint. The Midpoint Formula states that if (x_1, y_1) and (x_2, y_2) are two points on the coordinate plane, then the midpoint of the line segment that joins these two points is given by $\left(\dfrac{x_1 + x_2}{2}, \dfrac{y_1 + y_2}{2}\right)$.

Example

Calculate the midpoint of a line segment with the endpoints $(-8, -3)$ and $(4, 6)$.

$x_1 = -8, y_1 = -3, x_2 = 4, y_2 = 6$

$$\left(\frac{x_1 + x_2}{2}, \frac{y_1 + y_2}{2}\right) = \left(\frac{-8 + 4}{2}, \frac{-3 + 6}{2}\right)$$

$$= \left(\frac{-4}{2}, \frac{3}{2}\right)$$

$$= \left(-2, \frac{3}{2}\right)$$

The midpoint of the line segment is $\left(-2, \dfrac{3}{2}\right)$.

1.3 Bisecting a Line Segment Using Construction Tools

Construction tools can be used to bisect a line segment.

Example

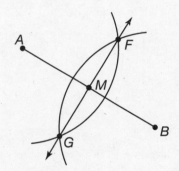

Open the radius of the compass to more than half the length of the original line segment. Construct an arc using one endpoint as the center. Keeping the compass at the same radius, construct an arc using the other endpoint as center. Label and connect the points created by the intersection of the arcs. Line segment FG bisects $\overline{AB}$.

Translating an Angle on the Coordinate Plane

Translating an angle on the coordinate plane is a rigid motion that slides the angle, either horizontally or vertically, on the coordinate plane. Because it is a rigid motion, the angle measures of the image and the pre-image are the same. Horizontal translations only impact the *x*-coordinates of the endpoints; vertical translations only impact the *y*-coordinates of the endpoints.

Example

Angle *JDL* is translated horizontally 11 units right to form ∠*J'D'L'*. Angle *J'D'L'* is translated vertically 12 units down to create ∠*J"D"L"*.

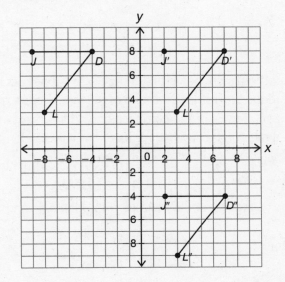

Line Segment	$\overline{JD}$	$\overline{J'D'}$	$\overline{J''D''}$
Coordinates of Endpoints	(−9, 8) (−4, 8)	(2, 8) (7, 8)	(2, −4) (7, −4)

Line Segment	$\overline{DL}$	$\overline{D'L'}$	$\overline{D''L''}$
Coordinates of Endpoints	(−4, 8) (−8, 3)	(7, 8) (3, 3)	(7, −4) (3, −9)

The measure of the angle images and pre-images remain the same after each translation.

1.4 Bisecting an Angle Using Construction Tools

An angle bisector is a ray drawn through the vertex of an angle that divides the angle into two angles of equal measure.

Example

Angle *F* can be bisected using construction tools.

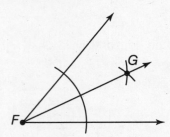

Place the compass on the vertex of the angle. Construct an arc that intersects both sides of the angle. Place the compass at one of the intersection points and construct an arc, then using the same radius of the compass construct an arc using the other intersection point. Construct a ray connecting the vertex to the intersection of the arcs. Ray *FG* bisects ∠*F*.

1.5 Constructing Perpendicular Lines

Perpendicular lines can be constructed through a given point using construction tools.

Example

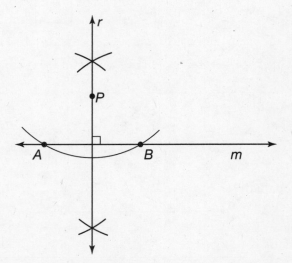

Use the given point *P* as the center and construct an arc that passes through the given line. Open the compass radius. Construct an arc above and below the given line using one of the intersection points just created. Keeping the radius the same, construct an arc above and below the given line using the other intersection point. Connect the intersection points of the arcs which should also pass through the given point. Line *r* is perpendicular to line *m*.

1.5 Constructing Equilateral Triangles

Equilateral triangles have 3 congruent sides. Construction tools can be used to construct an equilateral triangle given the length of one side.

Example

Construct an equilateral triangle with the side length shown.

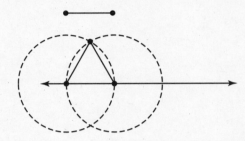

Construct a starter line and duplicate the given segment onto the starter line. Construct a circle using an endpoint of the line segment as the center. Then construct another circle using the other endpoint as the center. Connect the point of intersection of the circles to each endpoint using line segments.

1.5 Constructing Isosceles Triangles

An isosceles triangle is a triangle that has at least two sides of equal length.

Example

Construct an isosceles triangle with the side length shown.

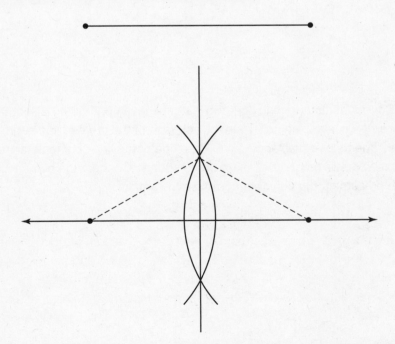

Construct a starter line and duplicate the given line segment. Then construct a perpendicular bisector through the line segment. Connect the endpoints of each line segment to a point on the bisector.

1.5 Constructing Squares

A square can be constructed using construction tools.

Example

Construct a square using the perimeter given.

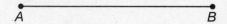

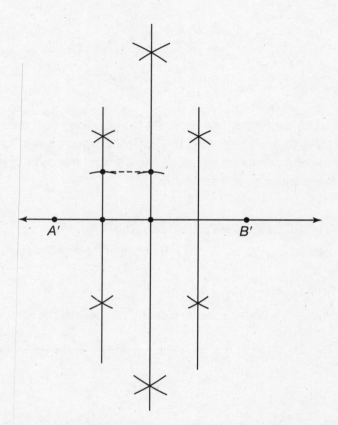

Construct a starter line and duplicate the given perimeter. Bisect the line segment using a perpendicular bisector. Then, bisect each of the created line segments to create 4 line segments of equal length. Duplicate one of the line segments along two perpendicular bisectors to create the height of the square. Connect the two endpoints of the line segments representing the height to complete the square.

1.5 Constructing Rectangles That Are Not Squares

A rectangle can be constructed in a similar method to constructing a square using a given perimeter of the rectangle.

Example

Construct a rectangle using the perimeter given.

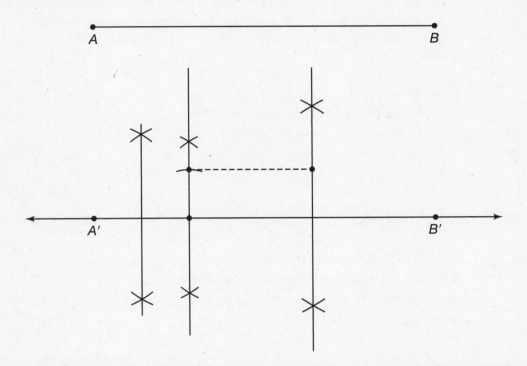

Construct a starter line and duplicate the given perimeter. Place a point anywhere on the line segment except in the middle dividing the line segment into two unequal line segments. Then, draw perpendicular bisectors through each of the line segments to create four line segments. Choose one of the line segments to use as the base of the rectangle. Duplicate another line segment that is not the same size as the base on two of the perpendicular bisectors to use as the height of the rectangle. Finally, connect the endpoints of the line segments representing the height to create a rectangle.

Identifying Points of Concurrency

When three or more lines intersect at the same point, the lines are called concurrent lines. The point at which the concurrent lines intersect is called the point of concurrency.

There are special types of points of concurrency in triangles. The incenter of a triangle is the point at which the three angle bisectors of a triangle are concurrent. The circumcenter of a triangle is the point at which the three perpendicular bisectors of a triangle are concurrent. The centroid is the point at which the three medians of a triangle are concurrent. The orthocenter is the point at which the three altitudes of a triangle are concurrent.

Examples

In $\triangle ABC$, $\overline{AE}$, $\overline{BF}$, and $\overline{CD}$ are angle bisectors. So, point G is the incenter, and $DG = EG = FG$.

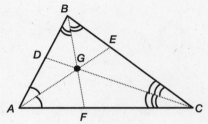

In $\triangle DEF$, $\overline{JK}$, $\overline{LM}$, and $\overline{NP}$ are perpendicular bisectors. So, point Q is the circumcenter, and the distances from the circumcenter to each vertex are the same.

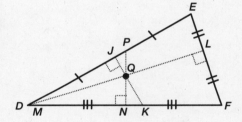

In $\triangle PQR$, $\overline{PT}$, $\overline{QV}$, and $\overline{RS}$ are medians. So, point W is the centroid, and $PW = 2TW$, $QW = 2VW$, and $RW = 2SW$.

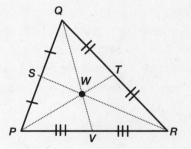

In $\triangle XYZ$, $\overline{XB}$, $\overline{YC}$, and $\overline{ZA}$ are altitudes. So, point D is the orthocenter.

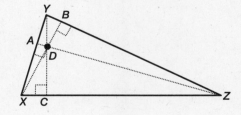

Introduction to Proof

2

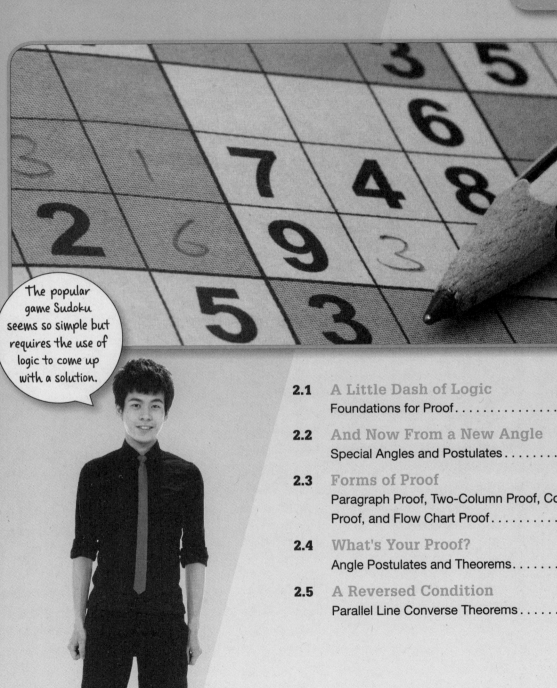

The popular game Sudoku seems so simple but requires the use of logic to come up with a solution.

A Little Dash of Logic
Foundations for Proof

LEARNING GOALS

In this lesson, you will:

- Define inductive and deductive reasoning.
- Identify methods of reasoning.
- Compare and contrast methods of reasoning.
- Create examples using inductive and deductive reasoning.
- Identify the hypothesis and conclusion of a conditional statement.
- Explore the truth values of conditional statements.
- Use a truth table.

KEY TERMS

- induction
- deduction
- counterexample
- conditional statement
- propositional form
- propositional variables
- hypothesis
- conclusion
- truth value
- truth table

One of the most famous literary detectives is Sherlock Holmes. Created by author Sir Arthur Conan Doyle, Sherlock Holmes first appeared in print in 1887 in the novel *A Study in Scarlet*. The character has gone on to appear in four novels, 56 short stories, and over 200 films. The Guinness Book of World Records lists Holmes as the most portrayed movie character, with more than 70 different actors playing the part.

Holmes is most famous for his keen powers of observation and logical reasoning, which always helped him solve the case. In many literary and film adaptations, Holmes is known to remark, "Elementary, my dear Watson," after explaining to his assistant how he solved the mystery. However, this well-known phrase doesn't actually appear in any of the stories written by Doyle. It first appeared in the 1915 novel *Psmith, Journalist* by P.G. Wodehouse and also appeared at the end of the 1929 film *The Return of Sherlock Holmes*. Regardless, this phrase will probably always be associated with the famous detective.

1. Emma considered the following statements.

   - $4^2 = 4 \times 4$

   - Nine cubed is equal to nine times nine times nine.

   - 10 to the fourth power is equal to four factors of 10 multiplied together.

   Emma concluded that raising a number to a power is the same as multiplying the number as many times as indicated by the exponent. How did Emma reach this conclusion?

2. Ricky read that raising a number to a power is the same as multiplying that number as many times as indicated by the exponent. He had to determine seven to the fourth power using a calculator. So, he entered $7 \times 7 \times 7 \times 7$. How did Ricky reach this conclusion?

3. Compare Emma's reasoning to Ricky's reasoning.

4. Jennifer is a writing consultant. She is paid $900 for a ten-hour job and $1980 for a twenty-two-hour job.

   a. How much does Jennifer charge per hour?

   b. To answer Question 4, part (a), did you start with a general rule and make a conclusion, or did you start with specific information and create a general rule?

5. Your friend Aaron tutors elementary school students. He tells you that the job pays $8.25 per hour.

   a. How much does Aaron earn from working 4 hours?

   b. To answer Question 5, part (a), did you start with a general rule and make a conclusion, or did you start with specific information and create a general rule?

Is This English Class or Algebra?

The ability to use information to reason and make conclusions is very important in life and in mathematics. There are two common methods of reasoning. You can construct the name for each method of reasoning using your knowledge of prefixes, root words, and suffixes.

> Remember, a prefix is at the beginning of a word and a suffix is at the end.

Word Fragment	Prefix, Root Word, or Suffix	Meaning
in-	Prefix	*toward* or *up to*
de-	Prefix	*down from*
-duc-	Root Word	*to lead* and often *to think*, from the Latin word *duco*
-tion	Suffix	*the act of*

1. Form a word that means "the act of thinking down from."

2. Form a word that means "the act of thinking toward or up to."

Induction is reasoning that uses specific examples to make a conclusion. Sometimes you will make generalizations about observations or patterns and apply these generalizations to new or unfamiliar situations. For example, you may notice that when you don't study for a test, your grade is lower than when you do study for a test. You apply what you learned from these observations to the next test you take.

> These types of reasoning can also be known as inductive and deductive reasoning.

Deduction is reasoning that uses a general rule to make a conclusion. For example, you may learn the rule for which direction to turn a screwdriver: "righty tighty, lefty loosey." If you want to remove a screw, you apply the rule and turn the screwdriver counterclockwise.

3. Consider the reasoning used by Emma, Ricky, Jennifer, and Aaron in Problem 1.

   a. Who used inductive reasoning?

   b. Who used deductive reasoning?

PROBLEM 3 Coming to Conclusions

A problem situation can provide you with a great deal of information that you can use to make conclusions. It is important to identify specific and general information in a problem situation to reach appropriate conclusions. Some information may be irrelevant to reach the appropriate conclusion.

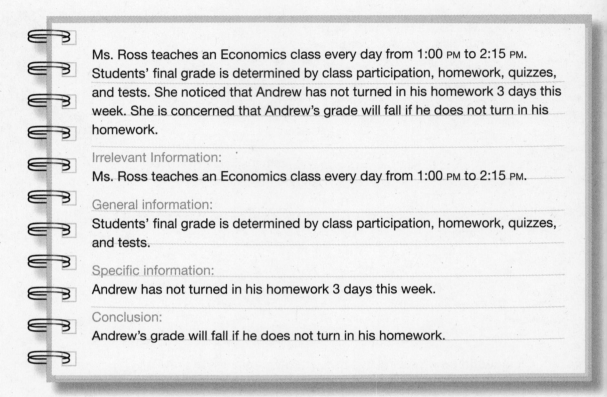

Ms. Ross teaches an Economics class every day from 1:00 PM to 2:15 PM. Students' final grade is determined by class participation, homework, quizzes, and tests. She noticed that Andrew has not turned in his homework 3 days this week. She is concerned that Andrew's grade will fall if he does not turn in his homework.

Irrelevant Information:
Ms. Ross teaches an Economics class every day from 1:00 PM to 2:15 PM.

General information:
Students' final grade is determined by class participation, homework, quizzes, and tests.

Specific information:
Andrew has not turned in his homework 3 days this week.

Conclusion:
Andrew's grade will fall if he does not turn in his homework.

1. Did Ms. Ross use induction or deduction to make this conclusion? Explain your answer.

2. Conner read an article that claimed that tobacco use greatly increases the risk of getting cancer. He then noticed that his neighbor Matilda smokes. Conner is concerned that Matilda has a high risk of getting cancer.

    a. Which information is specific and which information is general in this problem situation?

    b. What is the conclusion in this problem?

    c. Did Conner use inductive or deductive reasoning to make the conclusion? Explain your reasoning.

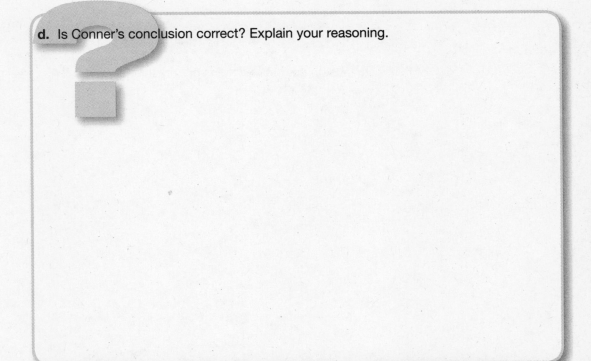

    d. Is Conner's conclusion correct? Explain your reasoning.

3. Molly returned from a trip to England and tells you, "It rains every day in England!" She explains that it rained each of the five days she was there.

   a. Which information is specific and which information is general in this problem situation?

   b. What is the conclusion in this problem?

   c. Did Molly use inductive or deductive reasoning to make the conclusion? Explain your answer.

   d. Is Molly's conclusion correct? Explain your reasoning.

4. Dontrell takes detailed notes in history class and math class. His classmate Trang will miss biology class tomorrow to attend a field trip. Trang's biology teacher asks him if he knows someone who always takes detailed notes. Trang tells his biology teacher that Dontrell takes detailed notes. Trang's biology teacher suggests that Trang should borrow Dontrell's notes because he concludes that Dontrell's notes will be detailed.

a. What conclusion did Trang make? What information supports this conclusion?

b. What type of reasoning did Trang use? Explain your reasoning.

c. What conclusion did the biology teacher make? What information supports this conclusion?

d. What type of reasoning did the biology teacher use? Explain your reasoning.

e. Will Trang's conclusion always be true? Will the biology teacher's conclusion always be true? Explain your reasoning.

5. The first four numbers in a sequence are 4, 15, 26, and 37.

   a. What is the next number in the sequence? How did you calculate the next number?

   b. Describe how you used both induction and deduction, and what order you used these reasonings to make your conclusion.

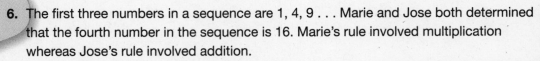

6. The first three numbers in a sequence are 1, 4, 9 . . . Marie and Jose both determined that the fourth number in the sequence is 16. Marie's rule involved multiplication whereas Jose's rule involved addition.

   a. What types of reasoning did Marie and Jose use to determine the fourth number in the sequence?

   b. What rule did Marie use to determine the fourth number in the sequence?

   c. What rule did Jose use to determine the fourth number in the sequence?

   d. Who used the correct rule? Explain your reasoning.

PROBLEM 4 Why Is This False?

There are two reasons why a conclusion may be false. Either the assumed information is false, or the argument is not valid.

1. Derek tells his little brother that it will not rain for the next 30 days because he "knows everything." Why is this conclusion false?

2. Two lines are not parallel, so the lines must intersect. Why is this conclusion false?

3. Write an example of a conclusion that is false because the assumed information is false.

4. Write an example of a conclusion that is false because the argument is not valid.

To show that a statement is false, you can provide a *counterexample*. A **counterexample** is a specific example that shows that a general statement is not true.

5. Provide a counterexample for each of these statements to demonstrate that they are not true.

   a. All prime numbers are odd.

   b. The sum of the measures of two acute angles is always greater than 90°.

A **conditional statement** is a statement that can be written in the form "If p, then q." This form is the **propositional form** of a conditional statement. It can also be written using symbols as $p \rightarrow q$, which is read as "p implies q." The variables p and q are **propositional variables**. The **hypothesis** of a conditional statement is the variable p. The **conclusion** of a conditional statement is the variable q.

In this case, p and q represent statements, not numbers.

The **truth value** of a conditional statement is whether the statement is true or false. If a conditional statement could be true, then the truth value of the statement is considered true. The truth value of a conditional statement is either true or false, but not both.

You can identify the hypothesis and conclusion from a conditional statement.

Conditional Statement
If $x^2 = 36$, then $x = 6$ or $x = -6$.

Hypothesis of the Conditional Statement
$x^2 = 36$

Conclusion of the Conditional Statement
$x = 6$ or $x = -6$.

Consider the conditional statement: If the measure of an angle is 32°, then the angle is acute.

1. What is the hypothesis p?

2. What is the conclusion q?

3. If p is true and q is true, then the truth value of a conditional statement is true.

    a. What does the phrase "If p is true" mean in terms of the conditional statement?

    b. What does the phrase "If q is true" mean in terms of the conditional statement?

    c. Explain why the truth value of the conditional statement is true if both p and q are true.

4. If p is true and q is false, then the truth value of a conditional statement is false.

   a. What does the phrase "If p is true" mean in terms of the conditional statement?

   b. What does the phrase "If q is false" mean in terms of the conditional statement?

   c. Explain why the truth value of the conditional statement is false if p is true and q is false.

5. If p is false and q is true, then the truth value of a conditional statement is true.

   a. What does the phrase "If p is false" mean in terms of the conditional statement?

   b. What does the phrase "If q is true" mean in terms of the conditional statement?

   c. Explain why the truth value of the conditional statement is true if p is false and q is true.

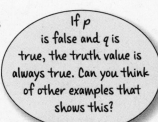

If p is false and q is true, the truth value is always true. Can you think of other examples that shows this?

6. If p is false and q is false, then the truth value of a conditional statement is true.

   a. What does the phrase "If p is false" mean in terms of the conditional statement?

   b. What does the phrase "If q is false" mean in terms of the conditional statement?

   c. Explain why the truth value of the conditional statement is true if both p and q are false.

A **truth table** is a table that summarizes all possible truth values for a conditional statement $p \to q$. The first two columns of a truth table represent all possible truth values for the propositional variables p and q. The last column represents the truth value of the conditional statement $p \to q$.

The truth values for the conditional statement "If the measure of an angle is 32°, then the angle is acute" is shown.

The truth value of the conditional statement $p \to q$ is determined by the truth value of p and the truth value of q.

- If p is true and q is true, then $p \to q$ is true.
- If p is true and q is false, then $p \to q$ is false.
- If p is false and q is true, then $p \to q$ is true.
- If p is false and q is false, then $p \to q$ is true.

p	q	$p \to q$
the measure of an angle is 32°	the angle is acute	If the measure of an angle is 32°, then the angle is acute.
T	T	T
T	F	F
F	T	T
F	F	T

7. Consider the conditional statement: If $m\overline{AB}$ = 6 inches and $m\overline{BC}$ = 6 inches, then $\overline{AB} \cong \overline{BC}$.

   a. What is the hypothesis p?

   b. What is the conclusion q?

   c. If both p and q are true, what does that mean? What is the truth value of the conditional statement if both p and q are true?

d. If p is true and q is false, what does that mean? What is the truth value of the conditional statement if p is true and q is false?

e. If p is false and q is true, what does that mean? What is the truth value of the conditional statement if p is false and q is true?

f. If both p and q are false, what does that mean? What is the truth value of the conditional statement if both p and q are false?

g. Summarize your answers to parts (a) through (f) by completing a truth table for the conditional statement.

p	q	$p \rightarrow q$

So, the only way to get a truth value of false is if the conclusion is false?

For each conditional statement, draw a diagram and then write the hypothesis as the "Given" and the conclusion as the "Prove."

1. If $\overrightarrow{BD}$ bisects $\angle ABC$, then $\angle ABD \cong \angle CBD$.

Given:

Prove:

2. $\overline{AM} \cong \overline{MB}$, if M is the midpoint of $\overline{AB}$.

Given:

Prove:

3. If $\overleftrightarrow{AB} \perp \overrightarrow{CD}$ at point C, then $\angle ACD$ is a right angle and $\angle BCD$ is a right angle.

Given:

Prove:

4. $\overrightarrow{WX}$ is the perpendicular bisector of $\overline{PR}$, if $\overrightarrow{WX} \perp \overline{PR}$ and $\overrightarrow{WX}$ bisects $\overline{PR}$.

Given:

Prove:

5. Mr. David wrote the following information on the board.

If $\overline{AC} \cong \overline{BC}$, then C is the midpoint of $\overline{AB}$.

He asked his students to discuss the truth of this conditional statement.

Susan said she believed the statement to be true in all situations. Marcus disagreed with Susan and said that the statement was not true all of the time.

What is Marcus thinking and who is correct?

Talk the Talk

1. Write a short note to a friend explaining induction and deduction. Include definitions of both terms and examples that are very easy to understand.

 Be prepared to share your solutions and methods.

And Now From a New Angle
Special Angles and Postulates

LEARNING GOALS

In this lesson, you will:

- Calculate the complement and supplement of an angle.
- Classify adjacent angles, linear pairs, and vertical angles.
- Differentiate between postulates and theorems.
- Differentiate between Euclidean and non-Euclidean geometries.

KEY TERMS

- supplementary angles
- complementary angles
- adjacent angles
- linear pair
- vertical angles
- postulate
- theorem
- Euclidean geometry
- Linear Pair Postulate
- Segment Addition Postulate
- Angle Addition Postulate

A compliment is an expression of praise, admiration, or congratulations. Often when someone does something noteworthy, you may "pay them a compliment" to recognize the person's accomplishments.

Even though they are spelled similarly, the word "complement" means something very different. To complement something means to complete or to make whole. This phrase is used in mathematics, linguistics, music, and art. For example, complementary angles have measures that sum to 180 degrees—making the straight angle "whole." In music, a complement is an interval that when added to another spans an octave—makes it "whole."

The film *Jerry McGuire* features the famous line "You complete me," meaning that the other person complements them or that together they form a whole. So, a complement can be quite a compliment indeed!

Two angles are **supplementary angles** if the sum of their angle measures is equal to 180°.

Supplementary angles that share a side form a straight line, or a straight angle.

1. Use a protractor to draw a pair of supplementary angles that share a common side, and then measure each angle.

2. Use a protractor to draw a pair of supplementary angles that do not share a common side, and then measure each angle.

3. Calculate the measure of an angle that is supplementary to ∠KJL.

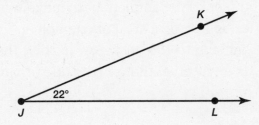

Two angles are **complementary angles** if the sum of their angle measures is equal to 90°.

4. Use a protractor to draw a pair of complementary angles that share a common side, and then measure each angle.

Complementary angles that share a side form a right angle.

5. Use a protractor to draw a pair of complementary angles that do not share a common side, and then measure each angle.

6. Calculate the measure of an angle that is complementary to ∠J.

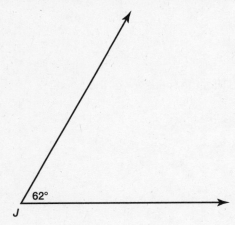

7. Determine the measure of each angle. Show your work and explain your reasoning.

   a. Two angles are congruent and supplementary.

   b. Two angles are congruent and complementary.

   c. The complement of an angle is twice the measure of the angle.

   d. The supplement of an angle is half the measure of the angle.

8. Determine the angle measures in each diagram.

a.

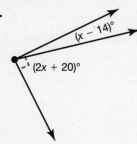

$(x - 14)°$

$(2x + 20)°$

b.

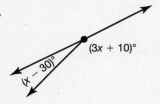

$(3x + 10)°$

$(x - 30)°$

You have learned that angles can be supplementary or complementary. Let's explore other angle relationships.

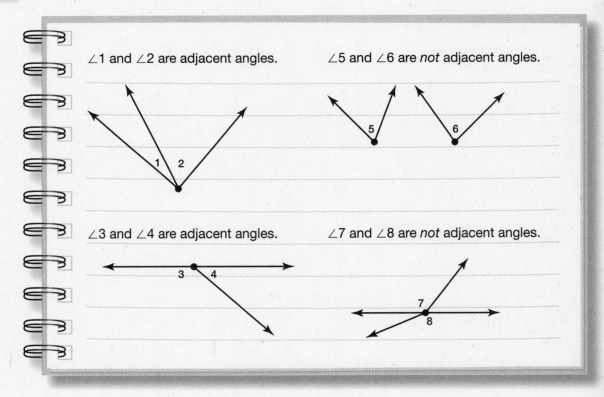

∠1 and ∠2 are adjacent angles.

∠5 and ∠6 are *not* adjacent angles.

∠3 and ∠4 are adjacent angles.

∠7 and ∠8 are *not* adjacent angles.

1. Analyze the worked example. Then answer each question.

   a. Describe adjacent angles.

b. Draw ∠2 so that it is adjacent to ∠1.

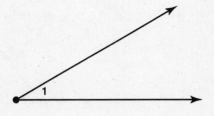

c. Is it possible to draw two angles that share a common vertex but do not share a common side? If so, draw an example. If not, explain why not.

d. Is it possible to draw two angles that share a common side, but do not share a common vertex? If so, draw an example. If not, explain why not.

Adjacent angles are two angles that share a common vertex and share a common side.

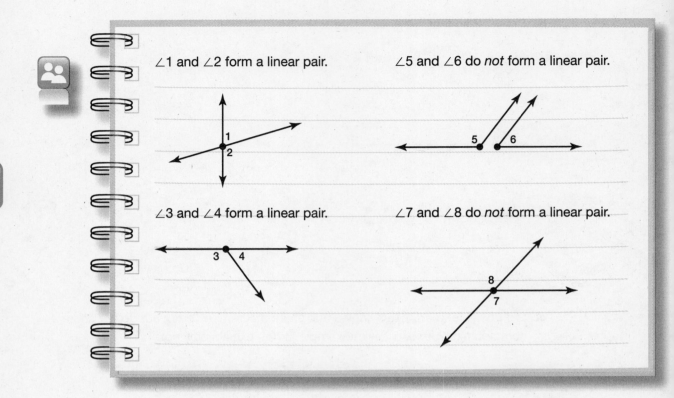

∠1 and ∠2 form a linear pair.

∠5 and ∠6 do *not* form a linear pair.

∠3 and ∠4 form a linear pair.

∠7 and ∠8 do *not* form a linear pair.

2. Analyze the worked example. Then answer each question.

    a. Describe a linear pair of angles.

b. Draw ∠2 so that it forms a linear pair with ∠1.

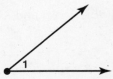

So, are the angles in a linear pair always supplementary?

c. Name all linear pairs in the figure shown.

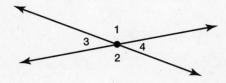

d. If the angles that form a linear pair are congruent, what can you conclude?

A **linear pair** of angles are two adjacent angles that have noncommon sides that form a line.

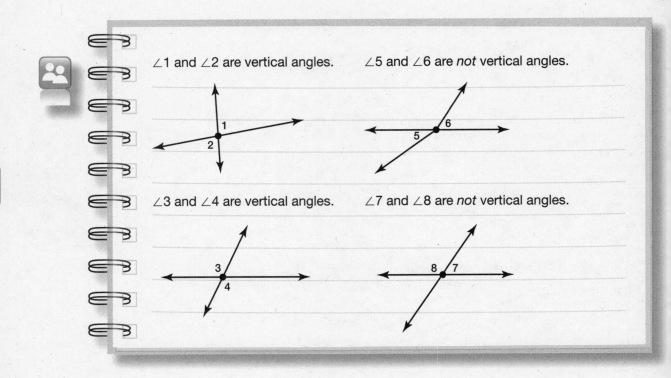

∠1 and ∠2 are vertical angles.

∠5 and ∠6 are *not* vertical angles.

∠3 and ∠4 are vertical angles.

∠7 and ∠8 are *not* vertical angles.

3. Analyze the worked example. Then answer each question.

   a. Describe vertical angles.

b. Draw ∠2 so that it forms a vertical angle with ∠1.

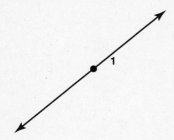

c. Name all vertical angle pairs in the diagram shown.

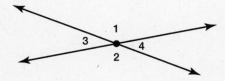

d. Measure each angle in part (c). What do you notice?

Vertical angles are two nonadjacent angles that are formed by two intersecting lines.

4. Determine $m\angle AED$. Explain how you determined the angle measure.

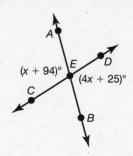

Make sure to carefully read the name of the angle whose measure you want to know.

2

5. For each conditional statement, draw a diagram and then write the hypothesis as the "Given" and the conclusion as the "Prove."

    a. $m\angle DEG + m\angle GEF = 180°$, if $\angle DEG$ and $\angle GEF$ are a linear pair.

       Given:

       Prove:

b. If $\angle ABD$ and $\angle DBC$ are complementary, then $\overrightarrow{BA} \perp \overrightarrow{BC}$.

Given:

Prove:

c. If $\angle 2$ and $\angle 3$ are vertical angles, then $\angle 2 \cong \angle 3$.

Given:

Prove:

A **postulate** is a statement that is accepted without proof.

A **theorem** is a statement that can be proven.

The Elements is a book written by the Greek mathematician Euclid. He used a small number of undefined terms and postulates to systematically prove many theorems. As a result, Euclid was able to develop a complete system we now know as **Euclidean geometry**.

Euclid's first five postulates are:

1. A straight line segment can be drawn joining any two points.

2. Any straight line segment can be extended indefinitely in a straight line.

3. Given any straight line segment, a circle can be drawn that has the segment as its radius and one endpoint as center.

4. All right angles are congruent.

5. If two lines are drawn that intersect a third line in such a way that the sum of the inner angles on one side is less than two right angles, then the two lines inevitably must intersect each other on that side if extended far enough. (This postulate is equivalent to what is known as the parallel postulate.)

Greek mathematician Euclid is sometimes referred to as the Father of Geometry.

Euclid used only the first four postulates to prove the first 28 propositions or theorems of *The Elements*, but was forced to use the fifth postulate, the parallel postulate, to prove the 29th theorem.

The *Elements* also includes five "common notions":

1. Things that equal the same thing also equal one another.

2. If equals are added to equals, then the wholes are equal.

3. If equals are subtracted from equals, then the remainders are equal.

4. Things that coincide with one another equal one another.

5. The whole is greater than the part.

It is important to note that Euclidean geometry is not the only system of geometry. Examples of non-Euclidian geometries include hyperbolic and elliptic geometry. The essential difference between Euclidean and non-Euclidean geometry is the nature of parallel lines.

Another way to describe the differences between these geometries is to consider two lines in a plane that are both perpendicular to a third line.

- In Euclidean geometry, the lines remain at a constant distance from each other and are known as parallels.

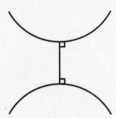

- In hyperbolic geometry, the lines "curve away" from each other.

- In elliptic geometry, the lines "curve toward" each other and eventually intersect.

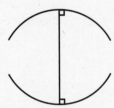

Using this textbook as a guide, you will develop your own system of geometry, just like Euclid. You already used the three undefined terms *point, line,* and *plane* to define related terms such as *line segment* and *angle.*

Your journey continues with the introduction of three fundamental postulates:

- The Linear Pair Postulate

- The Segment Addition Postulate

- The Angle Addition Postulate

You will use these postulates to make various conjectures. If you are able to prove your conjectures, then the conjectures will become theorems. These theorems can then be used to make even more conjectures, which may also become theorems. Mathematicians use this process to create new mathematical ideas.

The **Linear Pair Postulate** states: "If two angles form a linear pair, then the angles are supplementary."

1. Use the Linear Pair Postulate to complete each representation.

   a. Sketch and label a linear pair.

   b. Use your sketch and the Linear Pair Postulate to write the hypothesis.

   c. Use your sketch and the Linear Pair Postulate to write the conclusion.

   d. Use your conclusion and the definition of supplementary angles to write a statement about the angles in your figure.

The **Segment Addition Postulate** states: "If point B is on $\overline{AC}$ and between points A and C, then $AB + BC = AC$."

2. Use the Segment Addition Postulate to complete each representation.

   a. Sketch and label collinear points D, E, and F with point E between points D and F.

   b. Use your sketch and the Segment Addition Postulate to write the hypothesis.

   c. Use your sketch and the Segment Addition Postulate to write the conclusion.

   d. Write your conclusion using measure notation.

The **Angle Addition Postulate** states: "If point D lies in the interior of $\angle ABC$, then $m\angle ABD + m\angle DBC = m\angle ABC$."

3. Use the Angle Addition Postulate to complete each representation.

   a. Sketch and label $\angle DEF$ with $\overrightarrow{EG}$ drawn in the interior of $\angle DEF$.

   b. Use your sketch and the Angle Addition Postulate to write the hypothesis.

   c. Use your sketch and the Angle Addition Postulate to write the conclusion.

Be prepared to share your solutions and methods.

Forms of Proof

Paragraph Proof, Two-Column Proof, Construction Proof, and Flow Chart Proof

Have you ever heard the famous phrase, "The proof is in the pudding"? If you stop to think about what this phrase means, you might be left scratching your head!

The phrase used now is actually a shortened version of the original phrase, "The proof of the pudding is in the eating." This phrase meant that the pudding recipe may appear to be delicious, include fresh ingredients, and may even look delicious after it is made. However, the only way to really "prove" that the pudding is delicious is by eating it!

Today it is used to imply that the quality or truth of something can only be determined by putting it into action. For example, you don't know how good an idea is until you actually test the idea.

Can you think of any other popular phrases that don't seem to make sense? Perhaps you should do a little research to find out where these phrases came from.

PROBLEM 1 Properties of Real Numbers in Geometry

Many properties of real numbers can be applied in geometry. These properties are important when making conjectures and proving new theorems.

The **Addition Property of Equality** states: "If a, b, and c are real numbers and $a = b$, then $a + c = b + c$."

The Addition Property of Equality can be applied to angle measures, segment measures, and distances.

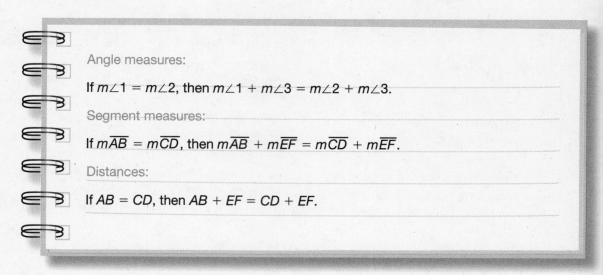

Angle measures:

If $m\angle 1 = m\angle 2$, then $m\angle 1 + m\angle 3 = m\angle 2 + m\angle 3$.

Segment measures:

If $m\overline{AB} = m\overline{CD}$, then $m\overline{AB} + m\overline{EF} = m\overline{CD} + m\overline{EF}$.

Distances:

If $AB = CD$, then $AB + EF = CD + EF$.

1. Sketch a diagram and write a statement that applies the Addition Property of Equality to angle measures.

2. Sketch a diagram and write a statement that applies the Addition Property of Equality to segment measures.

The **Subtraction Property of Equality** states: "If a, b, and c are real numbers and $a = b$, then $a - c = b - c$."

The Subtraction Property of Equality can be applied to angle measures, segment measures, and distances.

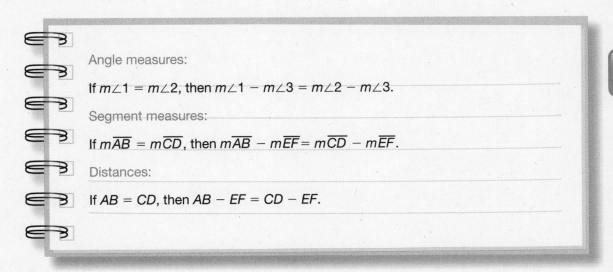

Angle measures:

If $m\angle 1 = m\angle 2$, then $m\angle 1 - m\angle 3 = m\angle 2 - m\angle 3$.

Segment measures:

If $m\overline{AB} = m\overline{CD}$, then $m\overline{AB} - m\overline{EF} = m\overline{CD} - m\overline{EF}$.

Distances:

If $AB = CD$, then $AB - EF = CD - EF$.

3. Sketch a diagram and write a statement that applies the Subtraction Property of Equality to angle measures.

4. Sketch a diagram and write a statement that applies the Subtraction Property of Equality to segment measures.

The **Reflexive Property** states: "If a is a real number, then $a = a$."

The Reflexive Property can be applied to angle measures, segment measures, distances, congruent angles, and congruent segments.

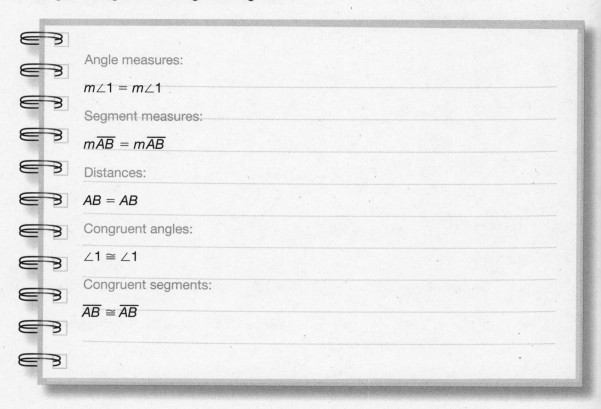

Angle measures:

$m\angle 1 = m\angle 1$

Segment measures:

$m\overline{AB} = m\overline{AB}$

Distances:

$AB = AB$

Congruent angles:

$\angle 1 \cong \angle 1$

Congruent segments:

$\overline{AB} \cong \overline{AB}$

5. Sketch a diagram and write a statement that applies the Reflexive Property to angles.

6. Sketch a diagram and write a statement that applies the Reflexive Property to segments.

The **Substitution Property** states: "If a and b are real numbers and $a = b$, then a can be substituted for b."

The Substitution Property can be applied to angle measures, segment measures, and distances.

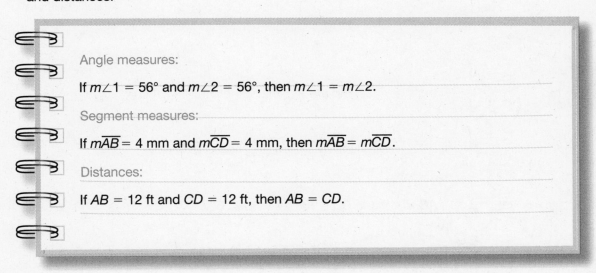

Angle measures:

If $m\angle 1 = 56°$ and $m\angle 2 = 56°$, then $m\angle 1 = m\angle 2$.

Segment measures:

If $m\overline{AB} = 4$ mm and $m\overline{CD} = 4$ mm, then $m\overline{AB} = m\overline{CD}$.

Distances:

If $AB = 12$ ft and $CD = 12$ ft, then $AB = CD$.

7. Sketch a diagram and write a statement that applies the Substitution Property to angles.

8. Sketch a diagram and write a statement that applies the Substitution Property to segments.

The **Transitive Property** states: "If *a*, *b*, and *c* are real numbers, *a* = *b*, and *b* = *c*, then *a* = *c*."

The Transitive Property can be applied to angle measures, segment measures, distances, congruent angles, and congruent segments.

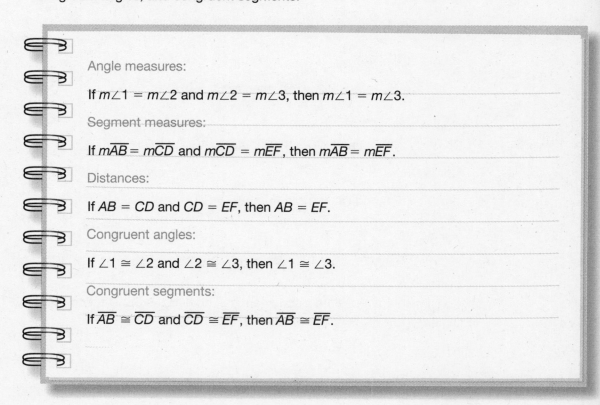

Angle measures:

If $m\angle 1 = m\angle 2$ and $m\angle 2 = m\angle 3$, then $m\angle 1 = m\angle 3$.

Segment measures:

If $m\overline{AB} = m\overline{CD}$ and $m\overline{CD} = m\overline{EF}$, then $m\overline{AB} = m\overline{EF}$.

Distances:

If $AB = CD$ and $CD = EF$, then $AB = EF$.

Congruent angles:

If $\angle 1 \cong \angle 2$ and $\angle 2 \cong \angle 3$, then $\angle 1 \cong \angle 3$.

Congruent segments:

If $\overline{AB} \cong \overline{CD}$ and $\overline{CD} \cong \overline{EF}$, then $\overline{AB} \cong \overline{EF}$.

9. Sketch a diagram and write a statement that applies the Transitive Property to angles.

Sometimes mathematical properties can seem obvious. So, why do we need them? When you learn about proofs, you will need these properties to justify your statements and conclusions.

10. Sketch a diagram and write a statement that applies the Transitive Property to congruent segments.

PROBLEM 2 · Various Forms of Proof

A **proof** is a logical series of statements and corresponding reasons that starts with a hypothesis and arrives at a conclusion. In this course, you will use four different kinds of proof.

1. The diagram shows four collinear points A, B, C, and D such that point B lies between points A and C, point C lies between points B and D, and $\overline{AB} \cong \overline{CD}$.

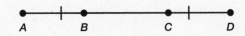

Consider the conditional statement: If $\overline{AB} \cong \overline{CD}$, then $\overline{AC} \cong \overline{BD}$.

a. Write the hypothesis as the "Given" and the conclusion as the "Prove."

Given:

Prove:

A **flow chart proof** is a proof in which the steps and reasons for each step are written in boxes. Arrows connect the boxes and indicate how each step and reason is generated from one or more other steps and reasons.

b. Cut out the steps on the flow chart proof.

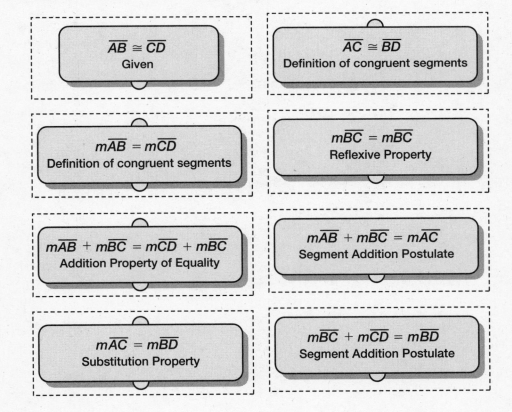

$\overline{AB} \cong \overline{CD}$
Given

$\overline{AC} \cong \overline{BD}$
Definition of congruent segments

$m\overline{AB} = m\overline{CD}$
Definition of congruent segments

$m\overline{BC} = m\overline{BC}$
Reflexive Property

$m\overline{AB} + m\overline{BC} = m\overline{CD} + m\overline{BC}$
Addition Property of Equality

$m\overline{AB} + m\overline{BC} = m\overline{AC}$
Segment Addition Postulate

$m\overline{AC} = m\overline{BD}$
Substitution Property

$m\overline{BC} + m\overline{CD} = m\overline{BD}$
Segment Addition Postulate

c. Complete the flow chart proof of the conditional statement in Question 1 by assembling your cutout steps in order. Use arrows to show the order of the flow chart proof.

Given:

Prove:

Don't forget the definitions and postulates you learned in the last lesson!

2

A **two-column proof** is a proof in which the steps are written in the left column and the corresponding reasons are written in the right column. Each step and corresponding reason are numbered.

d. Create a two-column proof of the conditional statement in Question 1.
Each box of the flow chart proof in Question 1, part (c) should appear as a row in the two-column proof.

Given:

Prove:

Statements	Reasons

A **paragraph proof** is a proof in which the steps and corresponding reasons are written in complete sentences.

e. Write a paragraph proof of the conditional statement in Question 1. Each row of the two-column proof in Question 1, part (d) should appear as a sentence in the paragraph proof.

A **construction proof** is a proof that results from creating an object with specific properties using only a compass and a straightedge.

f. Create a proof by construction of the conditional statement in Question 2.

Given:

Prove:

PROBLEM **3**   **Proof of the Right Angle Congruence Theorem**

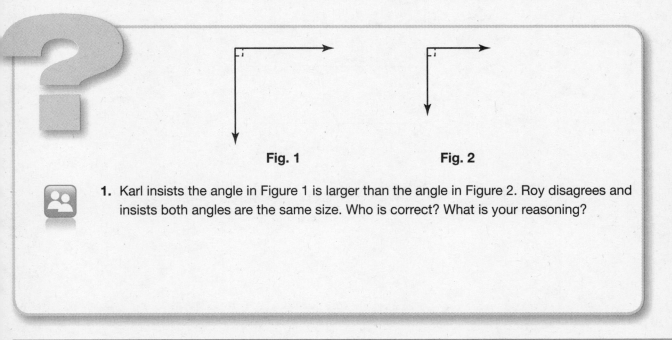

Fig. 1   Fig. 2

1. Karl insists the angle in Figure 1 is larger than the angle in Figure 2. Roy disagrees and insists both angles are the same size. Who is correct? What is your reasoning?

The **Right Angle Congruence Theorem** states: "All right angles are congruent."

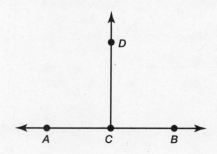

Given: ∠ACD and ∠BCD are right angles.

Prove: ∠ACD ≅ ∠BCD

Complete the flow chart of the Right Angle Congruence Theorem by writing the statement for each reason in the boxes provided.

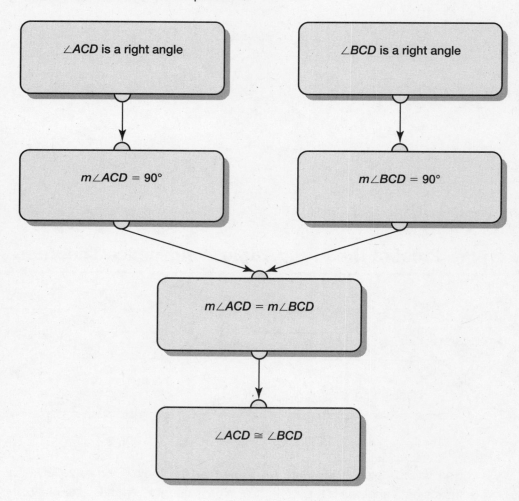

PROBLEM **4** **Proofs of the Congruent Supplement Theorem**

 The **Congruent Supplement Theorem** states: "If two angles are supplements of the same angle or of congruent angles, then the angles are congruent."

1. Use the diagram to write the "Given" statements for the Congruent Supplement Theorem. The "Prove" statement is provided.

   Given:

   Given:

   Given:

   Prove: $\angle 1 \cong \angle 3$

2. Cut out the steps of the flow chart proof.

   ∠1 is supplementary to ∠2
   Given

   ∠3 is supplementary to ∠4
   Given

   $m\angle 1 + m\angle 2 = 180°$
   Definition of supplementary angles

   ∠2 ≅ ∠4
   Given

   $m\angle 3 + m\angle 4 = 180°$
   Definition of supplementary angles

   $m\angle 1 = m\angle 3$
   Subtraction Property of Equality

   $m\angle 2 = m\angle 4$
   Definition of congruent angles

   $m\angle 1 + m\angle 2 = m\angle 3 + m\angle 4$
   Substitution Property

   ∠1 ≅ ∠3
   Definition of congruent angles

3. Complete the flow chart proof of the Congruent Supplements Theorem by assembling your cutout steps in order. Use arrows to show the order of the flow chart proof.

4. Create a two-column proof of the Congruent Supplement Theorem. Each box of the flow chart proof in Question 3 should appear as a row in the two-column proof.

Statements	Reasons

PROBLEM **5** **Proofs of the Congruent Complement Theorem**

The **Congruent Complement Theorem** states: "If two angles are complements of the same angle or of congruent angles, then they are congruent."

1. Draw and label a diagram illustrating this theorem.

2. Use your diagram to write the "Given" and "Prove" statements for the Congruent Complement Theorem.

Given:

Given:

Given:

Prove:

3. Create a flow chart proof of the Congruent Complement Theorem.

4. Create a two-column proof of the Congruent Complement Theorem. Each box of the flow chart proof in Question 3 should appear as a row in the two-column proof.

Statements	Reasons

2

PROBLEM **6** **Proofs of the Vertical Angle Theorem**

1. The **Vertical Angle Theorem** states: "Vertical angles are congruent."

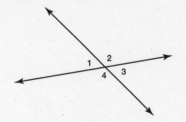

2. Use the diagram to write the "Prove" statements for the Vertical Angle Theorem. The "Given" statements are provided.

Given: ∠1 and ∠2 are a linear pair

Given: ∠2 and ∠3 are a linear pair

Given: ∠3 and ∠4 are a linear pair

Given: ∠4 and ∠1 are a linear pair

Prove:

Prove:

---

3. Create a flow chart proof of the first "Prove" statement of the Vertical Angle Theorem.

4. Create a two-column proof of the second "Prove" statement of the Vertical Angle Theorem.

Given:

Given:

Prove:

Statements	Reasons

Given: $\angle DEG \cong \angle HEF$

Prove: $\angle DEH \cong \angle GEF$

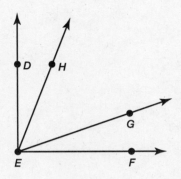

1. Prove the conditional statement using any method you choose.

Talk the Talk

1. List the advantages and disadvantages of each form of proof.

   a. flow chart proof

   b. two-column proof

   c. paragraph proof

   d. construction proof

2. Which form of proof do you prefer? Explain.

Once a theorem has been proven, it can be used as a reason in another proof. Using theorems that have already been proven allows you to write shorter proofs.

In this chapter, you proved these theorems:

- The Right Angle Congruence Theorem: All right angles are congruent.

- The Congruent Supplement Theorem: Supplements of congruent angles, or of the same angle, are congruent.

- The Congruent Complement Theorem: Complements of congruent angles, or of the same angle, are congruent.

- The Vertical Angle Theorem: Vertical angles are congruent.

A list of theorems that you prove throughout this course will be an excellent resource as you continue to make new conjectures and expand your system of geometry.

Be prepared to share your solutions and methods.

What's Your Proof?
Angle Postulates and Theorems

You are constantly bombarded with information through magazines, newspapers, television, and the Internet. However, not all "facts" that you read about are actually true! If you want to be an educated consumer of information, you should always be looking for the argument, or proof, to back up a statement. If you can't find such information then you should be skeptical.

Sometimes you need to carefully examine the evidence. For example, say someone claims that 4 out of 5 dentists recommend a certain toothpaste. Sounds pretty impressive, right? However, what if you learned that only five dentists were asked their opinions? You might start to question the claim. What if you also learned that the dentists were paid by the toothpaste company for their opinions? As you can see, sometimes the "truth" isn't always what it appears to be.

PROBLEM 1 The Corresponding Angle Postulate

The **Corresponding Angle Postulate** states: "If two parallel lines are intersected by a transversal, then corresponding angles are congruent."

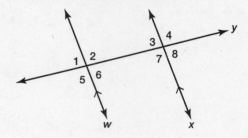

1. Name all pairs of angles that are congruent using the Corresponding Angle Postulate.

A **conjecture** is a hypothesis that something is true. The hypothesis can later be proved or disproved.

2. Write a conjecture about each pair of angles formed by parallel lines cut by a transversal. Explain how you made each conjecture.

   a. alternate interior angles.

   b. alternate exterior angles.

c. same-side interior angles

Test it out! Conjecture is all about testing.

2

d. same-side exterior angles

3. Did you use inductive or deductive reasoning to make each conjecture?

Conjecture or Theorem?

If you can prove that a conjecture is true, then it becomes a theorem.

1. The Alternate Interior Angle Conjecture states: "If two parallel lines are intersected by a transversal, then alternate interior angles are congruent."

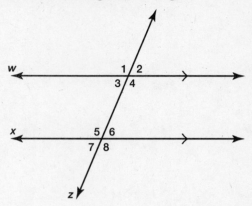

a. Use the diagram to write the "Given" and "Prove" statements for the Alternate Interior Angle Conjecture.

Given:

Prove:

b. Complete the flow chart proof of the Alternate Interior Angle Conjecture by writing the reason for each statement in the boxes provided.

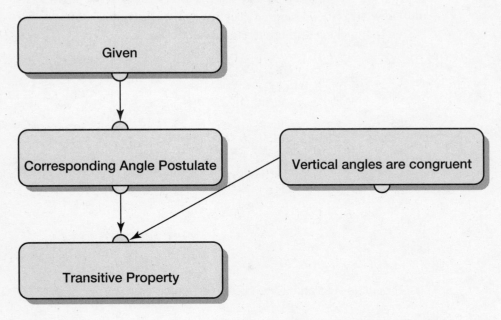

c. Create a two-column proof of the Alternate Interior Angle Theorem.

Statements	Reasons

Congratulations! You can now use this theorem as a valid reason in proofs.

 You have just proven the Alternate Interior Angle Conjecture. It is now known as the **Alternate Interior Angle Theorem**.

2. The Alternate Exterior Angle Conjecture states: "If two parallel lines are intersected by a transversal, then alternate exterior angles are congruent."

   a. Draw and label a diagram illustrating the Alternate Exterior Angle Conjecture. Then, write the given and prove statements.

   b. Prove the Alternate Exterior Angle Conjecture.

You have just proven the Alternate Exterior Angle Conjecture. It is now known as the **Alternate Exterior Angle Theorem**.

3. The Same-Side Interior Angle Conjecture states: "If two parallel lines are intersected by a transversal, then interior angles on the same side of the transversal are supplementary."

   a. Draw and label a diagram illustrating the Same-Side Interior Angle Conjecture. Then, write the given and prove statements.

   b. Prove the Same-Side Interior Angle Conjecture.

You're on a roll! Only one more conjecture to go.

You have just proven the Same-Side Interior Angle Conjecture. It is now known as the **Same-Side Interior Angle Theorem**.

4. The Same-Side Exterior Angle Conjecture states: "If two parallel lines are intersected by a transversal, then exterior angles on the same side of the transversal are supplementary."

a. Draw and label a diagram illustrating the Same-Side Exterior Angle Conjecture. Then, write the given and prove statements.

b. Prove the Same-Side Exterior Angle Conjecture.

You have just proven the Same-Side Exterior Angle Conjecture. It is now known as the **Same-Side Exterior Angle Theorem**.

Talk the Talk

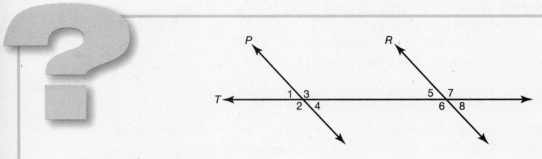

Given: $m\angle 4 = 37°$

1. Gail determined the measures of all eight angles labeled using the given information.
   Stu said she could only calculate the measure of four angles with certainty.
   Who is correct? Explain your reasoning.

If two parallel lines are intersected by a transversal, then:

- corresponding angles are congruent.
- alternate interior angles are congruent.
- alternate exterior angles are congruent.
- same-side interior angles are supplementary.
- same-side exterior angles are supplementary.

Each of these relationships is represented by a postulate or theorem.

- **Corresponding Angle Postulate**: If two parallel lines are intersected by a transversal, then corresponding angles are congruent.

- **Alternate Interior Angle Theorem**: If two parallel lines are intersected by a transversal, then alternate interior angles are congruent.

- **Alternate Exterior Angle Theorem**: If two parallel lines are intersected by a transversal, then alternate exterior angles are congruent.

- **Same-Side Interior Angle Theorem**: If two parallel lines are intersected by a transversal, then interior angles on the same side of the transversal are supplementary.

- **Same-Side Exterior Angle Theorem**: If two parallel lines are intersected by a transversal, then exterior angles on the same side of the transversal are supplementary.

2. Did you use inductive or deductive reasoning to prove each theorem?

 Be prepared to share your solutions and methods.

A Reversed Condition
Parallel Line Converse Theorems

LEARNING GOALS

In this lesson, you will:
- Write and prove parallel line converse conjectures.

KEY TERMS

- converse
- Corresponding Angle Converse Postulate
- Alternate Interior Angle Converse Theorem
- Alternate Exterior Angle Converse Theorem
- Same-Side Interior Angle Converse Theorem
- Same-Side Exterior Angle Converse Theorem

Lewis Carroll is best known as the author of *Alice's Adventures in Wonderland* and its sequel *Through the Looking Glass*. However, Carroll also wrote several mathematics books, many of which focus on logic. In fact, Carroll included logic in many of his fiction books. Sometimes these took the form of "logical nonsense" such as the tea party scene with the Mad Hatter.

At one point of the scene, Alice proclaims that she says what she means, or at least, that she means what she says, insisting that the two statements are the same thing. The numerous attendees of the tea party then correct her with a series of flipped sentences which have totally different meanings. For example, "I like what I get" and "I get what I like".

Are these two sentences saying the same thing? Can you think of other examples of flipped sentences?

PROBLEM 1 Converses

The **converse** of a conditional statement written in the form "If p, then q" is the statement written in the form "If q, then p." The converse is a new statement that results when the hypothesis and conclusion of the conditional statement are interchanged.

The Corresponding Angle Postulate states: "If two parallel lines are intersected by a transversal, then the corresponding angles are congruent."

The **Corresponding Angle Converse Postulate** states: "If two lines intersected by a transversal form congruent corresponding angles, then the lines are parallel."

The Corresponding Angle Converse Postulate is used to prove new conjectures formed by writing the converses of the parallel lines theorems.

1. For each theorem:

   • Identify the hypothesis p and conclusion q.

   • Write the converse of the theorem as a conjecture.

   a. Alternate Interior Angle Theorem: If two parallel lines are intersected by a transversal, then the alternate interior angles are congruent.

   Hypothesis p:

   Conclusion q:

   Alternate Interior Angle Converse Conjecture:

   b. Alternate Exterior Angle Theorem: If two parallel lines are intersected by a transversal, then the alternate exterior angles are congruent.

   Hypothesis p:

   Conclusion q:

   Alternate Exterior Angle Converse Conjecture:

   c. Same-Side Interior Angle Theorem: If two parallel lines are intersected by a transversal, then the same-side interior angles are supplementary.

   Hypothesis p:

   Conclusion q:

   Same-Side Interior Angle Converse Conjecture:

d. Same-Side Exterior Angle Theorem: If two parallel lines are intersected by a transversal, then the same-side exterior angles are supplementary.

Hypothesis *p*:

Conclusion *q*:

Same-Side Exterior Angle Converse Conjecture:

2. Consider lines *r* and *s*.

a. Use the Corresponding Angle Converse Postulate to construct a line parallel to line *r*. Write the steps.

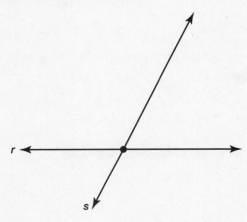

b. Which line is a transversal?

c. Which lines are parallel?

1. The Alternate Interior Angle Converse Conjecture states: "If two lines intersected by a transversal form congruent alternate interior angles, then the lines are parallel."

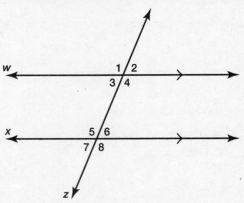

a. Use the diagram to write the given and prove statements for the Alternate Interior Angle Converse Conjecture.

Given:

Prove:

b. Prove the Alternate Interior Angle Converse Conjecture.

Congratulations! You can now use this theorem as a valid reason in proofs.

You have just proven the Alternate Interior Angle Converse Conjecture. It is now known as the **Alternate Interior Angle Converse Theorem**.

2. The Alternate Exterior Angle Converse Conjecture states: "If two lines intersected by a transversal form congruent alternate exterior angles, then the lines are parallel."

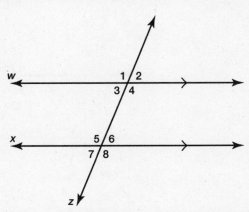

a. Use the diagram to write the given and prove statements for the Alternate Exterior Angle Converse Conjecture.

Given:

Prove:

b. Prove the Alternate Exterior Angle Converse Conjecture.

 You have just proven the Alternate Exterior Angle Converse Conjecture. It is now known as the **Alternate Exterior Angle Converse Theorem**.

3. The Same-Side Interior Angle Converse Conjecture states: "If two lines intersected by a transversal form supplementary same-side interior angles, then the lines are parallel."

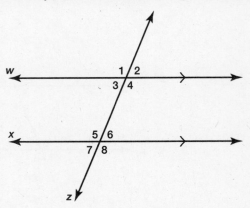

a. Use the diagram to write the given and prove statements for the Same-Side Interior Angle Converse Conjecture.

Given:

Prove:

b. Prove the Same-Side Interior Angle Converse Conjecture.

You're doing great. Only one more converse theorem.

You have just proven the Same-Side Interior Angle Converse Conjecture. It is now known as the **Same-Side Interior Angle Converse Theorem**.

4. The Same-Side Exterior Angle Converse Conjecture states: "If two lines intersected by a transversal form supplementary same-side exterior angles, then the lines are parallel."

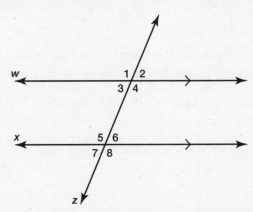

a. Use the diagram to write the given and prove statements for the Same-Side Exterior Angle Converse Conjecture.

Given:

Prove:

b. Prove the Same-Side Exterior Angle Converse Conjecture.

You have just proven the Same-Side Exterior Angle Converse Conjecture. It is now known as the **Same-Side Exterior Angle Converse Theorem**.

Talk the Talk

Here are all the converse postulates you have proven. Each converse conjecture you have proven is a new theorem.

Corresponding Angle Converse Postulate: If two lines intersected by a transversal form congruent corresponding angles, then the lines are parallel.

Alternate Interior Angle Converse Theorem: If two lines intersected by a transversal form congruent alternate interior angles, then the lines are parallel.

Alternate Exterior Angle Converse Theorem: If two lines intersected by a transversal form congruent alternate exterior angles, then the lines are parallel.

Same-Side Interior Angle Converse Theorem: If two lines intersected by a transversal form supplementary same-side interior angles, then the lines are parallel.

Same-Side Exterior Angle Converse Theorem: If two lines intersected by a transversal form supplementary same-side exterior angles, then the lines are parallel.

Use the diagram to answer the questions.

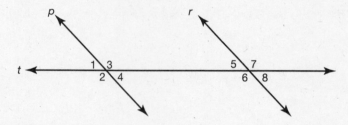

1. Which theorem or postulate would use $\angle 2 \cong \angle 7$ to justify line p is parallel to line r?

2. Which theorem or postulate would use $\angle 4 \cong \angle 5$ to justify line p is parallel to line r?

3. Which theorem or postulate would use $\angle 1 \cong \angle 5$ to justify line p is parallel to line r?

4. Which theorem or postulate would use $m\angle 4 + m\angle 6 = 180°$ to justify line p is parallel to line r?

5. Which theorem or postulate would use $m\angle 1 + m\angle 7 = 180°$ to justify line p is parallel to line r?

6. Which theorem or postulate would use line p is parallel to line r to justify $\angle 2 \cong \angle 7$?

7. Which theorem or postulate would use line p is parallel to line r to justify $\angle 4 \cong \angle 5$?

8. Which theorem or postulate would use line p is parallel to line r to justify $\angle 1 \cong \angle 5$?

9. Which theorem or postulate would use line p is parallel to line r to justify $m\angle 4 + m\angle 6 = 180°$?

10. Which theorem or postulate would use line p is parallel to line r to justify $m\angle 1 + m\angle 7 = 180°$?

 Be prepared to share your methods and solutions.

2

Chapter 2 Summary

KEY TERMS

- induction (2.1)
- deduction (2.1)
- counterexample (2.1)
- conditional statement (2.1)
- propositional form (2.1)
- propositional variables (2.1)
- hypothesis (2.1)
- conclusion (2.1)
- truth value (2.1)
- truth table (2.1)
- supplementary angles (2.2)
- complementary angles (2.2)
- adjacent angles (2.2)
- linear pair (2.2)
- vertical angles (2.2)
- postulate (2.2)
- theorem (2.2)
- Euclidean geometry (2.2)
- Addition Property of Equality (2.3)
- Subtraction Property of Equality (2.3)
- Reflexive Property (2.3)
- Substitution Property (2.3)
- Transitive Property (2.3)
- flow chart proof (2.3)
- two-column proof (2.3)
- paragraph proof (2.3)
- construction proof (2.3)
- conjecture (2.4)
- converse (2.5)

POSTULATES AND THEOREMS

- Linear Pair Postulate (2.2)
- Segment Addition Postulate (2.2)
- Angle Addition Postulate (2.2)
- Right Angle Congruence Theorem (2.3)
- Congruent Supplement Theorem (2.3)
- Congruent Complement Theorem (2.3)
- Vertical Angle Theorem (2.3)
- Corresponding Angle Postulate (2.4)
- Alternate Interior Angle Theorem (2.4)
- Alternate Exterior Angle Theorem (2.4)
- Same-Side Interior Angle Theorem (2.4)
- Same-Side Exterior Angle Theorem (2.4)
- Corresponding Angle Converse Postulate (2.5)
- Alternate Interior Angle Converse Theorem (2.5)
- Alternate Exterior Angle Converse Theorem (2.5)
- Same-Side Interior Angle Converse Theorem (2.5)
- Same-Side Exterior Angle Converse Theorem (2.5)

2.1   Identifying and Comparing Induction and Deduction

Induction uses specific examples to make a conclusion. Induction, also known as inductive reasoning, is used when observing data, recognizing patterns, making generalizations about the observations or patterns, and reapplying those generalizations to unfamiliar situations. Deduction, also known as deductive reasoning, uses a general rule or premise to make a conclusion. It is the process of showing that certain statements follow logically from some proven facts or accepted rules.

Example

Kyra sees coins at the bottom of a fountain. She concludes that if she throws a coin into the fountain, it too will sink. Tyler understands the physical laws of gravity and mass and decides a coin he throws into the fountain will sink.

The specific information is the coins Kyra and Tyler observed at the bottom of the fountain. The general information is the physical laws of gravity and mass.
Kyra's conclusion that her coin will sink when thrown into the fountain is induction.
Tyler's conclusion that his coin will sink when thrown into the fountain is deduction.

2.1   Identifying False Conclusions

It is important that all conclusions are tracked back to given truths. There are two reasons why a conclusion may be false. Either the assumed information is false or the argument is not valid.

Example

Erin noticed that every time she missed the bus, it rained. So, she concludes that next time she misses the bus it will rain.

Erin's conclusion is false because missing the bus is not related to what makes it rain.

2.1   Writing a Conditional Statement

A conditional statement is a statement that can be written in the form "If p, then q." The portion of the statement represented by p is the hypothesis. The portion of the statement represented by q is the conclusion.

Example

If I plant an acorn, then an oak tree will grow.

A solid line is drawn under the hypothesis, and a dotted line is drawn under the conclusion.

2.1   Using a Truth Table to Explore the Truth Value of a Conditional Statement

The truth value of a conditional statement is whether the statement is true or false. If a conditional statement could be true, then its truth value is considered "true." The first two columns of a truth table represent the possible truth values for p (the hypothesis) and q (the conclusion). The last column represents the truth value of the conditional statement ($p \rightarrow q$). Notice that the truth value of a conditional statement is either "true" or "false," but not both.

Example

Consider the conditional statement, "If I eat too much, then I will get a stomach ache."

p	q	$p \rightarrow q$
T	T	T
T	F	F
F	T	T
F	F	T

When p is true, I ate too much. When q is true, I will get a stomach ache. It is true that when I eat too much, I will get a stomach ache. So, the truth value of the conditional statement is true.

When p is true, I ate too much. When q is false, I will not get a stomach ache. It is false that when I eat too much, I will not get a stomach ache. So, the truth value of the conditional statement is false.

When p is false, I did not eat too much. When q is true, I will get a stomach ache. It could be true that when I did not eat too much, I will get a stomach ache for a different reason. So, the truth value of the conditional statement in this case is true.

When p is false, I did not eat too much. When q is false, I will not get a stomach ache. It could be true that when I did not eat too much, I will not get a stomach ache. So, the truth value of the conditional statement in this case is true.

2.1   Rewriting Conditional Statements

A conditional statement is a statement that can be written in the form "If p, then q." The hypothesis of a conditional statement is the variable p. The conclusion of a conditional statement is the variable q.

Example

Consider the following statement: If two angles form a linear pair, then the sum of the measures of the angles is 180 degrees. The statement is a conditional statement. The hypothesis is "two angles form a linear pair," and the conclusion is "the sum of the measures of the angles is 180 degrees." The conditional statement can be rewritten with the hypothesis as the "Given" statement and the conclusion as the "Prove" statement.

Given: Two angles form a linear pair.

Prove: The sum of the measures of the angles is 180 degrees.

Identifying Complementary and Supplementary Angles

Two angles are supplementary if the sum of their measures is 180 degrees.
Two angles are complementary if the sum of their measures is 90 degrees.

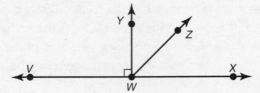

Example

In the diagram above, angles *YWZ* and *ZWX* are complementary angles.

In the diagram above, angles *VWY* and *XWY* are supplementary angles.
Also, angles *VWZ* and *XWZ* are supplementary angles.

Identifying Adjacent Angles, Linear Pairs, and Vertical Angles

Adjacent angles are angles that share a common vertex and a common side.

A linear pair of angles consists of two adjacent angles that have noncommon sides that form a line.

Vertical angles are nonadjacent angles formed by two intersecting lines.

Example

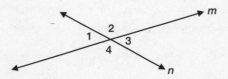

Angles 2 and 3 are adjacent angles.

Angles 1 and 2 form a linear pair. Angles 2 and 3 form a linear pair. Angles 3 and 4 form a iinear pair. Angles 4 and 1 form a linear pair.

Angles 1 and 3 are vertical angles. Angles 2 and 4 are vertical angles.

2.2 Determining the Difference Between Euclidean and Non-Euclidean Geometry

Euclidean geometry is a system of geometry developed by the Greek mathematician Euclid that included the following five postulates.

1. A straight line segment can be drawn joining any two points.
2. Any straight line segment can be extended indefinitely in a straight line.
3. Given any straight line segment, a circle can be drawn that has the segment as its radius and one point as the center.
4. All right angles are congruent.
5. If two lines are drawn that intersect a third line in such a way that the sum of the inner angles on one side is less than two right angles, then the two lines inevitably must intersect each other on that side if extended far enough.

Example

Euclidean geometry:

Non-Euclidean geometry:

2.2 Using the Linear Pair Postulate

The Linear Pair Postulate states: "If two angles form a linear pair, then the angles are supplementary."

Example

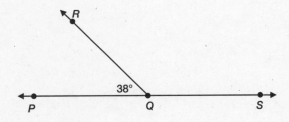

$m\angle PQR + m\angle SQR = 180°$

$38° + m\angle SQR = 180°$

$m\angle SQR = 180° - 38°$

$m\angle SQR = 142°$

2.2 Using the Segment Addition Postulate

The Segment Addition Postulate states: "If point *B* is on segment *AC* and between points *A* and *C*, then $AB + BC = AC$."

Example

A   B   C

|← 4 m →|←   10 m   →|

$$AB + BC = AC$$

$$4 \text{ m} + 10 \text{ m} = AC$$

$$AC = 14 \text{ m}$$

2.2 Using the Angle Addition Postulate

The Angle Addition Postulate states: "If point *D* lies in the interior of angle *ABC*, then $m\angle ABD + m\angle DBC = m\angle ABC$."

Example

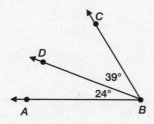

$$m\angle ABD + m\angle DBC = m\angle ABC$$

$$24° + 39° = m\angle ABC$$

$$m\angle ABC = 63°$$

2.3 Using Properties of Real Numbers in Geometry

The Addition Property of Equality states: "If a, b, and c are real numbers and $a = b$, then $a + c = b + c$."

The Subtraction Property of Equality states: "If a, b, and c are real numbers and $a = b$, then $a - c = b - c$."

The Reflexive Property states: "If a is a real number, then $a = a$."

The Substitution Property states: "If a and b are real numbers and $a = b$, then a can be substituted for b.

The Transitive Property states: "If a, b, and c are real numbers and $a = b$ and $b = c$, then $a = c$."

Example

Addition Property of Equality applied to angle measures: If $m\angle 1 = m\angle 2$, then $m\angle 1 + m\angle 3 = m\angle 2 + m\angle 3$.

Subtraction Property of Equality applied to segment measures: If $m\overline{AB} = m\overline{CD}$, then $m\overline{AB} - m\overline{EF} = m\overline{CD} - m\overline{EF}$.

Reflexive Property applied to distances: $AB = AB$

Substitution Property applied to angle measures: If $m\angle 1 = 20°$ and $m\angle 2 = 20°$, then $m\angle 1 = m\angle 2$.

Transitive Property applied to segment measures: If $m\overline{AB} = m\overline{CD}$ and $m\overline{CD} = m\overline{EF}$, then $m\overline{AB} = m\overline{EF}$.

2.3 Using the Right Angle Congruence Theorem

The Right Angle Congruence Theorem states: "All right angles are congruent."

Example

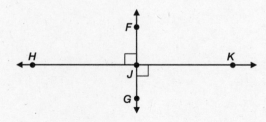

$\angle FJH \cong \angle GJK$

2.3   Using the Congruent Supplement Theorem

The Congruent Supplement Theorem states: "If two angles are supplements of the same angle or of congruent angles, then the angles are congruent."

Example

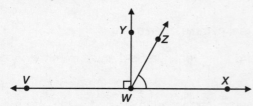

$\angle VWZ \cong \angle XWY$

2.3   Using the Congruent Complement Theorem

The Congruent Complement Theorem states: "If two angles are complements of the same angle or of congruent angles, then the angles are congruent."

Example

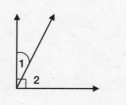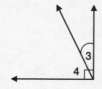

$\angle 2 \cong \angle 4$

2.3   Using the Vertical Angle Theorem

The Vertical Angle Theorem states: "Vertical angles are congruent."

Example

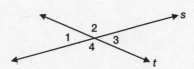

$\angle 1 \cong \angle 3$ and $\angle 2 \cong \angle 4$

2.4 Using the Corresponding Angle Postulate

The Corresponding Angle Postulate states: "If two parallel lines are intersected by a transversal, then corresponding angles are congruent."

Example

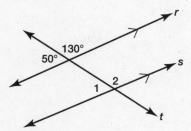

The angle that measures 50° and ∠1 are corresponding angles.
So, $m\angle 1 = 50°$.

The angle that measures 130° and ∠2 are corresponding angles.
So, $m\angle 2 = 130°$.

2.4 Using the Alternate Interior Angle Theorem

The Alternate Interior Angle Theorem states: "If two parallel lines are intersected by a transversal, then alternate interior angles are congruent."

Example

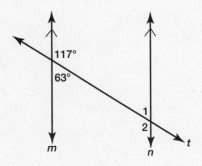

The angle that measures 63° and ∠1 are alternate interior angles.
So, $m\angle 1 = 63°$.

The angle that measures 117° and ∠2 are alternate interior angles.
So, $m\angle 2 = 117°$.

2.4   Using the Alternate Exterior Angle Theorem

The Alternate Exterior Angle Theorem states: "If two parallel lines are intersected by a transversal, then alternate exterior angles are congruent."

Example

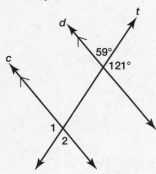

The angle that measures 121° and ∠1 are alternate exterior angles. So, $m\angle 1 = 121°$.

The angle that measures 59° and ∠2 are alternate exterior angles. So, $m\angle 2 = 59°$.

2.4   Using the Same-Side Interior Angle Theorem

The Same-Side Interior Angle Theorem states: "If two parallel lines are intersected by a transversal, then same-side interior angles are supplementary."

Example

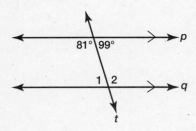

The angle that measures 81° and ∠1 are same-side interior angles.
So, $m\angle 1 = 180° - 81° = 99°$.

The angle that measures 99° and ∠2 are same-side interior angles.
So, $m\angle 2 = 180° - 99° = 81°$.

2.4 Using the Same-Side Exterior Angle Theorem

The Same-Side Exterior Angle Theorem states: "If two parallel lines are intersected by a transversal, then same-side exterior angles are supplementary."

Example

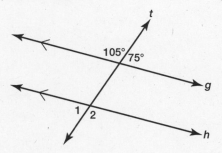

The angle that measures 105° and ∠1 are same-side exterior angles.
So, $m\angle 1 = 180° - 105° = 75°$.

The angle that measures 75° and ∠2 are same-side exterior angles.
So, $m\angle 2 = 180° - 75° = 105°$.

2.5 Using the Corresponding Angle Converse Postulate

The Corresponding Angle Converse Postulate states: "If two lines intersected by a transversal form congruent corresponding angles, then the lines are parallel."

Example

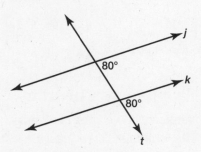

Corresponding angles have the same measure. So, $j \parallel k$.

2.5 Using the Alternate Interior Angle Converse Theorem

The Alternate Interior Angle Converse Theorem states: "If two lines intersected by a transversal form congruent alternate interior angles, then the lines are parallel."

Example

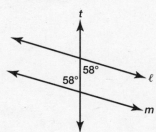

Alternate interior angles have the same measure. So, $\ell \parallel m$.

2.5 Using the Alternate Exterior Angle Converse Theorem

The Alternate Exterior Angle Converse Theorem states: "If two lines intersected by a transversal form congruent alternate exterior angles, then the lines are parallel."

Example

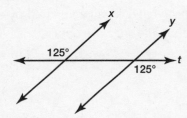

Alternate exterior angles have the same measure. So, $x \parallel y$.

2.5 Using the Same-Side Interior Angle Converse Theorem

The Same-Side Interior Angle Converse Theorem states: "If two lines intersected by a transversal form supplementary same-side interior angles, then the lines are parallel."

Example

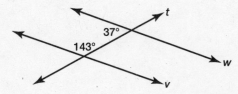

Same-side interior angles are supplementary: $37° + 143° = 180°$. So, $v \parallel w$.

2.5 Using the Same-Side Exterior Angle Converse Theorem

The Same-Side Exterior Angle Converse Theorem states: "If two lines intersected by a transversal form supplementary same-side exterior angles, then the lines are parallel."

Example

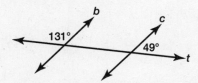

Same-side exterior angles are supplementary: 131° + 49° = 180°. So, $b \parallel c$.

2

Properties of Triangles

A lot of people use email but there is still a need to "snail" mail too. Mail isn't really delivered by snails—it's just a comment on how slow it is compared to a computer.

209

Inside Out

Triangle Sum, Exterior Angle, and Exterior Angle Inequality Theorems

LEARNING GOALS

In this lesson, you will:

- Prove the Triangle Sum Theorem.
- Explore the relationship between the interior angle measures and the side lengths of a triangle.
- Identify the remote interior angles of a triangle.
- Identify the exterior angle of a triangle.
- Explore the relationship between the exterior angle measure and two remote interior angles of a triangle.
- Prove the Exterior Angle Theorem.
- Prove the Exterior Angle Inequality Theorem.

KEY TERMS

- Triangle Sum Theorem
- remote interior angles of a triangle
- Exterior Angle Theorem
- Exterior Angle Inequality Theorem

Easter Island is one of the remotest islands on planet Earth. It is located in the southern Pacific Ocean approximately 2300 miles west of the coast of Chile. It was discovered by a Dutch captain in 1722 on Easter Day. When discovered, this island had few inhabitants other than 877 giant statues, which had been carved out of rock from the top edge of a wall of the island's volcano. Each statue weighs several tons, and some are more than 30 feet tall.

Several questions remain unanswered and are considered mysteries. Who built these statues? Did the statues serve a purpose? How were the statues transported on the island?

PROBLEM 1   Triangle Interior Angle Sums

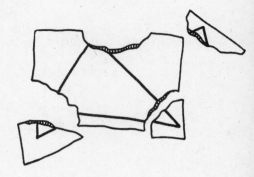

1. Draw any triangle on a piece of paper. Tear off the triangle's three angles. Arrange the angles so that they are adjacent angles. What do you notice about the sum of these three angles?

The **Triangle Sum Theorem** states: "the sum of the measures of the interior angles of a triangle is 180°."

2. Prove the Triangle Sum Theorem using the diagram shown.

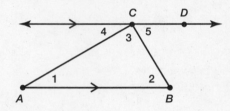

Given: Triangle *ABC* with $\overline{AB} \parallel \overline{CD}$

Prove: $m\angle 1 + m\angle 2 + m\angle 3 = 180°$

Think about the Angle Addition Postulate, alternate interior angles, and other theorems you know.

1. Consider the side lengths and angle measures of an acute triangle.

    a. Draw an acute scalene triangle. Measure each interior angle and label the angle measures in your diagram.

    b. Measure the length of each side of the triangle. Label the side lengths in your diagram.

    c. Which interior angle is opposite the longest side of the triangle?

    d. Which interior angle lies opposite the shortest side of the triangle?

2. Consider the side lengths and angle measures of an obtuse triangle.

    a. Draw an obtuse scalene triangle. Measure each interior angle and label the angle measures in your diagram.

    b. Measure the length of each side of the triangle. Label the side lengths in your diagram.

    c. Which interior angle lies opposite the longest side of the triangle?

    d. Which interior angle lies opposite the shortest side of the triangle?

3. Consider the side lengths and angle measures of a right triangle.

   a. Draw a right scalene triangle. Measure each interior angle and label the angle measures in your diagram.

   b. Measure each side length of the triangle. Label the side lengths in your diagram.

   c. Which interior angle lies opposite the longest side of the triangle?

   d. Which interior angle lies opposite the shortest side of the triangle?

4. The measures of the three interior angles of a triangle are 57°, 62°, and 61°. Describe the location of each side with respect to the measures of the opposite interior angles without drawing or measuring any part of the triangle.

a. longest side of the triangle

b. shortest side of the triangle

5. One angle of a triangle decreases in measure, but the sides of the angle remain the same length. Describe what happens to the side opposite the angle.

 6. An angle of a triangle increases in measure, but the sides of the angle remain the same length. Describe what happens to the side opposite the angle.

7. List the sides from shortest to longest for each diagram.

a.

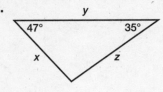

b.

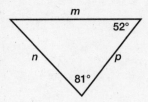

c.

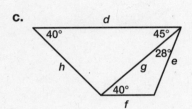

PROBLEM 3 · Exterior Angles

Use the diagram shown to answer Questions 1 through 12.

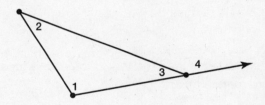

1. Name the interior angles of the triangle.

2. Name the exterior angles of the triangle.

3. What did you need to know to answer Questions 1 and 2?

4. What does $m\angle 1 + m\angle 2 + m\angle 3$ equal? Explain your reasoning.

5. What does $m\angle 3 + m\angle 4$ equal? Explain your reasoning.

6. Why does $m\angle 1 + m\angle 2 = m\angle 4$? Explain your reasoning.

7. Consider the sentence "The buried treasure is located on a remote island." What does the word *remote* mean?

8. The exterior angle of a triangle is $\angle 4$, and $\angle 1$ and $\angle 2$ are interior angles of the same triangle. Why would $\angle 1$ and $\angle 2$ be referred to as "remote" interior angles with respect to the exterior angle?

The **remote interior angles of a triangle** are the two angles that are non-adjacent to the specified exterior angle.

9. Write a sentence explaining $m\angle 4 = m\angle 1 + m\angle 2$ using the words *sum, remote interior angles of a triangle*, and *exterior angle of a triangle*.

10. Is the sentence in Question 9 considered a postulate or a theorem? Explain your reasoning.

11. The diagram was drawn as an obtuse triangle with one exterior angle. If the triangle had been drawn as an acute triangle, would this have changed the relationship between the measure of the exterior angle and the sum of the measures of the two remote interior angles? Explain your reasoning.

12. If the triangle had been drawn as a right triangle, would this have changed the relationship between the measure of the exterior angle and the sum of the measures of the two remote interior angles? Explain your reasoning.

The **Exterior Angle Theorem** states: "the measure of the exterior angle of a triangle is equal to the sum of the measures of the two remote interior angles of the triangle."

Think about the Triangle Sum Theorem, the definition of "linear pair," the Linear Pair Postulate, and other definitions or facts that you know.

13. Prove the Exterior Angle Theorem using the diagram shown.

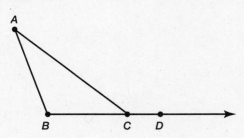

Given: Triangle ABC with exterior $\angle ACD$

Prove: $m\angle A + m\angle B = m\angle ACD$

14. Solve for *x* in each diagram.

a.

b.

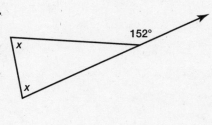

c.

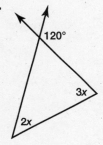

d.

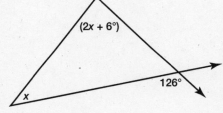

The **Exterior Angle Inequality Theorem** states: "the measure of an exterior angle of a triangle is greater than the measure of either of the remote interior angles of the triangle."

15. Why is it necessary to prove two different statements to completely prove this theorem?

16. Prove both parts of the Exterior Angle Inequality Theorem using the diagram shown.

a. Part 1

Given: Triangle *ABC* with exterior ∠*ACD*

Prove: *m*∠*ACD* > *m*∠*A*

Statements	Reasons
1.	**1.** Given
2.	**2.** Triangle Sum Theorem
3.	**3.** Linear Pair Postulate
4.	**4.** Definition of linear pair
5.	**5.** Substitution Property using step 2 and step 4
6.	**6.** Subtraction Property of Equality
7.	**7.** Definition of an angle measure
8.	**8.** Inequality Property (if *a* = *b* + *c* and *c* > 0, then *a* > *b*)

b. Part 2

Given: Triangle *ABC* with exterior ∠*ACD*

Prove: *m*∠*ACD* > *m*∠*B*

Easter Island is an island in the southeastern Pacific Ocean, famous for its statues created by the early Rapa Nui people.

Two maps of Easter Island are shown.

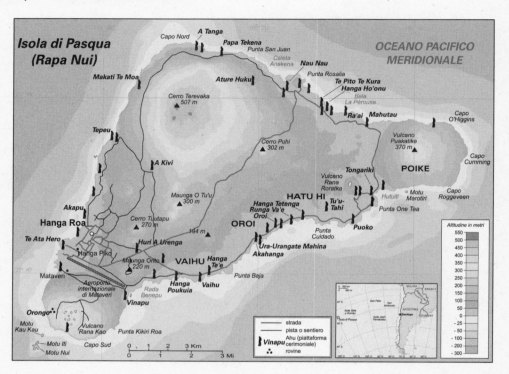

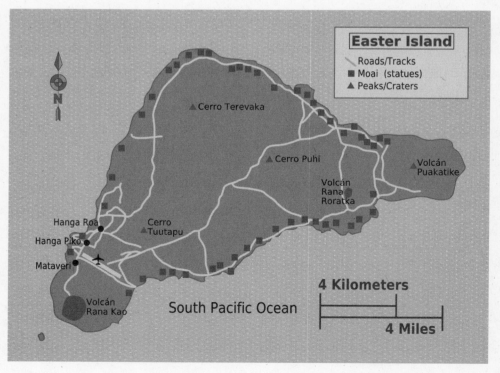

1. What questions could be answering using each map?

2. What geometric shape does Easter Island most closely resemble? Draw this shape on one of the maps.

3. Is it necessary to draw Easter Island on a coordinate plane to compute the length of its coastlines? Why or why not?

4. Predict which side of Easter Island appears to have the longest coastline and state your reasoning using a geometric theorem.

5. Use either map to validate your answer to Question 4.

6. Easter Island has 887 statues. How many statues are there on Easter Island per square mile?

 7. Suppose we want to place statues along the entire coastline of the island, and the distance between each statue was 1 mile. Would we need to build additional statues, and if so, how many?

Talk the Talk

Using only the information in the diagram shown, determine which two islands are farthest apart. Use mathematics to justify your reasoning.

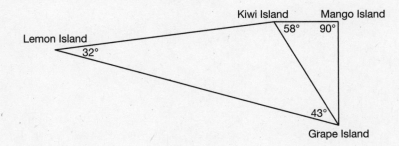

Be prepared to share your solutions and methods.

Trade Routes and Pasta Anyone?

The Triangle Inequality Theorem

Triangular trade best describes the Atlantic trade routes among several different destinations in Colonial times. The Triangular Trade Routes connected England, Europe, Africa, the Americas, and the West Indies. The Triangular Trade Routes included the following:

- Trade Route 1: England to Africa to the Americas
- Trade Route 2: England to Africa to the West Indies
- Trade Route 3: Europe to the West Indies to the Americas
- Trade Route 4: Americas to the West Indies to Europe

1. Sarah claims that any three lengths will determine three sides of a triangle. Sam does not agree. He thinks some combinations will not work. Who is correct?

All I need is one counterexample to disprove a statement.

2. Sam then claims that he can just look at the three lengths and know immediately if they will work. Sarah is unsure. She decides to explore this for herself.

   Help Sarah by working through the following activity.

   To begin, you will need a piece of strand pasta (like linguine). Break the pasta at two random points so the strand is divided into three pieces. Measure each of your three pieces of pasta in centimeters. Try to form a triangle from your three pieces of pasta. Try several pieces of pasta with different breaking points.

3. Collect and record your classmates' measurements.

Piece 1 (cm)	Piece 2 (cm)	Piece 3 (cm)	Forms a Triangle? (yes or no)

4. Examine the lengths of the pasta pieces that did form a triangle. Compare them with the lengths of the pasta pieces that did not form a triangle. What observations can you make?

5. Under what conditions were you able to form a triangle?

6. Under what conditions were you unable to form a triangle?

7. Based upon your observations, determine if it is possible to form a triangle using segments with the following measurements. Explain your reasoning.

   a. 2 centimeters, 5.1 centimeters, 2.4 centimeters

   b. 9.2 centimeters, 7 centimeters, 1.9 centimeters

The rule that Sam was using is known as the Triangle Inequality Theorem.

The **Triangle Inequality Theorem** states: "the sum of the lengths of any two sides of a triangle is greater than the length of the third side."

8. Prove the Triangle Inequality Theorem by completing each step.

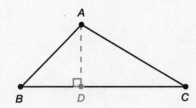

Given: Triangle ABC

Prove: $AB + AC > BC$

A perpendicular line segment AD is constructed through point A to side BC.

Statements	Reasons
1. Triangle ABC	**1.** Given
2. Draw $\overline{AD} \perp \overline{BC}$	**2.** Construction
3. $\angle ADB$ is a right angle.	**3.** Definition of perpendicular.
4. $\angle ADC$ is a right angle.	**4.** Definition of perpendicular.
5. $BD^2 + AD^2 = AB^2$	**5.** Pythagorean Theorem
6. $CD^2 + AD^2 = AC^2$	**6.** Pythagorean Theorem
7. $AB^2 > BD^2$	**7.** Definition of greater than.
8. $AC^2 > DC^2$	**8.** Definition of greater than.
9. $AB > BD$	**9.**
10. $AC > DC$	**10.**
11. $AB + AC > BD + DC$	**11.**
12. $BD + DC = BC$	**12.**
13. $AB + AC > BC$	**13.**

Be prepared to share your solutions and methods.

Stamps Around the World
Properties of a 45°–45°–90° Triangle

LEARNING GOALS

In this lesson, you will:

- Use the Pythagorean Theorem to explore the relationship between the side lengths of a triangle and the measures of its interior angles.
- Prove the 45°–45°–90° Triangle Theorem.

KEY TERM

- 45°–45°–90° Triangle Theorem

The first adhesive postage stamp was issued in the United Kingdom in 1840. It is commonly known as the Penny Black which makes sense because it cost one penny and had a black background. It featured a profile of 15-year-old former Princess Victoria.

You may think that the very first stamp is quite rare and valuable. However, that isn't quite true. The total print run was 68,808,000. During this time envelopes were not normally used. The address and the stamp was affixed to the folded letter itself. Many people kept personal letters and ended up keeping the stamp too.

As of 2012, the most valuable stamp was the Treskilling Yellow stamp from Sweden. Only one known copy exists. In 2010 it sold at auction for over three million dollars!

The first triangle-shaped U.S. stamps were issued on June 8, 1997. The pair of 32-cent commemorative stamps of triangular shape featured a mid-19th-century clipper ship and a U.S. mail stagecoach.

Each image shown is an enlargement of both stamps.

1. Can you use this enlargement to determine the measures of the angles of the actual stamp? Why or why not?

2. Measure the angles of one of the commemorative stamps.

3. Measure the length of the sides of one of the commemorative stamps and describe the relationship between the length of each side and the measure of the angle located opposite each side.

The **45°–45°–90° Triangle Theorem** states: "the length of the hypotenuse in a 45°–45°–90° triangle is $\sqrt{2}$ times the length of a leg."

4. Use the Pythagorean Theorem to prove the 45°–45°–90° Triangle Theorem. Let c represent the length of the hypotenuse and let ℓ represent the length of each leg.

5. Using the 45°–45°–90° Triangle Theorem, what is the length of the longest side of the enlargement of the commemorative stamp?

6. What additional information is needed to determine the length of the longest side of the actual commemorative stamp?

7. This stamp was issued in Mongolia.

Suppose the longest side of this stamp is 50 millimeters.

a. Use the Pythagorean Theorem to determine the approximate length of the other sides of this stamp. Round your answer to the nearest tenth of a millimeter.

b. Use the 45°–45°–90° Triangle Theorem to determine the approximate length of the other sides of this stamp. Round your answer to the nearest tenth of a millimeter.

8. This stamp was issued in Russia.

Suppose the longest side of this stamp is 50 millimeters. Use the 45°–45°–90° Triangle Theorem to determine the *actual* length of the shortest side of this stamp.

9. In 2007, another triangle-shaped stamp was issued in the United States. It was issued to commemorate the 400th anniversary of the Settlement of Jamestown, Virginia, by English colonists in 1607. This stamp features a painting of the three ships that carried the colonists from England to the United States. Was it a coincidence that the first fort built by the settlers was shaped like a triangle?

This is an enlargement of the Jamestown stamp.

Measure the length of the shortest side and use the 45°–45°–90° Triangle Theorem to determine the length of the longest side of the enlargement of the commemorative stamp.

10. The first triangular stamp was issued by the Cape of Good Hope in 1853. This is an enlargement of the Cape of Good Hope stamp.

Measure the length of the longest side and use the 45°–45°–90° Triangle Theorem to determine the length of the shortest side of the enlargement of the commemorative stamp.

1. Construct an isosceles right triangle with $\overline{CB}$ as a leg and $\angle C$ as the right angle.

C   B

After completing the construction, use a protractor and a ruler to confirm the following:

- $m\angle A = 45°$
- $m\angle B = 45°$
- $AC = BC$
- $AB = AC\sqrt{2}$
- $AB = BC\sqrt{2}$

2. Explain how you can use an alternate method for constructing a 45°–45°–90° triangle by constructing a square first.

Be prepared to share your solutions and methods.

3

More Stamps, Really?
Properties of a 30°–60°–90° Triangle

LEARNING GOALS

In this lesson, you will:

- Use the Pythagorean Theorem to explore the relationship between the side lengths of a triangle and the measures of its interior angles.
- Prove the 30°–60°–90° Triangle Theorem.

KEY TERM

- 30°–60°–90° Triangle Theorem

The US Postal Services doesn't have an official motto but an inscription on the James Farley Post Office in New York is well known. It reads, "Neither snow nor rain nor heat nor gloom of night stays these couriers from the swift completion of their appointed rounds."

There have been many popular characters on television who were mail carriers including Mister McFeely from the children's series *Mister Rogers' Neighborhood*, Cliff Clavin from the comedy series *Cheers*, and Newman from the comedy series *Seinfeld*.

Can you think of any other famous mail carriers? What other professions seem to inspire characters on television, the movies, or in books?

This stamp was issued in Malaysia.

1. How is this stamp different from the stamps you studied in the previous lesson?

2. This Malaysian stamp is shaped like an equilateral triangle. What is the measure of each interior angle of the triangle? Explain your reasoning.

3. Use the diagram of the stamp to draw an altitude to the base of the equilateral triangle. Describe the two triangles formed by the altitude.

4. How do you know that the two triangles formed by the altitude drawn to the base of an equilateral triangle are congruent.

5. If the length of each side of the Malaysian stamp is 50 millimeters, determine the length of the three sides in each of the two 30°–60°–90° triangles formed by the altitude drawn to the base of the equilateral triangle.

Don't rewrite radical side lengths as decimals. That will help you see the pattern.

6. How does the length of the hypotenuse in each of the two 30°–60°–90° triangles relate to the length of the shortest leg?

7. How does the length of the longer leg in each of the two 30°–60°–90° triangles relate to the length of the shortest leg?

The **30°–60°–90° Triangle Theorem** states: "the length of the hypotenuse in a 30°–60°–90° triangle is two times the length of the shorter leg, and the length of the longer leg is $\sqrt{3}$ times the length of the shorter leg."

8. Use the Pythagorean Theorem to demonstrate the 30°–60°–90° Triangle Theorem. Let x represent the length of the shortest leg.

9. This stamp was issued in the Netherlands.

Suppose the length of each side of the Netherlands stamp is 40 millimeters. Use the 30°–60°–90° Triangle Theorem to determine the height of the stamp.

10. In 1929, Uruguay issued a triangular parcel post stamp with a picture of wings, implying rapid delivery.

Suppose the height of the Uruguay stamp is 30 millimeters. Use the 30°–60°–90° Triangle Theorem to determine the length of the three sides of the stamp.

11. A mathematical society in India designed this stamp. The pyramidal design is an equilateral triangle.

Suppose the height of the pyramidal design on the stamp is 42 millimeters. Determine the area of the pyramidal design on the stamp.

PROBLEM 2   Construction

30°–60°–90° Triangle

Construct a 30°–60°–90° triangle by constructing an equilateral triangle and one altitude.

After completing the construction, use a protractor and a ruler to confirm that:

- one angle measure is 30°.
- one angle measure is 60°.
- one angle measure is 90°.
- the side opposite the 30° angle is one-half the length of the hypotenuse.
- the side opposite the 60° angle is one-half the hypotenuse times $\sqrt{3}$.

Talk the Talk

1. Label the shortest side of each triangle as *x*. Then label the remaining sides of each triangle in terms of *x*.

   a. 45°–45°–90° triangle

   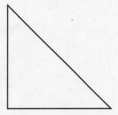

   b. 30°–60°–90° triangle

   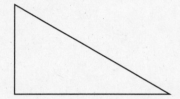

2. Explain how to calculate the following for a 45°–45°–90° triangle.

   a. The length of a leg given the length of the hypotenuse.

   b. The length of the hypotenuse given the length of a leg.

3. Explain how to calculate the following for a 30°–60°–90° triangle.

   a. The length of the hypotenuse given the length of the shorter leg.

   b. The length of the hypotenuse given the length of the longer leg.

   c. The length of the shorter leg given the length of the longer leg.

   d. The length of the shorter leg given the length of the hypotenuse.

   e. The length of the longer leg given the length of the shorter leg.

   f. The length of the longer leg given the length of the hypotenuse.

 Be prepared to share your solutions and methods.

3

- remote interior angles of a triangle (3.1)

- Triangle Sum Theorem (3.1)
- Exterior Angle Theorem (3.1)
- Exterior Angle Inequality Theorem (3.1)
- Triangle Inequality Theorem (3.2)
- 45°–45°–90° Triangle Theorem (3.3)
- 30°–60°–90° Triangle Theorem (3.4)

3.1 **Using the Triangle Sum Theorem**

The Triangle Sum Theorem states: "The sum of the measures of the interior angles of a triangle is 180°."

Example

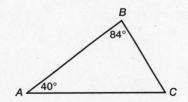

$$m\angle A + m\angle B + m\angle C = 180°$$

$$40° + 84° + m\angle C = 180°$$

$$m\angle C = 180° - (40° + 84°)$$

$$m\angle C = 180° - 124°$$

$$m\angle C = 56°$$

3.1   Using the Exterior Angle Theorem

The Exterior Angle Theorem states: "The measure of an exterior angle of a triangle is equal to the sum of the measures of the two remote interior angles of the triangle."

Example

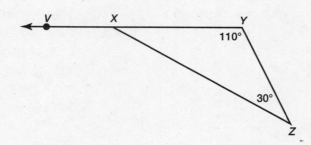

$m\angle VXZ = m\angle Y + m\angle Z$

$m\angle VXZ = 110° + 30°$

$m\angle VXZ = 140°$

3.2   Using the Triangle Inequality Theorem

The Triangle Inequality Theorem states: "The sum of the lengths of any two sides of a triangle is greater than the length of the third side."

Example

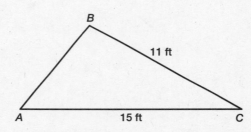

$AB < BC + AC$	$BC < AB + AC$	$AC < AB + BC$
$AB < 11 + 15$	$11 < AB + 15$	$15 < AB + 11$
$AB < 26$	$-4 < AB$	$4 < AB$

So, *AB* must be greater than 4 feet and less than 26 feet. (A length cannot be negative, so disregard the negative number.)

3.3 Using the 45°–45°–90° Triangle Theorem

The 45°–45°–90° Triangle Theorem states: "The length of the hypotenuse in a 45°–45°–90° triangle is $\sqrt{2}$ times the length of a leg."

Examples

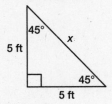

$x = 5\sqrt{2}$ ft

The length of the hypotenuse is $5\sqrt{2}$ feet.

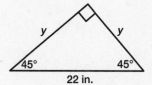

$y\sqrt{2} = 22$

$y = \dfrac{22}{\sqrt{2}} = \dfrac{22 \cdot \sqrt{2}}{\sqrt{2} \cdot \sqrt{2}} = \dfrac{22 \cdot \sqrt{2}}{2} = 11\sqrt{2}$ in.

The length of each leg is $11\sqrt{2}$ inches.

3.4 Using the 30°–60°–90° Triangle Theorem

The 30°–60°–90° Triangle Theorem states: "The length of the hypotenuse in a 30°–60°–90° triangle is two times the length of the shorter leg, and the length of the longer leg is $\sqrt{3}$ times the length of the shorter leg."

Examples

Hypotenuse:

$x = 2(8) = 16$ m

Longer leg:

$y = 8\sqrt{3}$ m

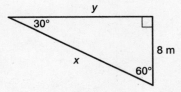

Shorter leg:

$a\sqrt{3} = 10$

$a = \dfrac{10}{\sqrt{3}} = \dfrac{10\sqrt{3}}{3}$ in.

Hypotenuse:

$b = 2a = 2\left(\dfrac{10\sqrt{3}}{3}\right)$

$= \dfrac{20\sqrt{3}}{3}$ in.

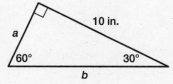

Shorter leg:

$2s = 6$

$s = 3$ ft

Longer leg:

$t = s\sqrt{3}$

$t = 3\sqrt{3}$ ft

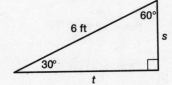

Similarity Through Transformations

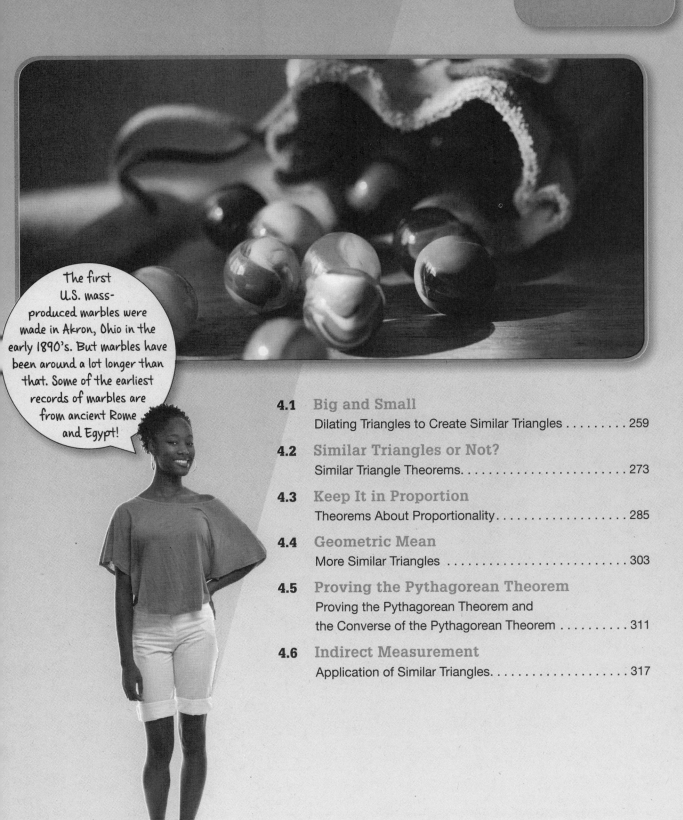

The first U.S. mass-produced marbles were made in Akron, Ohio in the early 1890's. But marbles have been around a lot longer than that. Some of the earliest records of marbles are from ancient Rome and Egypt!

Big and Small
Dilating Triangles to Create Similar Triangles

Making hand shadow puppets has a long history. This activity goes back to ancient China and India. Before the invention of television, or even radio, hand shadows were used to entertain people by telling stories.

Today, you can find tutorials online that will show you how to create really complicated and interesting shadow puppets. Groups of people can get together and create entire landscapes and scenes—all with the shadows made by their hands!

The game of marbles is played in a circle. The goal is to knock your opponents marbles outside of the circle by flicking a shooter marble at the other marbles in the circle. The shooter marble is often larger than the other marbles.

John placed a shooter marble near three smaller marbles as shown.

Can you describe the 3 smaller marbles as being collinear?

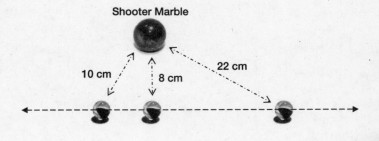

Shooter Marble

10 cm   8 cm   22 cm

1. Draw another row of three marbles under the first row of marbles using a dilation factor of 2 with the shooter marble as the center of the dilation.

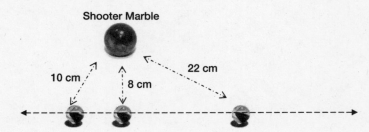

Shooter Marble

10 cm   8 cm   22 cm

2. Explain how you located the positions of each additional marble. Label the distances between the marbles in the first row and in the second row.

3. Describe the relationship between the first and second rows of marbles.

4. Use a ruler to compare the length of the line segments connecting each original marble to the line segments connecting each additional marble.

5. What can you conclude about dilating a line that does not pass through the center of a dilation?

6. Consider line P. How could you show a dilation of this line by a factor of 2 using P as the center of dilation? Explain your reasoning.

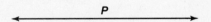

P

You have volunteered to help at the children's booth at an art festival. The children that visit the booth will be able to create objects, like animals or people, out of poster board and craft sticks. Then, they will use a flashlight to create shadow puppets. Your job is to show the children how to use a flashlight and a wall to make their own puppet show.

1. How does the size of the shadow puppet compare to the size of the object made out of poster board and craft sticks?

2. How does the shape of the shadow puppet compare to the shape of the object made out of poster board and craft sticks?

3. Do you think that the shadow is a transformation of the object? Why or why not?

Consider △ABC, △DEF, and point Y. Imagine that point Y is the flashlight and △DEF is the shadow of △ABC.

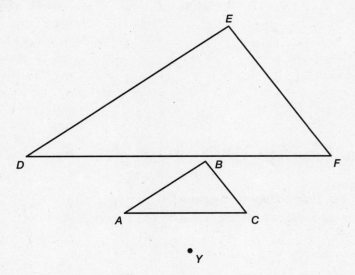

4. Draw the line segments $\overline{YD}, \overline{YE}, \overline{YF}$ on the figure shown. These line segments show the path of the light from the flashlight.

Describe what these line segments connect.

5. Use a metric ruler to determine the actual lengths of $\overline{YA}, \overline{YB}, \overline{YC}, \overline{YD}, \overline{YE}$, and $\overline{YF}$ to the nearest tenth of a centimeter.

4

6. Express the ratios $\dfrac{YD}{YA}, \dfrac{YE}{YB}$, and $\dfrac{YF}{YC}$ as decimals.

7. What do you notice about the ratios?

Remember that a ratio is a comparison of two numbers that uses division. The ratio of two numbers a and b (b cannot be zero), can be written in three ways.

a to b

a : b

$\frac{a}{b}$

8. Use a protractor to measure the corresponding angles in the triangles. What can you conclude?

9. What is the relationship between the image and pre-image in a dilation?

The shadow created by the flashlight is a dilation.

10. In any dilation:

    a. how will the corresponding angles in the image and pre-image compare?

    b. how will the ratios of the lengths of the corresponding sides compare?

11. What is the center of the dilation shown in Question 4?

12. Rectangle *L'M'N'P'* is a dilation of rectangle *LMNP*. The center of dilation is point *Z*.

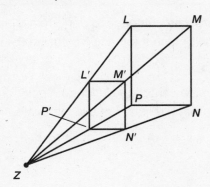

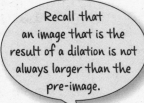

Recall that an image that is the result of a dilation is not always larger than the pre-image.

a. Use a metric ruler to determine the actual lengths of $\overline{ZL}$, $\overline{ZN}$, $\overline{ZM}$, $\overline{ZP}$, $\overline{ZL'}$, $\overline{ZN'}$, $\overline{ZM'}$, and $\overline{ZP'}$ to the nearest tenth of a centimeter.

Then express the ratios $\frac{ZL'}{ZL}$, $\frac{ZN'}{ZN}$, $\frac{ZM'}{ZM}$, and $\frac{ZP'}{ZP}$ as decimals.

b. What do you notice about the ratios?

4

13. How does the image compare to the pre-image when:

a. the scale factor is greater than 1?

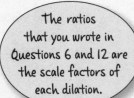
The ratios that you wrote in Questions 6 and 12 are the scale factors of each dilation.

b. the scale factor is less than 1?

You can use your compass and a straightedge to perform a dilation. Consider △GHJ shown on the coordinate plane. You will dilate the triangle by using the origin as the center and by using a scale factor of 2.

1. How will the distance from the center of dilation to a point on the image of △G′H′J′ compare to the distance from the center of dilation to a corresponding point on △GHJ? Explain your reasoning.

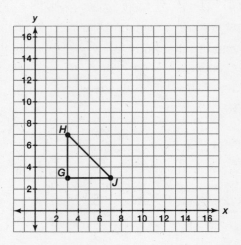

2. For each vertex of △GHJ, draw a ray that starts at the origin and passes through the vertex.

3. Use the duplicate segment construction to locate the vertices of △G′H′J′.

4. List the coordinates of the vertices of △GHJ and △G′H′J′. How do the coordinates of the image compare to the coordinates of the pre-image?

5. Triangle *J'K'L'* is a dilation of △*JKL*. The center of dilation is the origin.

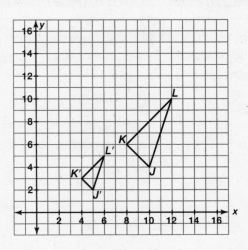

a. List the coordinates of the vertices of △*JKL* and △*J'K'L'*. How do the coordinates of the image compare to the coordinates of the pre-image?

b. What is the scale factor of the dilation? Explain your reasoning.

c. How do you think you can use the scale factor to determine the coordinates of the vertices of an image?

6. Use coordinate notation to describe the dilation of point (*x*, *y*) when the center of dilation is at the origin using a scale factor of *k*.

Similar triangles are triangles that have all pairs of corresponding angles congruent and all corresponding sides are proportional. Similar triangles have the same shape but not always the same size.

1. Triangle *HRY* ~ Triangle *JPT*

   Draw a diagram that illustrates this similarity statement and list all of the pairs of congruent angles and all of the proportional sides.

2.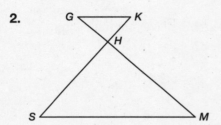

   a. What conditions are necessary to show triangle *GHK* is similar to triangle *MHS*?

b. Suppose $4GH = HM$.

Determine whether this given information is enough to prove that the two triangles are similar. Explain why you think they are similar or provide a counter-example if you think the triangles are not similar.

c. Suppose $\overline{GK}$ is parallel to $\overline{MS}$.

Determine whether this given information is enough to prove that the two triangles are similar. Explain why you think they are similar or provide a counter-example if you think the triangles are not similar.

d. Suppose $\angle G \cong \angle S$.

Determine whether this given information is enough to prove that the two triangles are similar. Explain why you think they are similar or provide a counter-example if you think the triangles are not similar.

In each of the following situations you have concluded that given the information provided, the triangles could be proven similar using geometric theorems. The triangles could also be proven similar using a sequence of transformations. These transformations result in mapping one triangle to the other.

1.

G   K

H

S   M

a. Suppose $\overline{KG}$ is parallel to $\overline{MS}$.

Describe a sequence of transformations that maps one triangle to the other triangle.

b. Suppose $\angle G \cong \angle S$.

Describe a sequence of transformations that maps one triangle to the other triangle.

c. Suppose $(KH)(GH) = (SH)(MH)$

Describe a sequence of transformations that maps one triangle to the other triangle.

 Be prepared to share your solutions and methods.

4

Similar Triangles or Not?

Similar Triangle Theorems

An art projector is a piece of equipment that artists have used to create exact copies of artwork, to enlarge artwork, or to reduce artwork. A basic art projector uses a light bulb and a lens within a box. The light rays from the art being copied are collected onto a lens at a single point. The lens then projects the image of the art onto a screen as shown.

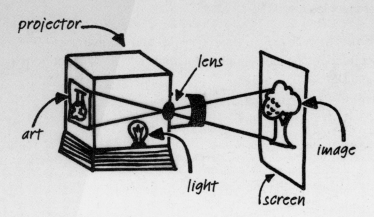

If the projector is set up properly, the triangles shown will be similar polygons. You can show that these triangles are similar without measuring all of the side lengths and all of the interior angles.

PROBLEM 1 Using Two Angles

In the previous lesson, you used transformations to prove that triangles are similar when their corresponding angles are congruent and their corresponding sides are proportional. In this problem, you will explore the similarity of two triangles using construction tools.

1. Identify all of the corresponding congruent angles and all of the corresponding proportional sides using the similar triangles shown.

   △RST ~ △WXY

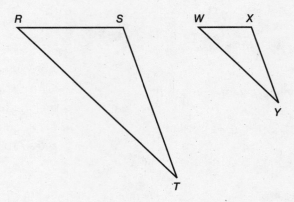

You can conclude that two triangles are similar if you are able to prove that all of their corresponding angles are congruent and all of their corresponding sides are proportional.

Let's use constructions to see if you can use fewer pairs of angles or fewer pairs of sides to show that triangles are similar.

2. Construct triangle D′E′F′ using only ∠D and ∠E in triangle DEF as shown. Make all the corresponding side lengths of triangle D′E′F′ different from the side lengths of triangle DEF.

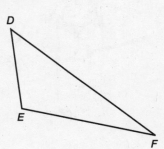

3. Measure the angles and sides of triangle $D'E'F'$ and triangle *DEF*. Are the two triangles similar? Explain your reasoning.

Did everyone construct the same triangle?

4. In triangles *DEF* and $D'E'F'$, two pairs of corresponding angles are congruent. Determine if this is sufficient information to conclude that the triangles are similar.

The **Angle-Angle Similarity Theorem** states: "If two angles of one triangle are congruent to two angles of another triangle, then the triangles are similar."

4

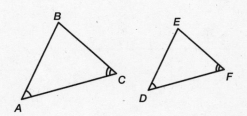

If $m\angle A = m\angle D$ and $m\angle C = m\angle F$, then $\triangle ABC \sim \triangle DEF$.

5. Explain why this similarity theorem is Angle-Angle instead of Angle-Angle-Angle.

6. The triangles shown are isosceles triangles. Do you have enough information to show that the triangles are similar? Explain your reasoning.

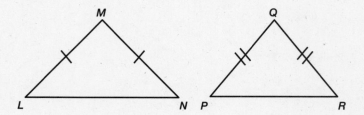

7. The triangles shown are isosceles triangles. Do you have enough information to show that the triangles are similar? Explain your reasoning.

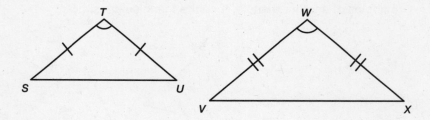

1. Construct triangle $D'E'F'$ by doubling the lengths of sides $\overline{DE}$ and $\overline{EF}$. Construct the new $D'E'$ and $E'F'$ separately and then construct the triangle. This will ensure a ratio of 2:1. Do not duplicate angles.

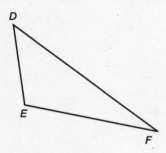

 2. Measure the angles and sides of triangle $D'E'F'$ and triangle DEF. Are the two triangles similar? Explain your reasoning.

Did everyone construct the same triangle?

3. Two pairs of corresponding sides are proportional. Determine if this is sufficient information to conclude that the triangles are similar.

Not having sufficient information doesn't mean that the triangle are NOT similar. It just means that you can't know for sure whether the triangles are or are not similar.

4. Construct triangle $D'E'F'$ by doubling the lengths of sides $\overline{DE}$, $\overline{EF}$, and $\overline{FD}$. Construct the new side lengths separately, and then construct the triangle. Do not duplicate angles.

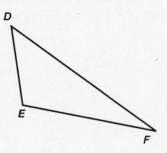

What about now? Did everyone construct the same triangle?

5. Measure the angles and sides of triangle $D'E'F'$ and triangle DEF. Are the two triangles similar? Explain your reasoning.

6. Three pairs of corresponding sides are proportional. Determine if this is sufficient information to conclude that the triangles are similar.

The **Side-Side-Side Similarity Theorem** states: "If all three corresponding sides of two triangles are proportional, then the triangles are similar."

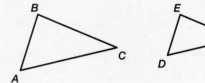

If $\dfrac{AB}{DE} = \dfrac{BC}{EF} = \dfrac{AC}{DF}$, then $\triangle ABC \sim \triangle DEF$.

Stacy says that the Side-Side-Side Similarity Theorem tells us that two triangles can have proportional sides, but not congruent angles, and still be similar. Michael doesn't think that's right, but he can't explain why.

7. Is Stacy correct? If not, explain why not.

8. Determine whether $\triangle UVW$ is similar to $\triangle XYZ$. If so, use symbols to write a similarity statement.

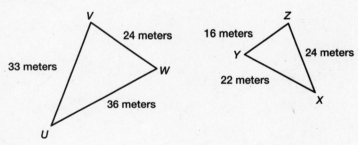

9. Describe how transformations could be used to determine whether two triangles are similar when all pairs of corresponding sides are proportional.

PROBLEM 3 Using Two Proportional Sides and an Angle

An **included angle** is an angle formed by two consecutive sides of a figure.

An **included side** is a line segment between two consecutive angles of a figure.

1. Construct triangle *D'E'F'* by duplicating an angle and doubling the length of the two sides that make up that angle. Construct the new side lengths separately, and then construct the triangle.

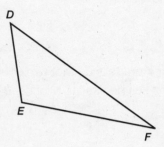

2. Measure the angles and sides of triangle *D'E'F'* and triangle *DEF*. Are the two triangles similar? Explain your reasoning.

3. Two pairs of corresponding sides are proportional and the corresponding included angles are congruent. Determine if this is sufficient information to conclude that the triangles are similar.

4. Describe how transformations could be used to determine whether two triangles are similar when two pairs of corresponding sides are proportional and the included angles are congruent.

The **Side-Angle-Side Similarity Theorem** states: "If two of the corresponding sides of two triangles are proportional and the included angles are congruent, then the triangles are similar."

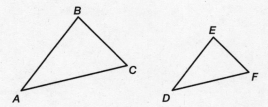

 If $\dfrac{AB}{DE} = \dfrac{AC}{DF}$ and $\angle A \cong \angle D$, then $\triangle ABC \sim \triangle DEF$.

Talk the Talk

1. Gaelin is thinking of a triangle and he wants everyone in his class to draw a similar triangle. Complete the graphic organizer to describe the sides and angles of triangles he could provide.

  Be prepared to share your solutions and methods.

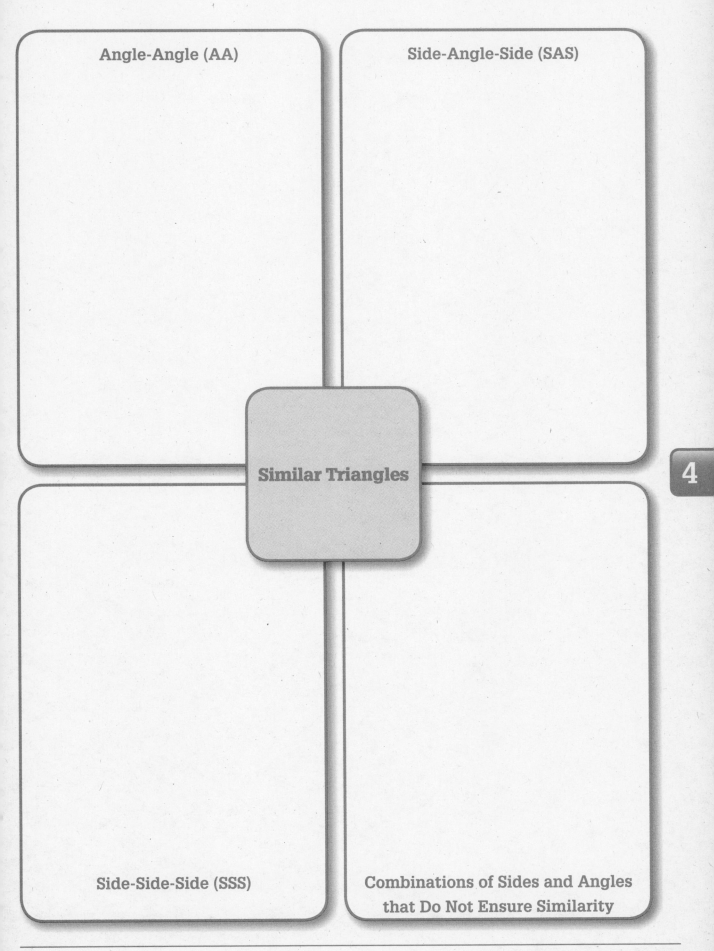

Angle-Angle (AA)

Side-Angle-Side (SAS)

Similar Triangles

Side-Side-Side (SSS)

Combinations of Sides and Angles that Do Not Ensure Similarity

4

4

Keep It in Proportion

Theorems About Proportionality

LEARNING GOALS

In this lesson, you will:

- Prove the Angle Bisector/Proportional Side Theorem.
- Prove the Triangle Proportionality Theorem.
- Prove the Converse of the Triangle Proportionality Theorem.
- Prove the Proportional Segments Theorem associated with parallel lines.
- Prove the Triangle Midsegment Theorem.

KEY TERMS

- Angle Bisector/Proportional Side Theorem
- Triangle Proportionality Theorem
- Converse of the Triangle Proportionality Theorem
- Proportional Segments Theorem
- Triangle Midsegment Theorem

Although geometry is a mathematical study, it has a history that is very much tied up with ancient and modern religions. Certain geometric ratios have been used to create religious buildings, and the application of these ratios in construction even extends back into ancient times.

Music, as well, involves work with ratios and proportions.

When an interior angle of a triangle is bisected, you can observe proportional relationships among the sides of the triangles formed. You will be able to prove that these relationships apply to all triangles.

The **Angle Bisector/Proportional Side Theorem** states: "A bisector of an angle in a triangle divides the opposite side into two segments whose lengths are in the same ratio as the lengths of the sides adjacent to the angle."

To prove the Angle Bisector/Proportional Side Theorem, consider the statements and figure shown.

Given: $\overline{AD}$ bisects $\angle BAC$

Prove: $\dfrac{AB}{AC} = \dfrac{BD}{CD}$

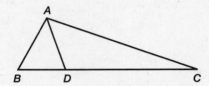

1. Draw a line parallel to $\overline{AB}$ through point C. Extend $\overline{AD}$ until it intersects the line. Label the point of intersection, point E.

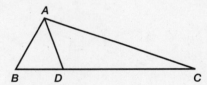

2. Complete the proof of the Angle Bisector/Proportional Side Theorem.

Statements	Reasons
1.	**1.** Given
2.	**2.** Construction
3.	**3.** Definition of angle bisector
4. $\angle BAE \cong \angle CEA$	**4.**
5.	**5.** Transitive Property of $\cong$
6.	**6.** If two angles of a triangle are congruent, then the sides opposite the angles are congruent.
7.	**7.** Definition of congruent segments
8.	**8.** Alternate Interior Angle Theorem
9. $\triangle DAB \sim \triangle DEC$	**9.**
10. $\dfrac{AB}{EC} = \dfrac{BD}{CD}$	**10.**
11.	**11.** Rewrite as an equivalent proportion
12. $\dfrac{AB}{BD} = \dfrac{AC}{CD}$	**12.**

Applying the Angle Bisector/Proportional Side Theorem

1. On the map shown, North Craig Street bisects the angle formed between Bellefield Avenue and Ellsworth Avenue.

   • The distance from the ATM to the Coffee Shop is 300 feet.

   • The distance from the Coffee Shop to the Library is 500 feet.

   • The distance from your apartment to the Library is 1200 feet.

   Determine the distance from your apartment to the ATM.

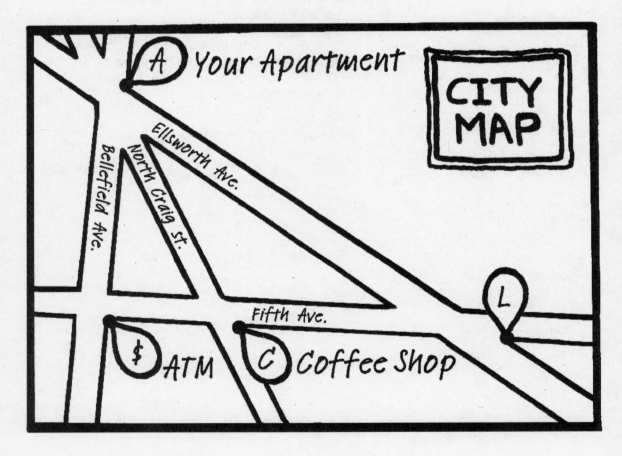

2. $\overline{CD}$ bisects $\angle C$. Solve for DB.

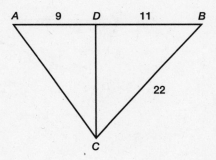

3. $\overline{CD}$ bisects $\angle C$. Solve for AC.

4. $\overline{AD}$ bisects $\angle A$. $AC + AB = 36$. Solve for AC and AB.

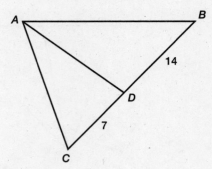

5. $\overline{BD}$ bisects $\angle B$. Solve for AC.

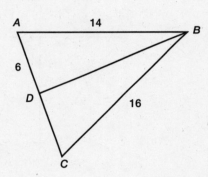

The **Triangle Proportionality Theorem** states: "If a line parallel to one side of a triangle intersects the other two sides, then it divides the two sides proportionally."

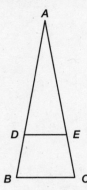

Given: $\overline{BC} \parallel \overline{DE}$

Prove: $\dfrac{BD}{DA} = \dfrac{CE}{EA}$

1. Write a paragraph proof to prove triangle *ADE* is similar to triangle *ABC*.

2. Cut out each statement and reason on the next page. Match them together, and then rearrange them in an appropriate order by numbering them to create a proof for the Triangle Proportionality Theorem.

Triangle ADE is similar to triangle ABC	Corresponding sides of similar triangles are proportional
$\dfrac{BD}{DA} = \dfrac{CE}{EA}$	Corresponding Angle Postulate
$\angle AED \cong \angle C$	Given
$\overline{BC} \parallel \overline{DE}$	Corresponding Angle Postulate
$\dfrac{BA}{DA} = \dfrac{CA}{EA}$	AA Similarity Theorem
$BA = BD + DA$ and $CA = CE + EA$	Substitution
$\dfrac{BD + DA}{DA} = \dfrac{CE + EA}{EA}$	Segment Addition Postulate
$\angle ADE \cong \angle B$	Simplify

4

Statements	**Reasons**

The **Converse of the Triangle Proportionality Theorem** states: "If a line divides two sides of a triangle proportionally, then it is parallel to the third side."

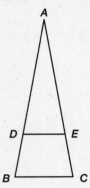

Given: $\dfrac{BD}{DA} = \dfrac{CE}{EA}$

Prove: $\overline{BC} \parallel \overline{DE}$

Prove the Converse of the Triangle Proportionality Theorem.

PROBLEM **Proportional Segments Theorem**

The **Proportional Segments Theorem** states: "If three parallel lines intersect two transversals, then they divide the transversals proportionally."

Given: $L_1 \parallel L_2 \parallel L_3$

Prove: $\dfrac{AB}{BC} = \dfrac{DE}{EF}$

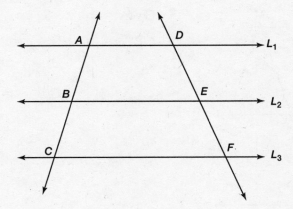

1. Through any two points there is exactly one line. Draw line segment *CD* to form triangle *ACD* and triangle *FDC*.

2. Let *H* be the point at which L_2 intersects line segment *CD*. Label point *H*.

3. Using the Triangle Proportionality Theorem and triangle *ACD*, what can you conclude?

4. Using the Triangle Proportionality Theorem and triangle *FDC*, what can you conclude?

5. What property of equality will justify the prove statement?

PROBLEM 6   Triangle Midsegment Theorem

 The **Triangle Midsegment Theorem** states: "The midsegment of a triangle is parallel to the third side of the triangle and is half the measure of the third side of the triangle."

1. Use the diagram to write the "Given" and "Prove" statements for the Triangle Midsegment Theorem.

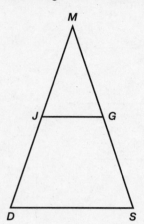

Given:

Prove:

2. Prove the Triangle Midsegment Theorem.

3. Ms. Zoid asked her students to determine whether $\overline{RD}$ is a midsegment of $\triangle TUY$, given $TY = 14$ cm and $RD = 7$ cm.

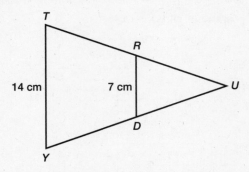

Carson told Alicia that using the Triangle Midsegment Theorem, he could conclude that $\overline{RD}$ is a midsegment. Is Carson correct? How should Alicia respond if Carson is incorrect?

4. Ms. Zoid drew a second diagram on the board and asked her students to determine if $\overline{RD}$ is a midsegment of triangle TUY, given $\overline{RD} \parallel \overline{TY}$.

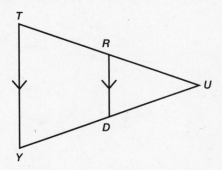

Alicia told Carson that using the Triangle Midsegment Theorem, she could conclude that $\overline{RD}$ is a midsegment. Is Alicia correct? How should Carson respond if Alicia is incorrect?

In △*BJG*, the midpoint of $\overline{BJ}$ is *F* (−3, 5). The midpoint of $\overline{BG}$ is *A* (−6, −5). The midpoint of $\overline{GJ}$ is *R* (6, −5).

5. Use the Triangle Midsegment Theorem to determine the coordinates of the vertices of △*BJG*. Show all of your work.

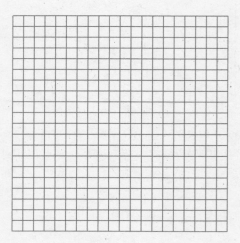

6. Determine the perimeter of $\triangle BJG$ and the perimeter of $\triangle FAR$.
Round each radical to the nearest tenth. Show all of your work.

 Be prepared to share your solutions and methods.

4

Geometric Mean
More Similar Triangles

LEARNING GOALS

In this lesson, you will:

- Explore the relationships created when an altitude is drawn to the hypotenuse of a right triangle.
- Prove the Right Triangle/Altitude Similarity Theorem.
- Use the geometric mean to solve for unknown lengths.

KEY TERMS

- Right Triangle/Altitude Similarity Theorem
- geometric mean
- Right Triangle Altitude/Hypotenuse Theorem
- Right Triangle Altitude/Leg Theorem

People have been building bridges for centuries so that they could cross rivers, valleys, or other obstacles. The earliest bridges probably consisted of a log that connected one side to the other—not exactly the safest bridge!

The longest bridge in the world is the Danyang-Kunshan Grand Bridge in China. Spanning 540,700 feet, it connects Shanghai to Nanjing. Construction was completed in 2010 and employed 10,000 people, took 4 years to build, and cost approximately $8.5 billion.

Lake Pontchartrain Causeway is the longest bridge in the United States. Measuring *only* 126,122 feet, that's less than a quarter of the Danyang-Kunshan Grand Bridge. However, it currently holds the record for the longest bridge over continuous water. Not too shabby!

A bridge is needed to cross over a canyon. The dotted line segment connecting points S and R represents the bridge. The distance from point P to point S is 45 yards. The distance from point Q to point S is 130 feet. How long is the bridge?

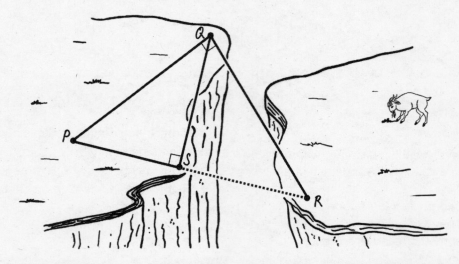

To determine the length of the bridge, you must first explore what happens when an altitude is drawn to the hypotenuse of a right triangle.

When an altitude is drawn to the hypotenuse of a right triangle, it forms two smaller triangles. All three triangles have a special relationship.

We're going to explore these relationships in several triangles first. Then we can answer the question at the beginning of this problem.

1. Construct an altitude to the hypotenuse in the right triangle ABC. Label the altitude CD.

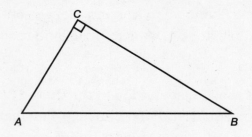

2. Name all right triangles in the figure.

3. Trace each of the triangles on separate pieces of paper and label all the vertices on each triangle. Cut out each triangle. Label the vertex of each triangle. Arrange the triangles so that all of the triangles have the same orientation. The hypotenuse, the shortest leg, and the longest leg should all be in corresponding positions. You may have to flip triangles over to do this.

4. Name each pair of triangles that are similar. Explain how you know that each pair of triangles are similar.

5. Write the corresponding sides of each pair of triangles as proportions.

 The **Right Triangle/Altitude Similarity Theorem** states: "If an altitude is drawn to the hypotenuse of a right triangle, then the two triangles formed are similar to the original triangle and to each other."

PROBLEM 2 Geometric Mean

When an altitude of a right triangle is constructed from the right angle to the hypotenuse, three similar right triangles are created. This altitude is a *geometric mean*.

The **geometric mean** of two positive numbers a and b is the positive number x such that $\frac{a}{x} = \frac{x}{b}$.

Two theorems are associated with the altitude to the hypotenuse of a right triangle.

The **Right Triangle Altitude/Hypotenuse Theorem** states: "The measure of the altitude drawn from the vertex of the right angle of a right triangle to its hypotenuse is the geometric mean between the measures of the two segments of the hypotenuse."

The **Right Triangle Altitude/Leg Theorem** states: "If the altitude is drawn to the hypotenuse of a right triangle, each leg of the right triangle is the geometric mean of the hypotenuse and the segment of the hypotenuse adjacent to the leg."

1. Use the diagram from Problem 1 to answer each question.

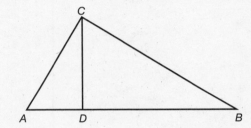

a. Write a proportion to demonstrate the Right Triangle Altitude/Hypotenuse Theorem?

b. Write a proportion to demonstrate the Right Triangle Altitude/Leg Theorem?

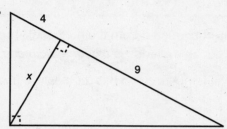

2. In each triangle, solve for *x*.

a.

b.

c.

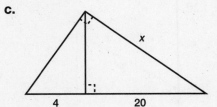

d.

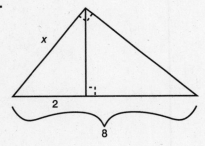

3. In the triangle shown, solve for *x*, *y*, and *z*.

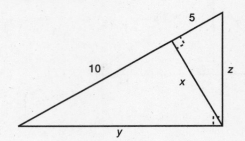

Bridge Over the Canyon

 1. Solve for the length of the bridge in Problem 1 using the geometric mean.

> Now I know everything that I need to answer that "bridge" question. Bring it on!

 Be prepared to share your solutions and methods.

Proving the Pythagorean Theorem

Proving the Pythagorean Theorem and the Converse of the Pythagorean Theorem

LEARNING GOALS

In this lesson, you will:

- Prove the Pythagorean Theorem using similar triangles.
- Prove the Converse of the Pythagorean Theorem using algebraic reasoning.

The Pythagorean Theorem is one of the most famous theorems in mathematics. And the proofs of the theorem are just as famous. It may be the theorem with the most different proofs. The book *Pythagorean Proposition* alone contains 370 proofs.

The scarecrow in the film *The Wizard of Oz* even tries to recite the Pythagorean Theorem upon receiving his brain. He proudly states, "The sum of the square roots of any two sides of an isosceles triangle is equal to the square root of the remaining side. Oh, joy! Oh, rapture! I've got a brain!"

Sadly the scarecrow's version of the theorem is wrong—so much for that brain the wizard gave him!

Proving the Pythagorean Theorem with Similar Triangles

Use the Right Triangle/Altitude Similarity Theorem to prove the Pythagorean Theorem.

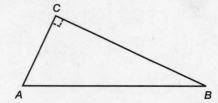

Given: Triangle ABC with right angle C

Prove: $AC^2 + CB^2 = AB^2$

1. Construct altitude CD to hypotenuse AB.

2. Applying the Right Triangle/Altitude Similarity Theorem, what can you conclude?

3. Write a proportional statement describing the relationship between the longest leg and hypotenuse of triangle ABC and triangle CBD.

4. Rewrite the proportional statement you wrote in Question 3 as a product.

5. Write a proportional statement describing the relationship between the shortest leg and hypotenuse of triangle ABC and triangle ACD.

6. Rewrite the proportional statement you wrote in Question 5 as a product.

7. Add the statement in Question 4 to the statement in Question 6.

8. Factor the statement in Question 7.

9. What is equivalent to $DB + AD$?

10. Substitute the answer to Question 9 into the answer to Question 8 to prove the Pythagorean Theorem.

PROBLEM 2 Proving the Pythagorean Theorem with Algebraic Reasoning

Use the diagram shown and the following questions to prove the Pythagorean Theorem.

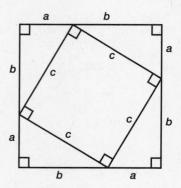

 1. What is the area of the larger square?

2. What is the total area of the four right triangles?

3. What is the area of the smaller square?

 4. What is the relationship between the area of the four right triangles, the area of the smaller square, and the area of the larger square?

Use the diagram shown and the following questions to prove the Converse of the Pythagorean Theorem.

A large square is composed with four identical right triangles in its corners.

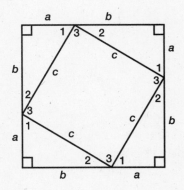

Recall, the Converse of the Pythagorean Theorem states: "If $a^2 + b^2 = c^2$, then a and b are the lengths of the legs of a right triangle and c is the length of the hypotenuse."

1. What can you conclude about $m\angle 1 + m\angle 2 + m\angle 3$?

2. Use the Triangle Sum Theorem to determine $m\angle 1 + m\angle 2$.

3. Knowing $m\angle 1 + m\angle 2$, what can you conclude about $m\angle 3$?

4. What does $m\angle 3$ tell you about the quadrilateral inside of the large square?

5. What is the area of one of the right triangles?

6. What is the area of the quadrilateral inside the large square?

7. Write an expression that represents the combined areas of the four right triangles and the quadrilateral inside the large square. Use your answers from Question 16, parts (e) and (f).

8. Write an expression to represent the area of the large square, given that one side is expressed as $(a + b)$. Simplify your answer.

9. Write an equation using the two different expressions representing the area of the large square from Questions 7 and 8. Then, solve the equation to prove the Converse of the Pythagorean Theorem.

 Be prepared to share your solutions and methods.

Indirect Measurement
Application of Similar Triangles

LEARNING GOALS

LEARNING GOALS

In this lesson, you will:

- Identify similar triangles to calculate indirect measurements.
- Use proportions to solve for unknown measurements.

KEY TERM

- indirect measurement

You would think that determining the tallest building in the world would be pretty straightforward. Well, you would be wrong.

There is actually an organization called the Council on Tall Buildings and Urban Habitat that officially certifies buildings as the world's tallest. It was founded at Lehigh University in 1969 with a mission to study and report "on all aspects of the planning, design, and construction of tall buildings."

So, what does it take to qualify for world's tallest? The Council only recognizes a building if at least 50% of it's height is made up of floor plates containing habitable floor area. Any structure that does not meet this criteria is considered a tower. These buildings might have to settle for being the world's tallest tower instead!

PROBLEM 1 How Tall Is That Flagpole?

At times, measuring something directly is impossible, or physically undesirable. When these situations arise, **indirect measurement,** the technique that uses proportions to calculate measurement, can be implemented. Your knowledge of similar triangles can be very helpful in these situations.

Use the following steps to measure the height of the school flagpole or any other tall object outside. You will need a partner, a tape measure, a marker, and a flat mirror.

Step 1: Use a marker to create a dot near the center of the mirror.

Step 2: Face the object you would like to measure and place the mirror between yourself and the object. You, the object, and the mirror should be collinear.

Step 3: Focus your eyes on the dot on the mirror and walk backward until you can see the top of the object on the dot, as shown.

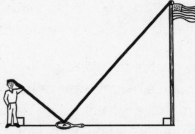

Step 4: Ask your partner to sketch a picture of you, the mirror, and the object.

Step 5: Review the sketch with your partner. Decide where to place right angles, and where to locate the sides of the two triangles.

Step 6: Determine which segments in your sketch can easily be measured using the tape measure. Describe their locations and record the measurements on your sketch.

1. How can similar triangles be used to calculate the height of the object?

2. Use your sketch to write a proportion to calculate the height of the object and solve the proportion.

3. Compare your answer with others measuring the same object. How do the answers compare?

4. What are some possible sources of error that could result when using this method?

5. Switch places with your partner and identify a second object to measure. Repeat this method of indirect measurement to solve for the height of the new object.

1. You go to the park and use the mirror method to gather enough information to calculate the height of one of the trees. The figure shows your measurements. Calculate the height of the tree.

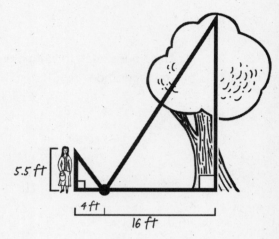

2. Stacey wants to try the mirror method to measure the height of one of her trees. She calculates that the distance between her and the mirror is 3 feet and the distance between the mirror and the tree is 18 feet. Stacey's eye height is 60 inches. Draw a diagram of this situation. Then, calculate the height of this tree.

Remember, whenever you are solving a problem that involves measurements like length (or weight), you may have to rewrite units so they are the same.

3. Stacey notices that another tree casts a shadow and suggests that you could also use shadows to calculate the height of the tree. She lines herself up with the tree's shadow so that the tip of her shadow and the tip of the tree's shadow meet. She then asks you to measure the distance from the tip of the shadows to her, and then measure the distance from her to the tree. Finally, you draw a diagram of this situation as shown below. Calculate the height of the tree. Explain your reasoning.

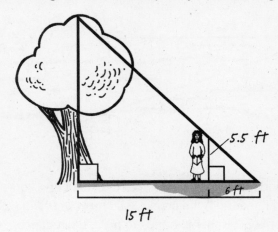

1. You stand on one side of the creek and your friend stands directly across the creek from you on the other side as shown in the figure.

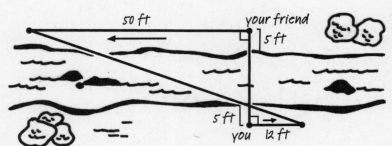

It is not reasonable for you to directly measure the width of a creek, but you can use indirect measurement to measure the width.

Your friend is standing 5 feet from the creek and you are standing 5 feet from the creek. You and your friend walk away from each other in opposite parallel directions. Your friend walks 50 feet and you walk 12 feet.

a. Label any angle measures and any angle relationships that you know on the diagram. Explain how you know these angle measures.

4

b. How do you know that the triangles formed by the lines are similar?

c. Calculate the distance from your friend's starting point to your side of the creek. Round your answer to the nearest tenth, if necessary.

d. What is the width of the creek? Explain your reasoning.

2. There is also a ravine (a deep hollow in the earth) on another edge of the park. You and your friend take measurements like those in Problem 3 to indirectly calculate the width of the ravine. The figure shows your measurements. Calculate the width of the ravine.

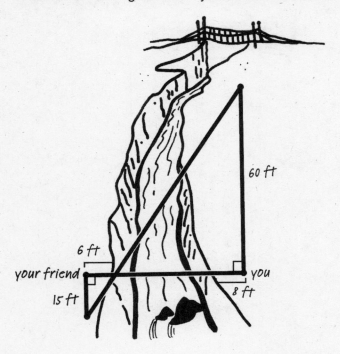

3. There is a large pond in the park. A diagram of the pond is shown below. You want to calculate the distance across the widest part of the pond, labeled as $\overline{DE}$. To indirectly calculate this distance, you first place a stake at point A. You chose point A so that you can see the edge of the pond on both sides at points D and E, where you also place stakes. Then, you tie a string from point A to point D and from point A to point E. At a narrow portion of the pond, you place stakes at points B and C along the string so that $\overline{BC}$ is parallel to $\overline{DE}$. The measurements you make are shown on the diagram. Calculate the distance across the widest part of the pond.

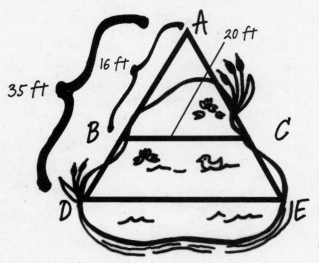

 Be prepared to share your solutions and methods.

- similar triangles (4.1)
- included angle (4.2)
- included side (4.2)
- geometric mean (4.4)
- indirect measurement (4.6)

- Angle-Angle Similarity Theorem (4.2)
- Side-Side-Side Similarity Theorem (4.2)
- Triangle Proportionality Theorem (4.3)
- Converse of the Triangle Proportionality Theorem (4.3)
- Proportional Segments Theorem (4.3)
- Triangle Midsegment Theorem (4.3)

- Side-Angle-Side Similarity Theorem (4.2)
- Angle Bisector/Proportional Side Theorem (4.3)
- Right Triangle/Altitude Similarity Theorem (4.4)
- Right Triangle Altitude/Hypotenuse Theorem (4.4)
- Right Triangle Altitude/Leg Theorem (4.4)

4.1 **Comparing the Pre-image and Image of a Dilation**

A dilation increases or decreases the size of a figure. The original figure is the pre-image, and the dilated figure is the image. A pre-image and an image are similar figures, which means they have the same shape but different sizes.

A dilation can be described by drawing line segments from the center of dilation through each vertex on the pre-image and the corresponding vertex on the image. The ratio of the length of the segment to a vertex on the pre-image and the corresponding vertex on the image is the scale factor of the dilation. A scale factor greater than 1 produces an image that is larger than the pre-image. A scale factor less than 1 produces an image that is smaller than the pre-image.

Example

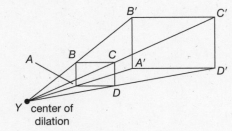

$YD = 3.5$ $YD' = 7.7$

$YB = 2.5$ $YB' = ?$

$YC = ?$ $YC' = 3.3$

$YA = 1.0$ $YA' = ?$

$$\text{scale factor} = \frac{YD'}{YD}$$

$$= \frac{7.7}{3.5}$$

$$= 2.2$$

$\dfrac{YB'}{YB} = 2.2$

$YB' = 2.2\overline{YB}$

$YB' = 2.2(2.5)$

$YB' = 5.5$

$\dfrac{YC'}{YC} = 2.2$

$YC' = 2.2YC$

$\dfrac{YC'}{2.2} = YC$

$\dfrac{3.3}{2.2} = YC$

$1.5 = \overline{YC}$

$\dfrac{YA'}{YA} = 2.2$

$YA' = 2.2YA$

$YA' = 2.2(1.0)$

$YA' = 2.2$

4

4.1 Dilating a Triangle on a Coordinate Grid

The length of each side of an image is the length of the corresponding side of the pre-image multiplied by the scale factor. On a coordinate plane, the coordinates of the vertices of an image can be found by multiplying the coordinates of the vertices of the pre-image by the scale factor. If the center of dilation is at the origin, a point (x, y) is dilated to (kx, ky) by a scale factor of k.

Example

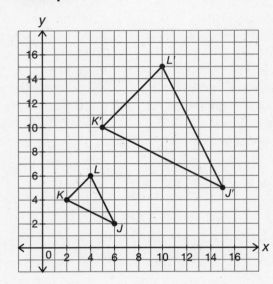

The center of dilation is the origin.

The scale factor is 2.5.

J(6, 2) ⟶ J′ (15, 5)

K(2, 4) ⟶ K′ (5, 10)

L(4, 6) ⟶ L′ (10, 15)

4.1 Using Geometric Theorems to Prove that Triangles are Similar

All pairs of corresponding angles and all corresponding sides of similar triangles are congruent. Geometric theorems can be used to prove that triangles are similar. The Alternate Interior Angle Theorem, the Vertical Angle Theorem, and the Triangle Sum Theorem are examples of theorems that might be used to prove similarity.

Example

By the Alternate Interior Angle Theorem, ∠A ≅ ∠D and ∠B ≅ ∠E. By the Vertical Angle Theorem, ∠ACB ≅ ∠ECD. Since the triangles have three pair of corresponding angles that are congruent, the triangles have the same shape and △ABC ≅ △DEC.

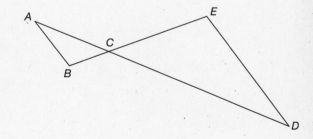

4.1 Using Transformations to Prove that Triangles are Similar

Triangles can also be proven similar using a sequence of transformations. The transformations might include rotating, dilating, and reflecting.

Example

Given: $\overline{AC} \parallel \overline{FD}$

Translate $\triangle ABC$ so that $\overline{AC}$ aligns with $\overline{FD}$. Rotate $\triangle ABC$ 180° about the point C so that $\overline{AC}$ again aligns with $\overline{FD}$. Translate $\triangle ABC$ until point C is at point F. If we dilate $\triangle ABC$ about point C to take point B to point E, then $\overline{AB}$ will be mapped onto $\overline{ED}$, and $\overline{BC}$ will be mapped onto $\overline{EF}$. Therefore, $\triangle ABC$ is similar to $\triangle DEF$.

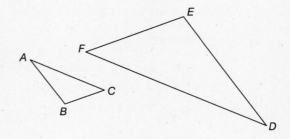

4.2 Using Triangle Similarity Theorems

Two triangles are similar if they have two congruent angles, if all of their corresponding sides are proportional, or if two of their corresponding sides are proportional and the included angles are congruent. An included angle is an angle formed by two consecutive sides of a figure. The following theorems can be used to prove that triangles are similar:

- The Angle-Angle (AA) Similarity Theorem—If two angles of one triangle are congruent to two angles of another triangle, then the triangles are similar.

- The Side-Side-Side (SSS) Similarity Theorem—If the corresponding sides of two triangles are proportional, then the triangles are similar.

- The Side-Angle-Side (SAS) Similarity Theorem—If two of the corresponding sides of two triangles are proportional and the included angles are congruent, then the triangles are similar.

Example

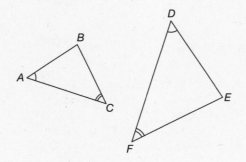

Given: $\angle A \cong \angle D$

$\angle C \cong \angle F$

Therefore, $\triangle ABC \sim \triangle DEF$ by the AA Similarity Theorem.

Applying the Angle Bisector/Proportional Side Theorem

When an interior angle of a triangle is bisected, you can observe proportional relationships among the sides of the triangles formed. You can apply the Angle Bisector/Proportional Side Theorem to calculate side lengths of bisected triangles.

- Angle Bisector/Proportional Side Theorem—A bisector of an angle in a triangle divides the opposite side into two segments whose lengths are in the same ratio as the lengths of the sides adjacent to the angle.

Example

The map of an amusement park shows locations of the various rides.

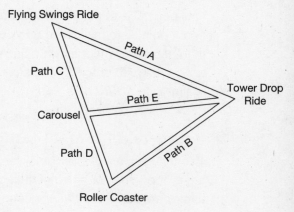

Given:

- Path E bisects the angle formed by Path A and Path B.

- Path A is 143 feet long.

- Path C is 65 feet long.

- Path D is 55 feet long.

Let x equal the length of Path B.

$$\frac{x}{55} = \frac{143}{63}$$

$$x = 121$$

Path B is 121 feet long.

Applying the Triangle Proportionality Theorem

The Triangle Proportionality Theorem is another theorem you can apply to calculate side lengths of triangles.

- Triangle Proportionality Theorem—If a line parallel to one side of a triangle intersects the other two sides, then it divides the two sides proportionally.

Example

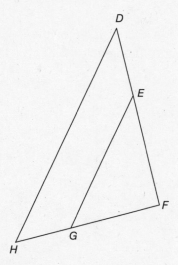

Given: $DH \parallel EG$

$DE = 30$

$EF = 45$

$GH = 25$

$FG = ?$

$$\frac{DE}{EF} = \frac{GH}{FG}$$

$$FG = \frac{GH \cdot EF}{DE}$$

$$= \frac{(25)(45)}{30}$$

$$= 37.5$$

4.3 Applying the Converse of the Triangle Proportionality Theorem

The Converse of the Triangle Proportionality Theorem allows you to test whether two line segments are parallel.

* Converse of the Triangle Proportionality Theorem—If a line divides two sides of a triangle proportionally, then it is parallel to the third side.

Example

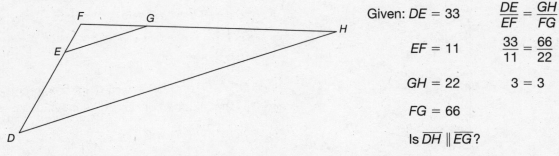

Given: $DE = 33$

$EF = 11$

$GH = 22$

$FG = 66$

$\dfrac{DE}{EF} = \dfrac{GH}{FG}$

$\dfrac{33}{11} = \dfrac{66}{22}$

$3 = 3$

Is $\overline{DH} \parallel \overline{EG}$?

Applying the Converse of the Triangle Proportionality, we can conclude that $\overline{DH} \parallel \overline{EG}$.

4.3 Applying the Proportional Segments Theorem

The Proportional Segments Theorem provides a way to calculate distances along three parallel lines, even though they may not be related to triangles.

* Proportional Segments Theorem—If three parallel lines intersect two transversals, then they divide the transversals proportionally.

Example

Given: $L_1 \parallel L_2 \parallel L_3$

$AB = 52$

$BC = 26$

$DE = 40$

$EF = \, ?$

$\dfrac{AB}{BC} = \dfrac{DE}{EF}$

$AB \cdot EF = DE \cdot BC$

$EF = \dfrac{DE \cdot BC}{AB}$

$= \dfrac{(40)(26)}{52}$

$= 20$

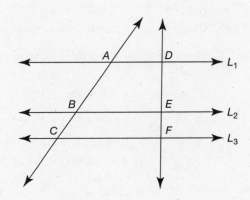

4.3 Applying the Triangle Midsegment Theorem

The Triangle Midsegment Theorem relates the lengths of the sides of a triangle when a segment is drawn parallel to one side.

- Triangle Midsegment Theorem—The midsegment of a triangle is parallel to the third side of the triangle and half the measure of the third side of the triangle.

Example

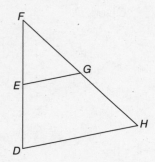

Given: $DE = 9$ $EF = 9$
$FG = 11$ $GH = 11$
$DH = 17$

Since $DE = EF$ and $FG = GH$, point E is the midpoint of $\overline{DF}$, and G is the midpoint of $\overline{FG}$. $\overline{EG}$ is the midsegment of $\triangle DEF$.

$EG = \dfrac{1}{2}DH = \dfrac{1}{2}(17) = 8.5$

4.4 Using the Geometric Mean and Right Triangle/Altitude Theorems

Similar triangles can be formed by drawing an altitude to the hypotenuse of a right triangle.

- Right Triangle/Altitude Similarity Theorem—If an altitude is drawn to the hypotenuse of a right triangle, then the two triangles formed are similar to the original triangle and to each other.

The altitude is the geometric mean of the triangle's bases. The geometric mean of two positive numbers a and b is the positive number x such as $\dfrac{a}{x} = \dfrac{x}{b}$. Two theorems are associated with the altitude to the hypotenuse as a geometric mean.

- The Right Triangle Altitude/Hypotenuse Theorem—The measure of the altitude drawn from the vertex of the right angle of a right triangle to its hypotenuse is the geometric mean between the measures of the two segments of the hypotenuse.

- The Right Triangle Altitude/Leg Theorem—If the altitude is drawn to the hypotenuse of a right triangle, each leg of the right triangle is the geometric mean of the hypotenuse and the segment of the hypotenuse adjacent to the leg.

Example

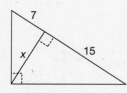

$\dfrac{7}{x} = \dfrac{x}{15}$
$x^2 = 105$
$x = \sqrt{105} \approx 10.2$

4.5 Proving the Pythagorean Theorem Using Similar Triangles

The Pythagorean Theorem relates the squares of the sides of a right triangle: $a^2 + b^2 = c^2$, where a and b are the bases of the triangle and c is the hypotenuse. The Right Triangle/Altitude Similarity Theorem can be used to prove the Pythagorean Theorem.

Example

Given: Triangle ABC with right angle C.

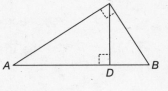

- Construct altitude CD to hypotenuse AB, as shown.

- According to the Right Triangle/Altitude Similarity Theorem, $\triangle ABC \sim \triangle CAD$.

- Since the triangles are similar, $\dfrac{AB}{CB} = \dfrac{CB}{DB}$ and $\dfrac{AB}{AC} = \dfrac{AC}{AD}$.

- Solve for the squares: $CB^2 = AB \times DB$ and $AC^2 = AB \times AD$.

- Add the squares: $CB^2 + AC^2 = AB \times DB + AB \times AD$

- Factor: $CB^2 + AC^2 = AB(DB + AD)$

- Substitute: $CB^2 + AC^2 = AB(AB) = AB^2$

This proves the Pythagorean Theorem: $CB^2 + AC^2 = AB^2$

4.5 Proving the Pythagorean Theorem Using Algebraic Reasoning

Algebraic reasoning can also be used to prove the Pythagorean Theorem.

Example

- Write and expand the area of the larger square:
  $(a + b)^2 = a^2 + 2ab + b^2$

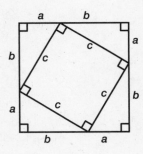

- Write the total area of the four right triangles:

  $4\left(\dfrac{1}{2}ab\right) = 2ab$

- Write the area of the smaller square:

  c^2

- Write and simplify an equation relating the area of the larger square to the sum of the areas of the four right triangles and the area of the smaller square:

  $a^2 + 2ab + b^2 = 2ab + c^2$
  $$a^2 + b^2 = c^2$$

4.5 Proving the Converse of the Pythagorean Theorem

Algebraic reasoning can also be used to prove the Converse of the Pythagorean Theorem: "If $a^2 + b^2 = c^2$, then a and b are the lengths of the legs of a right triangle and c is the length of the hypotenuse."

Example

Given: Triangle ABC with right angle C.

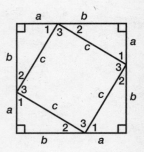

- Relate angles 1, 2, 3: $m\angle 1 + m\angle 2 + m\angle 3 = 180°$

- Use the Triangle Sum Theorem to determine $m\angle 1 + m\angle 2$.

  $m\angle 1 + m\angle 2 = 90°$

- Determine $m\angle 3$ from the small right angles:

  Since $m\angle 1 + m\angle 2 = 90°$, $m\angle 3$ must also equal $90°$.

- Identify the shape of the quadrilateral inside the large square: Since the quadrilateral has four congruent sides and four right angles, it must be a square.

- Determine the area of each right triangle: $A = \frac{1}{2}ab$

- Determine the area of the center square: c^2

- Write the sum of the areas of the four right triangles and the center square: $4\left(\frac{1}{2}ab\right) + c^2$

- Write and expand an expression for the area of the larger square: $(a + b)^2 = a^2 + 2ab + b^2$

- Write and simplify an equation relating the area of the larger square to the sum of the areas of the four right triangles and the area of the smaller square:

  $$a^2 + 2ab + b^2 = 2ab + c^2$$
  $$a^2 + b^2 = c^2$$

4.6 Use Similar Triangles to Calculate Indirect Measurements

Indirect measurement is a method of using proportions to calculate measurements that are difficult or impossible to make directly. A knowledge of similar triangles can be useful in these types of problems.

Example

Let x be the height of the tall tree.

$$\frac{x}{20} = \frac{32}{18}$$
$$x = \frac{(32)(20)}{18}$$
$$x \approx 35.6$$

The tall tree is about 35.6 feet tall.

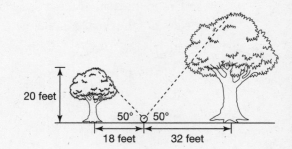

Congruence Through Transformations

The Louvre (pronounced Loov) Pyramid in Paris, France, serves as the entrance to the world famous Louvre Museum. It was constructed using 673 rhombus-shaped and triangular glass segments.

333

We Like to Move It!

Translating, Rotating, and Reflecting Geometric Figures

In this lesson, you will:

- Translate geometric figures on a coordinate plane.
- Rotate geometric figures on a coordinate plane.
- Reflect geometric figures on a coordinate plane.

Did you know that most textbooks are translated from English into at least one other language, usually Spanish? And in some school districts, general memos and letters to parents may be translated into up to five different languages! Of course, *translating* a language means something completely different from the word *translating* in geometry.

The same can be said for reflection. A "reflection pool" is a place where one can "reflect" on one's thoughts, while also admiring reflections in the pool of still water.

How about rotation? What do you think the term *rotation* means in geometry? Is this different from its meaning in common language?

5

PROBLEM 1 Translating Geometric Figures on the Coordinate Plane

To begin this chapter, cut out a copy of the figure shown.

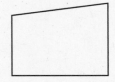

You will use this trapezoid throughout this lesson so don't lose it!

1. Graph trapezoid *ABCD* by plotting the points *A* (3, 9), *B* (3, 4), *C* (11, 4), and *D* (11, 10).

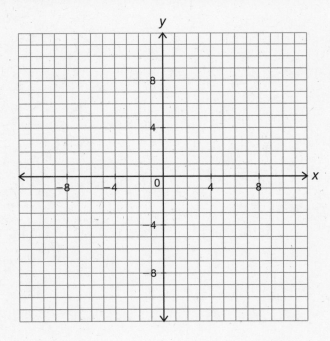

Use the model you cut out to help with the translations.

5

2. Translate trapezoid *ABCD* on the coordinate plane. Graph the image and record the vertex coordinates in the table.

   a. Translate trapezoid *ABCD* 15 units to the left to form trapezoid *A'B'C'D'*.

   b. Translate trapezoid *ABCD* 12 units down to form trapezoid *A"B"C"D"*.

Coordinates of Trapezoid *ABCD*	Coordinates of Trapezoid *A'B'C'D'*	Coordinates of Trapezoid *A"B"C"D"*
A (3, 9)		
B (3, 4)		
C (11, 4)		
D (11, 10)		

Let's consider translations without graphing.

3. The vertices of parallelogram DEFG are D (−9, 7), E (−12, 2), F (−3, 2), and G (0, 7).

   a. Determine the vertex coordinates of image D′E′F′G′ if parallelogram DEFG is translated 14 units down.

   b. How did you determine the image coordinates without graphing?

   c. Determine the vertex coordinates of image D″E″F″G″ if parallelogram DEFG is translated 8 units to the right.

   d. How did you determine the image coordinates without graphing?

PROBLEM 2 Rotating Geometric Figures on the Coordinate Plane

Recall that a rotation is a rigid motion that turns a figure about a fixed point, called the point of rotation. The figure is rotated in a given direction for a given angle, called the angle of rotation. The angle of rotation is the measure of the amount the figure is rotated about the point of rotation. The direction of a rotation can either be clockwise or counterclockwise.

Let's rotate point *A* about the origin. The origin will be the point of rotation and you will rotate point *A* 90°, 180°, and 270°.

First, let's rotate point *A* 90° counterclockwise about the origin.

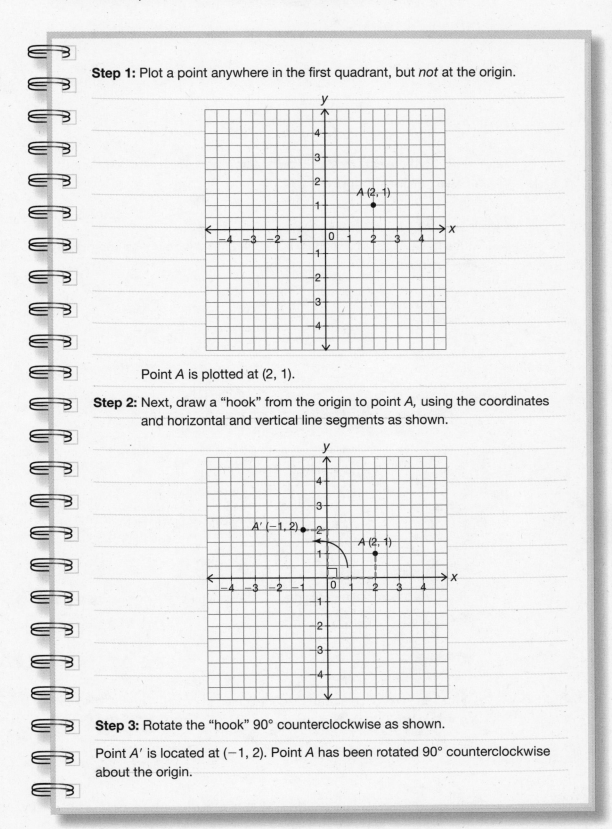

Step 1: Plot a point anywhere in the first quadrant, but *not* at the origin.

Point *A* is plotted at (2, 1).

Step 2: Next, draw a "hook" from the origin to point *A,* using the coordinates and horizontal and vertical line segments as shown.

Step 3: Rotate the "hook" 90° counterclockwise as shown.

Point *A'* is located at (−1, 2). Point *A* has been rotated 90° counterclockwise about the origin.

1. What do you notice about the coordinates of point A and the coordinates of point A'?

2. Predict what the coordinates of point A'' will be if you rotate point A' 90° counterclockwise about the origin.

3. Rotate point A' about the origin 90° counterclockwise on the coordinate plane shown. Label the point A''.

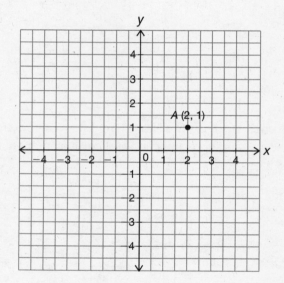

a. What are the coordinates of point A''? Was your prediction for the coordinates of point A'' correct?

b. What do you notice about the coordinates of points A and A''? How are the two points related?

4. Rotate point A'' about the origin 90 counterclockwise on the coordinate plane shown. Label the point A'''

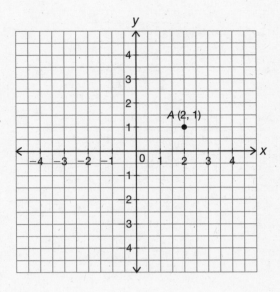

a. What are the coordinates of point A'''?

b. What do you notice about the coordinates of point A and point A'''? How are the two points related?

You may have noticed that the values of the x- and y-coordinates seem to switch places for every 90° rotation about the origin. You may have also noticed that the rotation from point A to A'' is a 180° counterclockwise rotation about the origin, and that the rotation from point A to A''' is a 270° counterclockwise rotation about the origin.

5. Determine the coordinates of point (x, y) after rotations of 90°, 180°, 270°, and 360°.

Original Point	Coordinates After a 90° Counterclockwise Rotation About the Origin	Coordinates After a 180° Counterclockwise Rotation About the Origin	Coordinates After a 270° Counterclockwise Rotation About the Origin	Coordinates After a 360° Counterclockwise Rotation About the Origin
(x, y)				

Verify that the information in the table is correct by using a test point. Plot a point on a coordinate plane and rotate the point 90°, 180°, 270°, and 360° counterclockwise about the origin.

6. Graph and label point *Q* at (5, 7) on the coordinate plane.

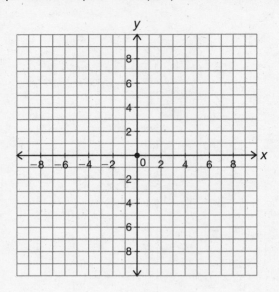

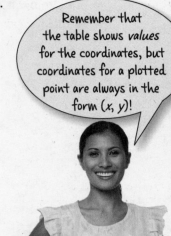

Remember that the table shows *values* for the coordinates, but coordinates for a plotted point are always in the form (*x, y*)!

7. Use the origin (0, 0) as the point of rotation.

  a. Rotate the pre-image *Q* 90° counterclockwise about the origin. Label the image *Q'*. Determine the coordinates of image *Q'*, then describe how you determined the location of point *Q'*.

  b. Rotate the pre-image *Q* 180° counterclockwise about the origin. Label the image *Q"*. Determine the coordinates of image *Q"*, then describe how you determined the location of image *Q"*.

  c. Rotate point *Q* 270° counterclockwise about the origin. Label the image *Q'''*. Determine the coordinates of point *Q'''*, then describe how you determined the location of image *Q'''*.

d. Rotate point Q 360° counterclockwise about the origin. Label the image Q″″. Determine the coordinates of point Q″″, then describe how you determined the location of image Q″″.

You have been rotating points about the origin on a coordinate plane. However, do you think polygons can also be rotated on the coordinate plane?

You can use models to help show that you *can* rotate polygons on a coordinate plane. However, before we start modeling the rotation of a polygon on a coordinate plane, let's graph the trapezoid to establish the pre-image.

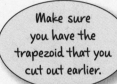

Make sure you have the trapezoid that you cut out earlier.

8. Graph trapezoid ABCD by plotting the points A (−12, 9), B (−12, 4), C (−4, 4), and D (−4, 10).

Now that you have graphed the pre-image, you are ready to model the rotation of the polygon on the coordinate plane.

- First, fold a piece of tape in half and tape it to both sides of the trapezoid you cut out previously.

- Then, take your trapezoid and set it on top of trapezoid ABCD on the coordinate plane, making sure that the tape covers the origin (0, 0).

- Finally, put a pin or your pencil point through the tape at the origin and rotate your model counterclockwise.

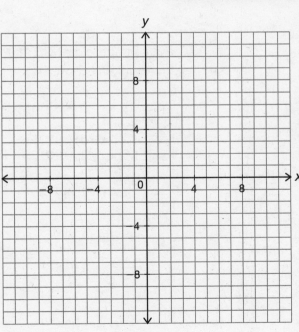

5

The 90° counterclockwise rotation of trapezoid *ABCD* about the origin is shown.

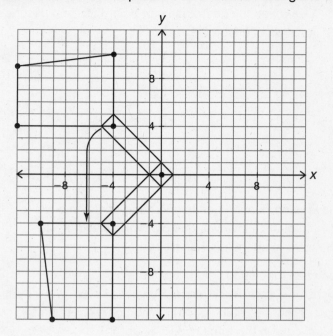

9. Rotate trapezoid *ABCD* about the origin for each given angle of rotation. Graph and label each image on the coordinate plane and record the coordinates in the table.

a. Rotate trapezoid *ABCD* 90° counterclockwise about the origin to form trapezoid *A'B'C'D'*.

b. Rotate trapezoid *ABCD* 180° counterclockwise about the origin to form trapezoid *A"B"C"D"*.

Coordinates of Trapezoid *ABCD*	Coordinates of Trapezoid *A'B'C'D'*	Coordinates of Trapezoid *A"B"C"D"*
A (−12, 9)		
B (−12, 4)		
C (−4, 4)		
D (−4, 10)		

10. What similarities do you notice between rotating a single point about the origin and rotating a polygon about the origin?

Let's consider rotations without graphing.

11. The vertices of parallelogram *DEFG* are *D* (−9, 7), *E* (−12, 2), *F* (−3, 2), and *G* (0, 7).

    a. Determine the vertex coordinates of image *D′E′F′G′* if parallelogram *DEFG* is rotated 90° counterclockwise about the origin.

    b. How did you determine the image coordinates without graphing?

    c. Determine the vertex coordinates of image *D″E″F″G″* if parallelogram *DEFG* is rotated 180° counterclockwise about the origin.

    d. How did you determine the image coordinates without graphing?

5

e. Determine the vertex coordinates of image $D'''E'''F'''G'''$ if parallelogram $DEFG$ is rotated 270° counterclockwise about the origin.

f. How did you determine the image coordinates without graphing?

12. Dante claims that if he is trying to determine the coordinates of an image that is rotated 180° about the origin, it does not matter which direction the rotation occurred. Desmond claims that the direction is important to know when determining the image coordinates. Who is correct? Explain why the correct student's rationale is correct.

PROBLEM 3 · Reflecting Geometric Figures on the Coordinate Plane

Recall that figures that are mirror images of each other are called reflections. A reflection is a rigid motion that reflects, or "flips," a figure over a given line called a line of reflection. A line of reflection is a line over which a figure is reflected so that corresponding points are the same distance from the line.

Let's reflect point *A* over the *y*-axis.

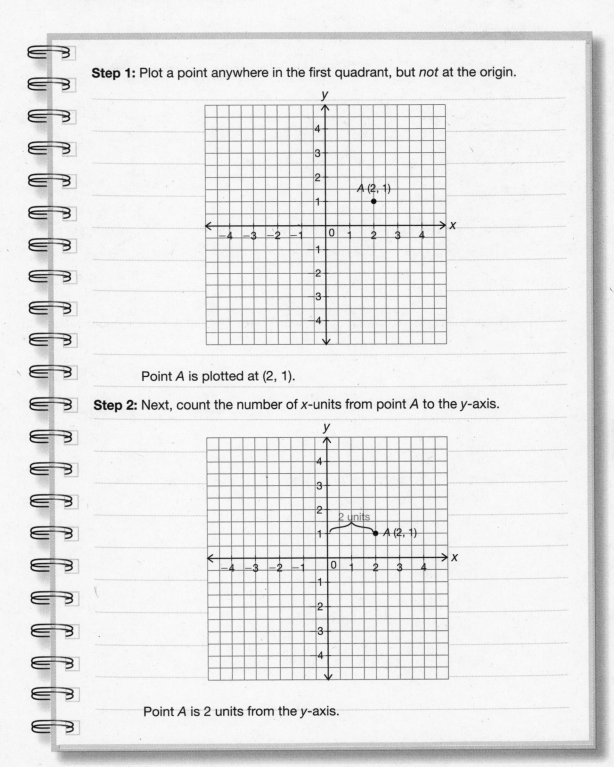

Step 1: Plot a point anywhere in the first quadrant, but *not* at the origin.

Point *A* is plotted at (2, 1).

Step 2: Next, count the number of *x*-units from point *A* to the *y*-axis.

Point *A* is 2 units from the *y*-axis.

Step 3: Then, count the same number of *x*-units on the opposite side of the *y*-axis to locate the reflection of point *A*. Label the point *A'*.

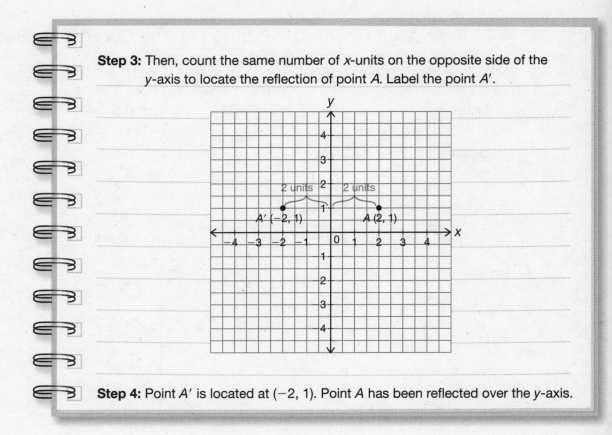

Step 4: Point *A'* is located at (−2, 1). Point *A* has been reflected over the *y*-axis.

1. What do you notice about the coordinates of point *A* and the coordinates of image *A'*?

2. Predict the coordinates of *A″* if point *A* is reflected over the *x*-axis. Explain your reasoning.

3. Reflect point *A* over the *x*-axis on the coordinate plane shown. Verify whether your prediction for the location of the image was correct. Graph the image and label it *A*".

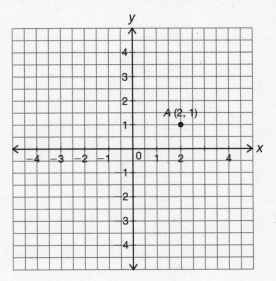

4. What do you notice about the coordinates of *A* and *A*"?

The coordinates of a pre-image reflected over either the *x*-axis or the *y*-axis can be used to determine the coordinates of the image.

5. Determine the coordinates of point (*x*, *y*) after reflections about the *x*-axis or *y*-axis.

Original Point	Coordinates of Image After a Reflection Over the *x*-axis	Coordinates of Image After a Reflection Over the *y*-axis
(*x*, *y*)		

Does this table still make sense if the line of reflection is not the *x*- or *y*-axis?

6. Graph point J at (5, 7) on the coordinate plane shown.

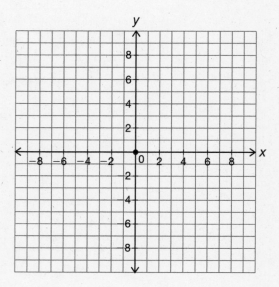

7. Reflect point J over the y-axis on the coordinate plane. Label the image J'. Determine the coordinates of J'. Then, describe how you determined the location of image J'.

8. Reflect point J over the x-axis on the coordinate plane. Label the image J''. Determine the coordinates of J''. Then, describe how you determined the location of image J''.

You can also reflect polygons on the coordinate plane. You can model the reflection of a polygon across a line of reflection. Just as with rotating a polygon on a coordinate plane, you will first need to establish a pre-image.

9. Graph trapezoid *ABCD* by plotting the points *A* (3, 9), *B* (3, 4), *C* (11, 4), and *D* (11, 10).

Now that you have graphed the pre-image, you are ready to model the reflection of the polygon on the coordinate plane. For this modeling, you will reflect the polygon over the *y*-axis.

- First, take your trapezoid that you cut out previously and set it on top of trapezoid *ABCD* on the coordinate plane.

- Next, determine the number of units point *A* is from the *y*-axis.

- Then, count the same number of units on the opposite side of the *y*-axis to determine where to place the image in Quadrant II.

- Finally, physically flip the trapezoid over the *y*-axis like you are flipping a page in a book.

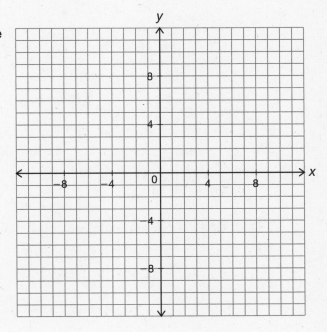

The reflection of trapezoid *ABCD* over the *y*-axis is shown.

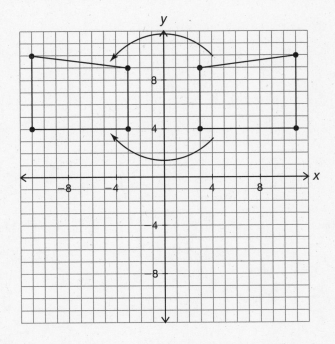

10. Reflect trapezoid *ABCD* over each given line of reflection. Graph and label each image on the coordinate plane and record each image's coordinates in the table.

   a. Reflect trapezoid *ABCD* over the *x*-axis to form trapezoid *A'B'C'D'*.

   b. Reflect trapezoid *ABCD* over the *y*-axis to form trapezoid *A"B"C"D"*.

Coordinates of Trapezoid *ABCD*	Coordinates of Trapezoid *A'B'C'D'*	Coordinates of Trapezoid *A"B"C"D"*
A (3, 9)		
B (3, 4)		
C (11, 4)		
D (11, 10)		

11. What similarities do you notice between reflecting a single point over the *x*- or *y*-axis and reflecting a polygon over the *x*- or *y*-axis?

Let's consider reflections without graphing.

12. The vertices of parallelogram *DEFG* are *D* (−9, 7), *E* (−12, 2), *F* (−3, 2), and *G* (0, 7).

   a. Determine the vertex coordinates of image *D'E'F'G'* if parallelogram *DEFG* is reflected over the *x*-axis.

   b. How did you determine the image coordinates without graphing?

c. Determine the vertex coordinates of image $D''E''F''G''$ if parallelogram $DEFG$ is reflected over the y-axis.

d. How did you determine the image coordinates without graphing?

Talk the Talk

You know that a line is determined by two points. The slope of any line represented on a coordinate plane can be given by $\frac{y_2 - y_1}{x_2 - x_1}$.

You also now know that when rotating a point (x, y) 90° counterclockwise about the origin, the x-coordinate of the original point maps to the y-coordinate of the transformed point and the y-coordinate of the original point maps to the opposite of the x-coordinate of the transformed point.

1. Rewrite the slope ratio above to describe the slope of a line that has been rotated 90° counterclockwise. What do you notice? Explain your reasoning.

When two lines are perpendicular to each other, how can you describe their slopes?

2. Complete the sentence using *always*, *sometimes*, or *never*.

   Images that result from a translation, rotation, or reflection are _____ congruent to the original figure.

Be prepared to share your solutions and methods.

Hey, Haven't I Seen You Before?

Congruent Triangles

LEARNING GOALS

In this lesson, you will:

- Identify corresponding sides and corresponding angles of congruent triangles.
- Explore the relationship between the corresponding sides of congruent triangles.
- Explore the relationship between the corresponding angles of congruent triangles.
- Write congruence statements for congruent triangles.
- Identify and use rigid motion to create new images.

In mathematics, when a geometric figure is transformed, the size and shape of the figure do not change. However, in physics, things are a little different. An idea known as length contraction explains that when an object is in motion, its length appears to be slightly less than it really is. This cannot be seen with everyday objects because they do not move fast enough. To truly see this phenomenon you would have to view an object moving close to the speed of light. In fact, if an object was moving past you at the speed of light, the length of the object would seem to be practically zero!

This theory is very difficult to prove and yet scientists came up with the idea in the late 1800s. How do you think scientists test and prove length contraction? Do you think geometry is used in these verifications?

1. Graph triangle *ABC* by plotting the points *A* (8, 10), *B* (1, 2), and *C* (8, 2).

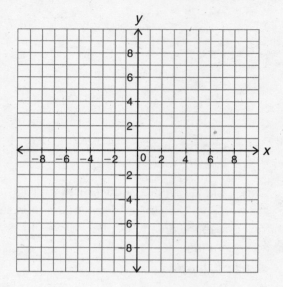

Let's explore the properties of congruent triangles.

a. Classify triangle *ABC*. Explain your reasoning.

b. Calculate the length of side $\overline{AB}$.

I would use the Pythagorean Theorem to calculate the length.

5

2. Translate triangle *ABC* 10 units to the left to form triangle *DEF*. Graph triangle *DEF* and list the coordinates of points *D, E,* and *F*.

Triangle *ABC* and triangle *DEF* in Question 1 are the same size and the same shape. Each side of triangle *ABC* matches, or corresponds to, a specific side of triangle *DEF*.

3. Given what you know about corresponding sides of congruent triangles, predict the side lengths of triangle *DEF*.

> Corresponding sides are sides that have the same relative positions in corresponding geometric figures.

4. Verify your prediction.

   a. Identify the pairs of corresponding sides of triangle *ABC* and triangle *DEF*.

   b. Determine the side lengths of triangle *DEF*.

   c. Compare the lengths of the sides of triangle *ABC* to the lengths of the corresponding sides of triangle *DEF*. What do you notice?

5. In general, what can you conclude about the relationship between the corresponding sides of congruent triangles?

> Would there ever be a time when corresponding sides of figures would not be congruent?

Use triangle *ABC* and triangle *DEF* from Question 1 to answer each question.

Each angle in triangle ABC corresponds to a specific angle in triangle DEF. Corresponding angles are angles that have the same relative positions in corresponding geometric figures.

6. Use a protractor to determine the measures of ∠*A*, ∠*B*, and ∠*C*.

7. What would you predict to be true about the measures of corresponding angles of congruent triangles?

8. Verify your prediction.

   a. Identify the corresponding angles of triangle *ABC* and triangle *DEF*.

   b. Use a protractor to determine the measures of angles *D*, *E*, and *F*.

   c. Compare the measures of the angles of triangle *ABC* to the measures of the corresponding angles of triangle *DEF*.

So, what can you say about corresponding sides and corresponding angles of congruent triangles?

9. In general, what can you conclude about the relationship between the corresponding angles of congruent triangles?

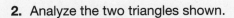

1. Consider the congruence statement △*JRB* ≅ △*MNS*.

   a. Identify the congruent angles.   b. Identify the congruent sides.

Remember, the ≅ means "is congruent to."

2. Analyze the two triangles shown.

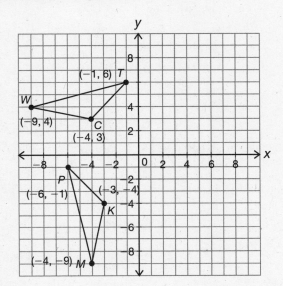

a. Determine the transformation used to create triangle *PMK*.

b. Does the transformation preserve the size and shape of the triangle in this problem situation? Why or why not?

5

c. Write a triangle congruence statement for the triangles.

d. Identify the congruent angles and congruent sides.

3. Analyze the two triangles shown.

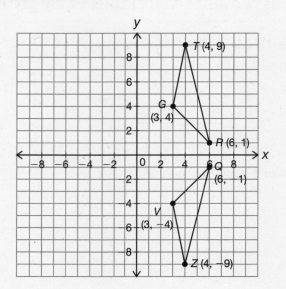

a. Determine the transformation used to create triangle *ZQV*.

b. Does the transformation preserve the size and shape of the triangle in this problem situation? Why or why not?

c. Write a triangle congruence statement for the triangles shown.

d. Identify the congruent angles.

e. Identify the congruent sides.

Talk the Talk

1. Given any triangle on a coordinate plane, how can you create a different triangle that you know will be congruent to the original triangle?

2. Describe the properties of congruent triangles.

Be prepared to share your solutions and methods.

It's All About the Sides
Side-Side-Side Congruence Theorem

Have you ever tried to construct something from scratch—a model car or a bird house, for example? If you have, you have probably discovered that it is a lot more difficult than it looks. To build something accurately, you must have a plan in place. You must think about materials you will need, measurements you will make, and the amount of time it will take to complete the project. You may need to make a model or blueprint of what you are building. Then, when the actual building begins, you must be very precise in all your measurements and cuts. The difference of half an inch may not seem like much, but it could mean the wall of your bird house is too small and now you may have to start again!

You will be constructing triangles throughout the next four lessons. While you won't be cutting or building anything, it is still important to measure accurately and be precise. Otherwise, you may think your triangles are accurate even though they're not!

While you can assume that all duplicated or transformed triangles are congruent, mathematically, you need to use a theorem to prove it.

The *Side-Side-Side Congruence Theorem* is one theorem that can be used to prove triangle congruence. The **Side-Side-Side Congruence Theorem** states: "If three sides of one triangle are congruent to the corresponding sides of another triangle, then the triangles are congruent."

1. Use the given line segments to construct triangle *ABC*. Then, write the steps you performed to construct the triangle.

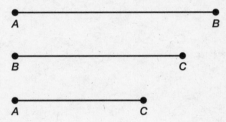

2. Analyze the triangle you created.

   a. Classify △*ABC*. Explain your reasoning.

   b. Compare your triangle to your classmates' triangles. Are the triangles congruent? Why or why not?

   c. How many different triangles can be formed given the lengths of three distinct sides?

3. Rico compares his triangle with his classmate Annette's. Rico gets out his ruler and protractor to verify that the triangles are congruent. Annette states he does not need to do that. Who is correct? Explain your reasoning.

In the previous problem, you proved that two triangles are congruent if three sides of one triangle are congruent to the corresponding sides of another triangle. When dealing with triangles on the coordinate plane, measurement must be used to prove congruence.

1. Graph triangle ABC by plotting the points A (8, −5), B (4, −12), and C (12, −8).

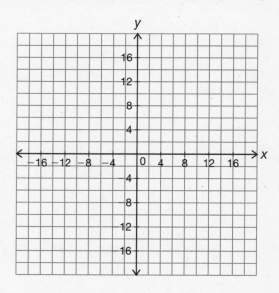

2. How can you determine the length of each side of this triangle?

3. Calculate the length of each side of triangle ABC. Record the measurements in the table.

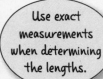

Use exact measurements when determining the lengths.

Side of Triangle *ABC*	Length of Side
$\overline{AB}$	
$\overline{BC}$	
$\overline{AC}$	

4. Translate line segments $\overline{AB}$, $\overline{BC}$, and $\overline{AC}$ up 7 units to form triangle $A'B'C'$. Graph the image.

5. Calculate the length of each side of triangle $A'B'C'$. Record the measurements in the table.

Side of Triangle $A'B'C'$	Length of Side
$\overline{A'B'}$	
$\overline{B'C'}$	
$\overline{A'C'}$	

6. Are the corresponding sides of the pre-image and image congruent? Explain your reasoning.

7. Do you need to determine the measures of the angles to verify that the triangles are congruent? Explain why or why not.

PROBLEM 3 Flipping for Congruence

1. Graph triangle *ABC* by plotting the points *A* (8, 25), *B* (4, 212), and *C* (12, 28).

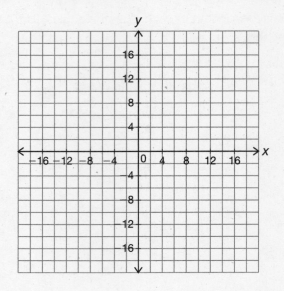

2. Reflect line segments $\overline{AB}$, $\overline{BC}$, and $\overline{AC}$ over the *x*-axis to form triangle *A″B″C″*.

3. Calculate the length of each side of triangle *A″B″C″*. Record the measurements in the table.

Side of Triangle *A″B″C″*	Length of Side
$\overline{A″B″}$	
$\overline{B″C″}$	
$\overline{A″C″}$	

4. Are the triangles congruent? Explain your reasoning.

PROBLEM 4 And Finally the Proof . . .

Complete the proof of the Side-Side-Side Congruence Theorem.

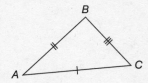 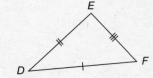

Given: $\overline{AB} \cong \overline{DE}, \overline{BC} \cong \overline{EF}, \overline{AC} \cong \overline{DF}$

Prove: $\triangle ABC \cong \triangle DEF$

Statements	Reasons
1.	1. Given
2.	2. Definition of congruence
3. $\dfrac{AB}{DE} = 1, \dfrac{BC}{EF} = 1, \dfrac{AC}{DF} = 1$	3.
4. $\dfrac{AB}{DE} = \dfrac{BC}{EF} = \dfrac{AC}{DF}$	4.
5.	5. Side-Side-Side Similarity Theorem
6. $\angle A \cong \angle D, \angle B \cong \angle E, \angle C \cong \angle F$	6.
7. $\triangle ABC \cong \triangle DEF$	7.

Be prepared to share your solutions and methods.

Make Sure the Angle Is Included

Side-Angle-Side Congruence Theorem

The smaller circle you see here has an infinite number of points. The larger circle also has an infinite number of points. But since the larger circle is, well, larger, shouldn't it have more points than the smaller circle?

Mathematicians use one-to-one correspondence to determine if two sets are equal. If you can show that each object in a set corresponds to one and only one object in another set, then the two sets are equal.

Look at the circles. Any ray drawn from the center will touch only two points—one on the smaller circle and one on the larger circle. This means that both circles contain the same number of points! Can you see how correspondence was used to come up with this answer?

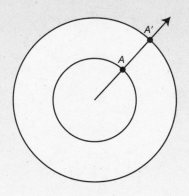

So far in this chapter, you have determined the congruence of two triangles by proving that if the sides of one triangle are congruent to the corresponding sides of another triangle, then the triangles are congruent.

There is another way to determine if two triangles are congruent that does not involve knowledge of three sides. You will prove the *Side-Angle-Side Congruence Theorem*.

The **Side-Angle-Side Congruence Theorem** states: "If two sides and the included angle of one triangle are congruent to the corresponding sides and the included angle of the second triangle, then the triangles are congruent."

First, let's prove this theorem through construction.

Recall that an included angle is the angle formed by two sides of a triangle.

1. Construct △*ABC* using the two line segments and included angle shown. Then, write the steps you performed to construct the triangle.

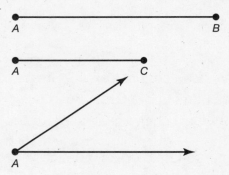

5

2. How does the length of side $\overline{BC}$ compare to the length of your classmates' side $\overline{BC}$?

3. Use a protractor to measure angle B and angle C in triangle ABC.

4. How do the measures of your corresponding angles compare to the measures of your classmates' corresponding angles?

5. Is your triangle congruent to your classmates' triangles? Why or why not?

6. If you were given one of the non-included angles, $\angle C$ or $\angle B$, instead of $\angle A$, do you think everyone in your class would have constructed an identical triangle? Explain your reasoning.

5

Through your construction, you and your classmates constructed congruent triangles using two given sides and the included angle of a triangle.

Let's now try to prove the Side-Angle-Side Theorem on the coordinate plane using algebra.

1. Graph triangle *ABC* by plotting the points *A* (5, 9), *B* (2, 3), and *C* (7, 2).

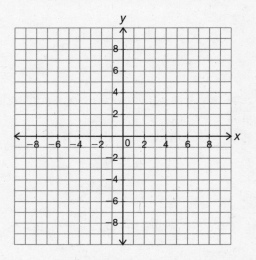

2. Calculate the length of each side of triangle *ABC* and record the measurements in the table. Record exact measurements.

Do you remember the difference between exact and approximate solutions?

Side of Triangle *ABC*	Length of Side
$\overline{AB}$	
$\overline{BC}$	
$\overline{AC}$	

3. Rotate side $\overline{AB}$, side $\overline{BC}$, and included angle B, in triangle ABC 270° counterclockwise about the origin. Then, connect points A' and C' to form triangle $A'B'C'$. Use the table to record the image coordinates.

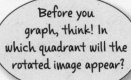

Before you graph, think! In which quadrant will the rotated image appear?

Coordinates of Triangle ABC	Coordinates of Triangle A'B'C'
A (5, 9)	
B (2, 3)	
C (14, 3)	

4. Calculate the length of each side of triangle $A'B'C'$ and record the measurements in the table. Record exact measurements.

Side of Triangle A'B'C'	Length of Side
$\overline{A'B'}$	
$\overline{B'C'}$	
$\overline{A'C'}$	

5. What do you notice about the corresponding side lengths of the pre-image and the image?

6. Use a protractor to measure angle B of triangle ABC and angle B' of triangle $A'B'C'$.

    a. What are the measures of each angle?

    b. What does this information tell you about the corresponding angles of the two triangles?

You have shown that the corresponding sides of the image and pre-image are congruent. Therefore, the triangles are congruent by the SSS Congruence Theorem.

You have also used a protractor to verify that the corresponding included angles of each triangle are congruent.

In conclusion, when two side lengths of one triangle and the measure of the included angle are equal to the two corresponding side lengths and the measure of the included angle of another triangle, the two triangles are congruent by the SAS Congruence Theorem.

7. Use the SAS Congruence Theorem and a protractor to determine if the two triangles drawn on the coordinate plane shown are congruent. Use a protractor to determine the measures of the included angles.

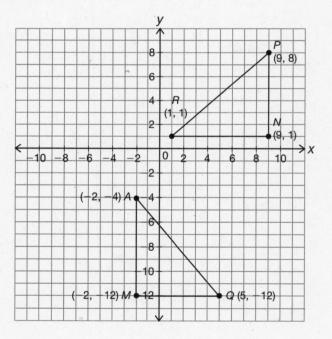

Prove the Side-Angle-Side Congruence Theorem.

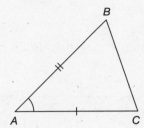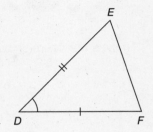

Given: $\overline{AB} \cong \overline{DE}$, $\overline{AC} \cong \overline{DF}$, and $\angle A \cong \angle D$

Prove: $\triangle ABC \cong \triangle DEF$

You can analyze diagrams and use SAS and SSS to determine if triangles are congruent.

Analyze the figure shown to determine if △*ABC* is congruent to △*DCB*.

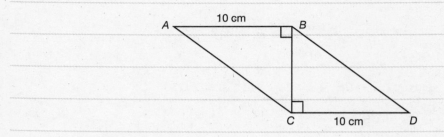

Notice, *m*$\overline{AB}$ = 10 cm and *m*$\overline{DC}$ = 10 cm, and the two line segments are corresponding sides of the two triangles. Also, notice that ∠*ABC* and ∠*DCB* are right angles, and they are corresponding angles of the two triangles.

In order to prove that the two triangles are congruent using SAS, you need to show that another side of triangle *ABC* is congruent to another side of triangle *DCB*. Notice that the two triangles share a side. Because $\overline{BC}$ is the same as $\overline{CB}$, you know that these two line segments are congruent.

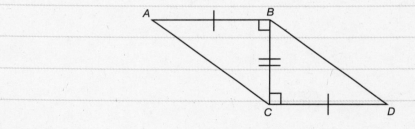

So, △*ABC* ≅ △*DCB* by the SAS Congruence Theorem.

1. Write the three congruence statements that show △*ABC* ≅ △*DCB* by the SAS Congruence Theorem.

2. Determine if there is enough information to prove that the two triangles are congruent by SSS or SAS. Write the congruence statements to justify your reasoning.

   a. $\triangle ABC \overset{?}{\cong} \triangle ADC$

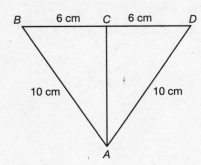

Use markers to identify all congruent line segments and angles.

   b. $\triangle ABC \overset{?}{\cong} \triangle DEF$

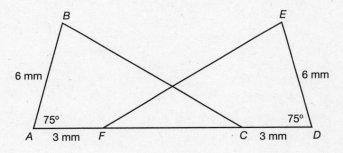

5

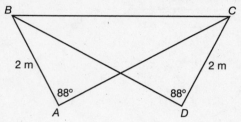

3. Simone says that since triangle *ABC* and triangle *DCB* have two pairs of congruent corresponding sides and congruent corresponding angles, then the triangles are congruent by SAS. Is Simone correct? Explain your reasoning.

B ━━━━━━━ C

2 m   2 m

88°   88°

A   D

 Be prepared to share your solutions and methods.

Angle to the Left of Me, Angle to the Right of Me

Angle-Side-Angle Congruence Theorem

LEARNING GOALS

LEARNING GOALS

In this lesson, you will:

- Explore the Angle-Side-Angle Congruence Theorem using constructions.
- Explore the Angle-Side-Angle Congruence Theorem on the coordinate plane.
- Prove the Angle-Side-Angle Congruence Theorem.

KEY TERM

- Angle-Side-Angle Congruence Theorem

"Don't judge a book by its cover." What does this saying mean to you? Usually it is said to remind someone not to make assumptions. Just because something (or someone!) looks a certain way on the outside, until you really get into it, you don't know the whole story. Often in geometry, it is easy to make assumptions. You assume that two figures are congruent because they look congruent. You assume two lines are perpendicular because they look perpendicular. Unfortunately, mathematics and assumptions do not go well together. Just as you should not judge a book by its cover, you should not assume anything about a measurement just because it looks a certain way.

Have you made any geometric assumptions so far in this chapter? Was your assumption correct or incorrect? Hopefully, it will only take you one incorrect assumption to learn not to assume!

PROBLEM 1 Putting the Pieces Together

So far you have looked at the Side-Side-Side Congruence Theorem and the Side-Angle-Side Congruence Theorem. But are there other theorems that prove triangle congruence as well?

1. Use the given two angles and included line segment to construct triangle *ABC*. Then, write the steps you performed to construct the triangle.

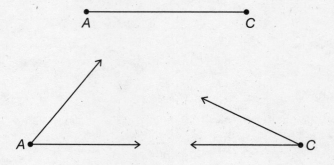

2. Compare your triangle to your classmates' triangles. Are the triangles congruent? Why or why not?

3. Wendy says that if the line segment and angles in the construction had not been labeled, then all the triangles would not have been congruent. Ian disagrees, and says that there is only one way to put two angles and a side together to form a triangle, whether they are labeled or not. Who is correct? Explain your reasoning.

Recall that an included side is the side between two angles of a triangle.

 You just used construction to prove the *Angle-Side-Angle Congruence Theorem*. The **Angle-Side-Angle Congruence Theorem** states: "If two angles and the included side of one triangle are congruent to the corresponding two angles and the included side of another triangle, then the triangles are congruent."

1. Analyze triangles *ABC* and *DEF*.

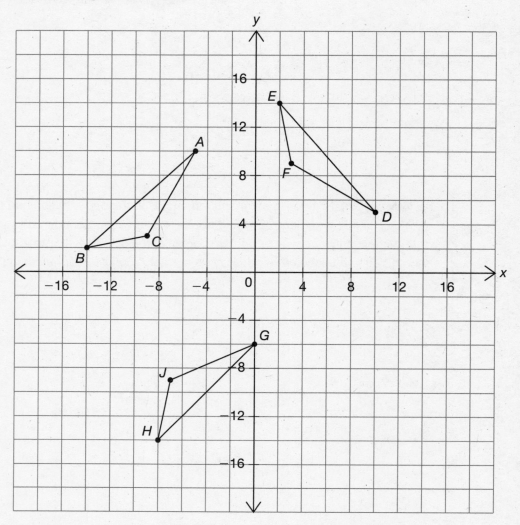

a. Measure the angles and calculate the side lengths of each triangle.

b. Describe the possible transformation(s) that could have occurred to transform pre-image *ABC* into image *DEF*.

c. Identify two pairs of corresponding angles and a pair of corresponding included sides that could be used to determine congruence through the ASA Congruence Theorem.

d. Use the ASA Congruence Theorem to determine if the two triangles are congruent.

2. Analyze triangles *DEF* and *GHJ*.

   a. Measure the angles and calculate the side lengths of triangle *GHJ*.

   b. Describe the possible transformation(s) that could have occurred to transform pre-image *DEF* to image *GHJ*.

   c. Identify two pairs of corresponding angles and a pair of corresponding included sides that could be used to determine congruence through the ASA Congruence Theorem.

   d. Use the ASA Congruence Theorem to determine if the two triangles are congruent.

3. What can you conclude about the relationship between triangle *ABC* and triangle *GHJ*? Explain your reasoning.

PROBLEM ❸ And Finally the Proof . . .

Prove the Angle-Side-Angle Congruence Theorem.

Given: $\angle A \cong \angle D, \overline{AC} \cong \overline{DF}, \angle C \cong \angle F$

Prove: $\triangle ABC \cong \triangle DEF$

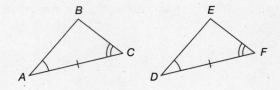

Sides Not Included

Angle-Angle-Side Congruence Theorem

LEARNING GOALS

In this lesson, you will:

- Explore the Angle-Angle-Side Congruence Theorem using constructions.
- Explore the Angle-Angle-Side Congruence Theorem on the coordinate plane.
- Prove the Angle-Angle-Side Congruence Theorem.

KEY TERM

- Angle-Angle-Side Congruence Theorem

Sometimes, good things must come to an end, and that can be said for determining if triangles are congruent, given certain information.

You have used many different theorems to prove that two triangles are congruent based on different criteria. Specifically,

- Side-Side-Side Congruence Theorem

- Side-Angle-Side Congruence Theorem

- and Angle-Side-Angle Congruence Theorem.

So, do you think there are any other theorems that can be used to prove that two triangles are congruent? Here's a hint: we have another lesson—so there must be at least one more congruence theorem!

PROBLEM 1 Using Constructions to Support AAS

There is another way to determine if two triangles are congruent that is different from the congruence theorems you have already proven. You will prove the *Angle-Angle-Side Congruence Theorem*.

The **Angle-Angle-Side Congruence Theorem** states: "If two angles and a non-included side of one triangle are congruent to the corresponding angles and the corresponding non-included side of a second triangle, then the triangles are congruent."

First, you will prove this theorem through construction.

> Recall that a non-included side is a side that is not located between the two angles.

1. Construct triangle *ABC* given $\overline{AB}$ and angles *A* and *C*. Then, write the steps you performed to construct the triangle.

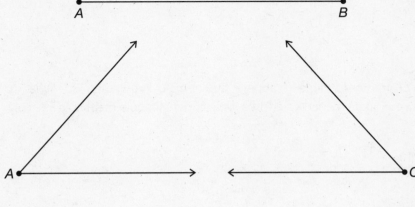

It might be helpful to construct angle B first and use that to create your triangle.

2. How does the length of side $\overline{AB}$ compare to the length of your classmates' side $\overline{AB}$?

3. Use a protractor to measure angle A and angle C in triangle ABC. What do you notice about your angle measures and your classmates' angle measures?

4. Thomas claims that his constructed triangle is not congruent because he drew a vertical starter line that created a triangle that has side AB being vertical rather than horizontal. Denise claims that all the constructed triangles are congruent even though Thomas's triangle looks different. Who's correct? Why is this student correct?

5. Is your triangle congruent to your classmates' triangles? Why or why not?

PROBLEM **2**   Using Reflection to Support AAS

If two angles and the non-included side of a triangle are reflected, is the image of the triangle congruent to the pre-image of the triangle?

1. Graph triangle *ABC* by plotting the points *A* (−3, −6), *B* (−9, −10), and *C* (−1, −10).

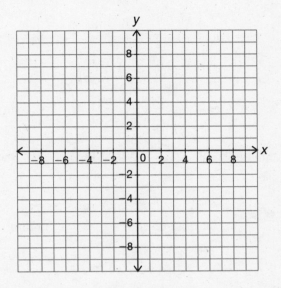

2. Calculate the length of each side of triangle *ABC*. Record the exact measurements in the table.

Side of Triangle *ABC*	Length of Side
$\overline{AB}$	
$\overline{BC}$	
$\overline{AC}$	

3. Reflect angle *A*, angle *B*, and side $\overline{BC}$ over the line of reflection $y = -2$ to form angle *D*, angle *E*, and side $\overline{EF}$. Then, connect points *D* and *E* to form triangle *DEF*. Record the image coordinates in the table.

Coordinates of Triangle *ABC*	Coordinates of Triangle *DEF*
A (−3, −6)	
B (−9, −10)	
C (−1, −10)	

4. Calculate the length of each side of triangle *DEF*. Record the exact measurements in the table.

Side of Triangle *DEF*	Length of Side
$\overline{DE}$	
$\overline{EF}$	
$\overline{DF}$	

5. Compare the corresponding side lengths of the pre-image and image. What do you notice?

You have shown that the corresponding sides of the image and pre-image are congruent. Therefore, the triangles are congruent by the SSS Congruence Theorem. However, you are proving the Angle-Angle-Side Congruence Theorem. Therefore, you need to verify that angle *A* and angle *C* are congruent to the corresponding angles in triangle *DEF*.

6. Use a protractor to determine the angle measures of each triangle.

   a. What is the measure of angle *A* and angle *C*?

   b. Which angles in triangle *DEF* correspond to angle *A* and angle *C*?

   c. What do you notice about the measures of the corresponding angles in the triangles? What can you conclude from this information?

You have used a protractor to verify that the corresponding angles of the two triangles are congruent.

In conclusion, when the measure of two angles and the length of the non-included side of one triangle are equal to the measure of the two corresponding angles and the length of the non-included side of another triangle, the two triangles are congruent by the AAS Congruence Theorem.

Prove the Angle-Angle-Side Congruence Theorem.

Given: $\angle A \cong \angle D$, $\angle B \cong \angle E$, $\overline{BC} \cong \overline{EF}$

Prove: $\triangle ABC \cong \triangle DEF$

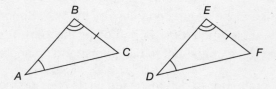

Determine if there is enough information to prove that the two triangles are congruent by ASA or AAS. Write the congruence statements to justify your reasoning.

1. $\triangle ABS \overset{?}{\cong} \triangle AVF$

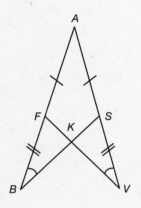

2. $\triangle GAB \overset{?}{\cong} \triangle SBA$

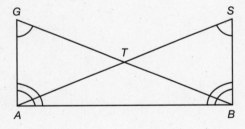

3. $\triangle EQD \overset{?}{\cong} \triangle DWE$

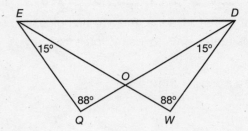

4. $\triangle ABC \overset{?}{\cong} \triangle PQR$

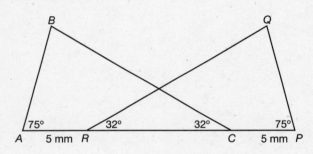

Talk the Talk

This chapter focused on four methods that you can use to prove that two triangles are congruent. Complete the graphic organizer by providing an illustration of each theorem.

Use markers to show congruent sides and congruent angles.

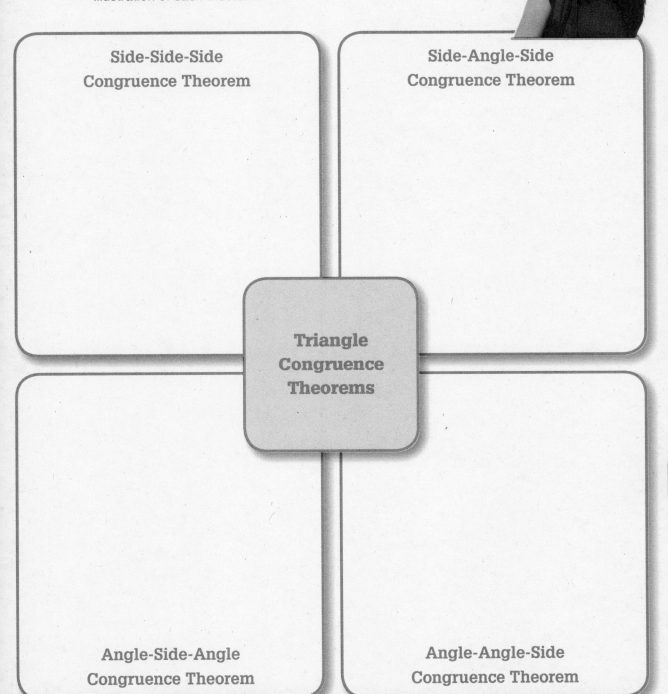

Side-Side-Side
Congruence Theorem

Side-Angle-Side
Congruence Theorem

Triangle
Congruence
Theorems

Angle-Side-Angle
Congruence Theorem

Angle-Angle-Side
Congruence Theorem

Be prepared to share your solutions and methods.

Any Other Theorems You Forgot to Mention?

Using Congruent Triangles

In this lesson, you will:

- Prove that the points on a perpendicular bisector of a line segment are equidistant to the endpoints of the line segment.
- Show that AAA for congruent triangles does not work.
- Show that SSA for congruent triangles does not work.
- Use the congruence theorems to determine triangle congruency.

Name That Tune was a popular game show that aired from 1974 to 1981. Contestants played against each other based on their knowledge of popular songs. One of the rounds was named Bid-a-Note in which contestants took turns stating, "I can name that tune in X notes," each time lowering the number of notes. Eventually one of the contestants would declare, "Name that tune!"

The goal was to name the tune in the fewest number of notes. You have been exploring congruent triangles and determining the fewest measurements that are needed to name that triangle. Although, *Name That Triangle* probably wouldn't be as popular a game show as *Name That Tune*!

Theorem: Points on a perpendicular bisector of a line segment are equidistant to the endpoints of the segment.

    1. Construct the perpendicular bisector of line segment *AB*.

$A \bullet\!\!\!-\!\!\!-\!\!\!-\!\!\!-\!\!\!-\!\!\!-\!\!\!-\!\!\!-\!\!\!-\!\!\!-\!\!\!-\!\!\!-\!\!\!-\!\!\!- \bullet B$

2. Locate point *C* on the perpendicular bisector above line segment *AB*.

3. Locate point *D* on the perpendicular bisector below line segment *AB*.

4. Locate point *E* on the perpendicular bisector where it intersects line segment *AB*.

5. Connect point *A* and point *C* to form triangle *AEC*.

6. Connect point *B* and point *C* to form triangle *BEC*.

7. Use a triangle congruence theorem to prove point *C* is equidistant to points *A* and *B*. Write each statement and reason.

8. Use a triangle congruence theorem to prove point *D* is equidistant to points *A* and *B*. Write each statement and reason.

9. How many other points on the perpendicular bisector can be proven equidistant from the endpoints of line segment *AB* using the same strategy?

10. Explain how rigid motion could be used to prove points on the perpendicular bisector are equidistant from the endpoints of line segment *AB*.

Thus far, you have explored and proven each of the triangle congruence theorems:

- Side-Side-Side (SSS)

- Side-Angle-Side (SAS)

- Angle-Side-Angle (ASA)

- Angle-Angle-Side (AAS)

1. Juno wondered why AAA isn't on the list of congruence theorems.

   Provide a counterexample to show Juno why Angle-Angle-Angle (AAA) **is not** considered a congruence theorem.

2. Juno also wondered why SSA isn't on the list of congruence theorems.

Provide a counterexample to show Juno why Side-Side-Angle (SSA) *is not* considered a triangle congruence theorem.

Determine which given information results in △*DFG* ≅ △*EFG*. State the appropriate congruence theorem if the triangles can be proven congruent, or state that there is not enough information if additional givens are needed to determine congruent triangles.

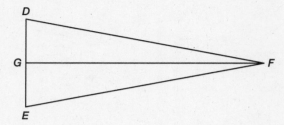

1. Given: *G* is the midpoint of $\overline{DE}$

2. Given: $\overline{DE} \perp \overline{FG}$

3. Given: $\overline{FG}$ bisects ∠*DFE*, $\overline{FD} \cong \overline{FE}$

4. Given: Triangle *DEF* is isosceles with $\overline{FD} \cong \overline{FE}$

5. Given: $\overline{FG}$ bisects ∠*DFE*, ∠*DGF* is a right angle

6. Given: ∠*D* ≅ ∠*E*, $\overline{FG}$ bisects ∠*DFE*

1. Determine what additional information is needed to prove the specified triangles congruent.

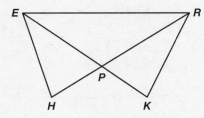

a. Given: ∠H ≅ ∠K

   Prove: △EPH ≅ △RPK by the ASA Congruence Triangle Theorem

b. Given: $\overline{HE}$ ≅ $\overline{KR}$

   Prove: △EHR ≅ △RKE by the SSS Congruence Triangle Theorem

c. Given: Triangle EPR is isosceles with $\overline{EP}$ ≅ $\overline{RP}$

   Prove: △EPH ≅ △RPK by the SAS Congruence Triangle Theorem

2. Determine what additional information is needed to prove the specified triangles congruent.

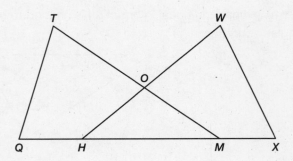

a. Given: $\overline{QH} \cong \overline{XM}$, $\overline{TQ} \cong \overline{WX}$

Prove: $\triangle TQM \cong \triangle WXH$ by the SAS Congruence Triangle Theorem

b. Given: $\angle Q \cong \angle X$, $\angle T \cong \angle W$

Prove: $\triangle TQM \cong \triangle WXH$ by the AAS Congruence Triangle Theorem

1. Use this diagram to answer each question.

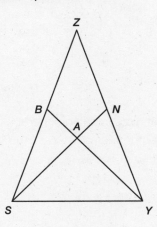

a. Name three possible sets of congruent triangles by writing triangle congruency statements.

b. Which set of triangles share a common side?

c. Which set of triangles share a common angle?

d. Which set of triangles contain a pair of vertical angles?

e. Knowing triangle ZSN is isosceles with $\overline{ZS} \cong \overline{ZY}$ would be helpful in determining the congruence of which set of triangles?

f. Knowing triangle SAY is equilateral would be helpful in determining the congruence of which set of triangles?

g. Knowing $\angle Z \cong \angle Z$ would be helpful in determining the congruence of which set of triangles?

h. Knowing $\overline{SY} \cong \overline{SY}$ would be helpful in determining the congruence of which set of triangles?

 Be prepared to share your solutions and methods.

Chapter **5** Summary

- Side-Side-Side Congruence Theorem (5.3)
- Side-Angle-Side Congruence Theorem (5.4)
- Angle-Side-Angle Congruence Theorem (5.5)
- Angle-Angle-Side Congruence Theorem (5.6)

5.1 Translating Triangles on the Coordinate Plane

A translation is a rigid motion that slides each point of a figure the same distance and direction.

Example

Triangle *ABC* has been translated 10 units to the left and 2 units down to create triangle *A'B'C'*.

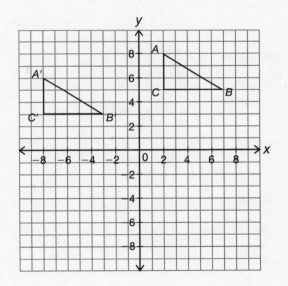

The coordinates of triangle *ABC* are *A* (2, 8), *B* (7, 5), and *C* (2, 5).

The coordinates of triangle *A'B'C'* are *A'* (−8, 6), *B'* (−3, 3), and *C'* (−8, 3).

5

411

5.1 Rotating Triangles in the Coordinate Plane

A rotation is a rigid motion that turns a figure about a fixed point, called the point of rotation. The figure is rotated in a given direction for a given angle, called the angle of rotation. The angle of rotation is the measure of the amount the figure is rotated about the point of rotation. The direction of a rotation can either be clockwise or counterclockwise. To determine the new coordinates of a point after a 90° counterclockwise rotation, change the sign of the y-coordinate of the original point and then switch the x-coordinate and the y-coordinate. To determine the new coordinates of a point after a 180° rotation, change the signs of the x-coordinate and the y-coordinate of the original point.

Example

Triangle ABC has been rotated 180° counterclockwise about the origin to create triangle $A'B'C'$.

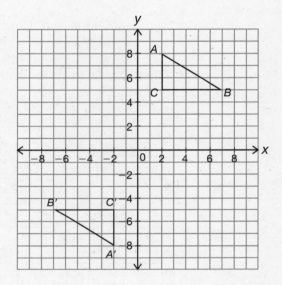

The coordinates of triangle ABC are A (2, 8), B (7, 5), and C (2, 5).

The coordinates of triangle $A'B'C'$ are A' (−2, −8), B' (−7, −5), and C' (−2, −5).

Reflecting Triangles on a Coordinate Plane

A reflection is a rigid motion that reflects or "flips" a figure over a given line called a line of reflection. Each point in the new triangle will be the same distance from the line of reflection as the corresponding point in the original triangle. To determine the coordinates of a point after a reflection across the x-axis, change the sign of the y-coordinate of the original point. The x-coordinate remains the same. To determine the coordinates of a point after a reflection across the y-axis, change the sign of the x-coordinate of the original point. The y-coordinate remains the same.

Example

Triangle ABC has been reflected across the x-axis to create triangle $A'B'C'$.

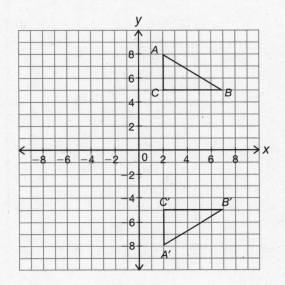

The coordinates of triangle ABC are A (2, 8), B (7, 5), and C (2, 5).

The coordinates of triangle $A'B'C'$ are A' (2, −8), B' (7, −5), and C' (2, −5).

5

5.3 **Using the SSS Congruence Theorem to Identify Congruent Triangles**

The Side-Side-Side (SSS) Congruence Theorem states that if three sides of one triangle are congruent to the corresponding sides of another triangle, then the triangles are congruent.

Example

Use the SSS Congruence theorem to prove $\triangle CJS$ is congruent to $\triangle C'J'S'$.

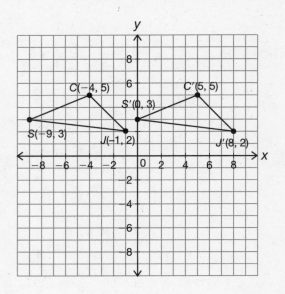

$SC = \sqrt{[-4 - (-9)]^2 + (5 - 3)^2}$

$\quad = \sqrt{5^2 + 2^2}$

$\quad = \sqrt{25 + 4}$

$\quad = \sqrt{29}$

$S'C' = \sqrt{(5 - 0)^2 + (5 - 3)^2}$

$\quad = \sqrt{5^2 + 2^2}$

$\quad = \sqrt{25 + 4}$

$\quad = \sqrt{29}$

$CJ = \sqrt{[-1 - (-4)]^2 + (2 - 5)^2}$

$\quad = \sqrt{3^2 + (-3)^2}$

$\quad = \sqrt{9 + 9}$

$\quad = \sqrt{18}$

$C'J' = \sqrt{(8 - 5)^2 + (2 - 5)^2}$

$\quad = \sqrt{3^2 + (-3)^2}$

$\quad = \sqrt{9 + 9}$

$\quad = \sqrt{18}$

$SJ = \sqrt{[-1 - (-9)]^2 + (2 - 3)^2}$

$\quad = \sqrt{8^2 + (-1)^2}$

$\quad = \sqrt{64 + 1}$

$\quad = \sqrt{65}$

$S'J' = \sqrt{(8 - 0)^2 + (2 - 3)^2}$

$\quad = \sqrt{8^2 + (-1)^2}$

$\quad = \sqrt{64 + 1}$

$\quad = \sqrt{65}$

The lengths of the corresponding sides of the pre-image and the image are equal, so the corresponding sides of the image and the pre-image are congruent. Therefore, the triangles are congruent by the SSS Congruence Theorem.

Using the SAS Congruence Theorem to Identify Congruent Triangles

The Side-Angle-Side (SAS) Congruence Theorem states that if two sides and the included angle of one triangle are congruent to the corresponding two sides and the included angle of a second triangle, then the triangles are congruent. An included angle is the angle formed by two sides of a triangle.

Example

Use the SAS Congruence Theorem to prove that $\triangle AMK$ is congruent to $\triangle A'M'K'$.

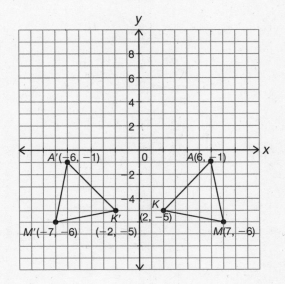

$KA = \sqrt{(6-2)^2 + [-1-(-5)]^2}$

$\qquad = \sqrt{4^2 + 4^2}$

$\qquad = \sqrt{16 + 16}$

$\qquad = \sqrt{32}$

$K'A' = \sqrt{[-5-(-1)]^2 + [-2-(-6)]^2}$

$\qquad = \sqrt{(-4)^2 + 4^2}$

$\qquad = \sqrt{16 + 16}$

$\qquad = \sqrt{32}$

$KM = \sqrt{(7-2)^2 + [-6-(-5)]^2}$

$\qquad = \sqrt{5^2 + (-1)^2}$

$\qquad = \sqrt{25 + 1}$

$\qquad = \sqrt{26}$

$K'M' = \sqrt{[-7-(-2)]^2 + [-6-(-5)]^2}$

$\qquad = \sqrt{(-5)^2 + (-1)^2}$

$\qquad = \sqrt{25 + 1}$

$\qquad = \sqrt{26}$

$m\angle K = 58°$

$m\angle K' = 58°$

The lengths of the pairs of the corresponding sides and the measures of the pair of corresponding included angles are equal. Therefore, the triangles are congruent by the SAS Congruence Theorem.

5.5 Using the ASA Congruence Theorem to Identify Congruent Triangles

The Angle-Side-Angle (ASA) Congruence Theorem states that if two angles and the included side of one triangle are congruent to the corresponding two angles and the included side of another triangle, then the triangles are congruent. An included side is the line segment between two angles of a triangle.

Example

Use the ASA Congruence Theorem to prove that $\triangle DLM$ is congruent to $\triangle D'L'M'$.

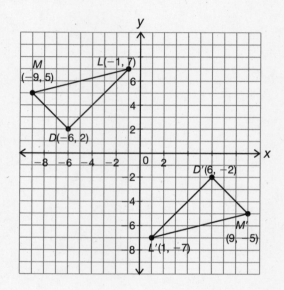

$$DM = \sqrt{[-9-(-6)]^2 + (5-2)^2}$$
$$= \sqrt{(-3)^2 + 3^2}$$
$$= \sqrt{9+9}$$
$$= \sqrt{18}$$

$m\angle D = 90°$

$m\angle M = 60°$

$$D'M' = \sqrt{(9-6)^2 + [-5-(-2)]^2}$$
$$= \sqrt{3^2 + (-3)^2}$$
$$= \sqrt{9+9}$$
$$= \sqrt{18}$$

$m\angle D' = 90°$

$m\angle M' = 60°$

The measures of the pairs of corresponding angles and the lengths of the corresponding included sides are equal. Therefore, the triangles are congruent by the ASA Congruence Theorem.

Using the AAS Congruence Theorem to Identify Congruent Triangles

The Angle-Angle-Side (AAS) Congruence Theorem states that if two angles and a non-included side of one triangle are congruent to the corresponding two angles and the corresponding non-included side of a second triangle, then the triangles are congruent.

Example

Use the AAS Congruence Theorem to prove $\triangle LSK$ is congruent to $\triangle L'S'K'$.

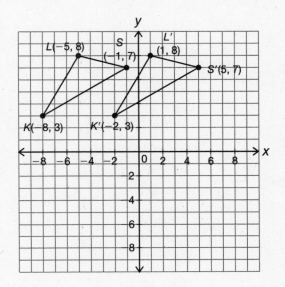

$m\angle L = 108°$

$m\angle K = 30°$

$KS = \sqrt{[-1 - (-8)]^2 + (7 - 3)^2}$

$\quad = \sqrt{7^2 + 4^2}$

$\quad = \sqrt{49 + 16}$

$\quad = \sqrt{65}$

$m\angle L' = 108°$

$m\angle K' = 30°$

$K'S' = \sqrt{[5 - (-2)]^2 + (7 - 3)^2}$

$\quad = \sqrt{7^2 + 4^2}$

$\quad = \sqrt{49 + 16}$

$\quad = \sqrt{65}$

The measures of the two pairs of corresponding angles and the lengths of the pair of corresponding non-included sides are equal. Therefore, the triangles are congruent by the AAS Congruence Theorem.

5

Using Congruence Theorems

> The Penrose Triangle is one of the most famous "impossible objects." It can be drawn in two dimensions but cannot be created in three dimensions.

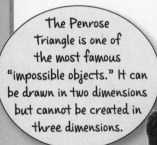

Time to Get Right
Right Triangle Congruence Theorems

LEARNING GOALS

In this lesson, you will:

- Prove the Hypotenuse-Leg Congruence Theorem using a two-column proof and construction.
- Prove the Leg-Leg, Hypotenuse-Angle, and Leg-Angle Congruence Theorems by relating them to general triangle congruence theorems.
- Apply right triangle congruence theorems.

KEY TERMS

- Hypotenuse-Leg (HL) Congruence Theorem
- Leg-Leg (LL) Congruence Theorem
- Hypotenuse-Angle (HA) Congruence Theorem
- Leg-Angle (LA) Congruence Theorem

You know the famous equation $E = mc^2$. But this equation is actually incomplete. The full equation is $E^2 = (m^2)^2 + (pc)^2$, where E represents energy, m represents mass, p represents momentum, and c represents the speed of light.

You can represent this equation on a right triangle.

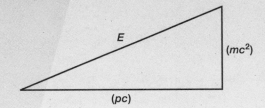

So, when an object's momentum is equal to 0, you get the equation $E = mc^2$.

But what about a particle of light, which has no mass? What equation would describe its energy?

1. List all of the triangle congruence theorems you explored previously.

How many pairs of measurements did you need to know for each congruence theorem?

The congruence theorems apply to all triangles. There are also theorems that only apply to right triangles. Methods for proving that two right triangles are congruent are somewhat shorter. You can prove that two right triangles are congruent using only two measurements.

2. Explain why only two pairs of corresponding parts are needed to prove that two right triangles are congruent.

3. Are all right angles congruent? Explain your reasoning.

The **Hypotenuse-Leg (HL) Congruence Theorem** states: "If the hypotenuse and leg of one right triangle are congruent to the hypotenuse and leg of another right triangle, then the triangles are congruent."

Mark up the diagram as you go with congruence marks to keep track of what you know.

4. Complete the two-column proof of the HL Congruence Theorem.

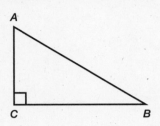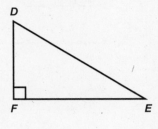

Given: ∠C and ∠F are right angles

$\overline{AC} \cong \overline{DF}$

$\overline{AB} \cong \overline{DE}$

Prove: △ABC ≅ △DEF

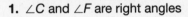

Statements	Reasons
1. ∠C and ∠F are right angles	
2. ∠C ≅ ∠F	
3. $\overline{AC} \cong \overline{DF}$	
4. $\overline{AB} \cong \overline{DE}$	
5. $AC = DF$	
6. $AB = DE$	
7. $AC^2 + CB^2 = AB^2$	
8. $DF^2 + FE^2 = DE^2$	
9. $AC^2 + CB^2 = DF^2 + FE^2$	
10. $CB^2 = FE^2$	
11. $CB = FE$	
12. $\overline{CB} \cong \overline{FE}$	
13. △ABC ≅ △DEF	

You can also use construction to demonstrate the Hypotenuse-Leg Theorem.

5. Construct right triangle *ABC* with right angle *C*, given leg $\overline{CA}$ and hypotenuse $\overline{AB}$. Then, write the steps you performed to construct the triangle.

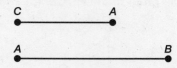

a. How does the length of side $\overline{CB}$ compare to the lengths of your classmates' sides $\overline{CB}$?

b. Use a protractor to measure ∠A and ∠B in triangle ABC. How do the measures of these angles compare to the measures of your classmates' angles A and B?

c. Is your triangle congruent to your classmates' triangles? Why or why not?

Through your two-column proof and your construction proof, you have proven that Hypotenuse-Leg is a valid method of proof for any right triangle. Now let's prove the Hypotenuse-Leg Theorem on the coordinate plane using algebra.

6. Consider right triangle ABC with right angle C and points A (0, 6), B (8, 0), and C (0, 0).

   a. Graph right triangle ABC.

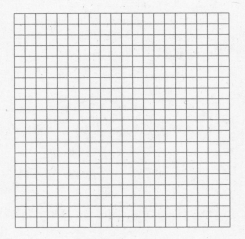

   b. Calculate the length of each line segment forming the sides of triangle ABC and record the measurements in the table.

Sides of Triangle ABC	Lengths of Sides of Triangle ABC (units)
$\overline{AB}$	
$\overline{BC}$	
$\overline{AC}$	

c. Rotate side AB, side AC, and $\angle C$ 180° counterclockwise about the origin. Then, connect points B' and C' to form triangle $A'B'C'$. Use the table to record the coordinates of triangle $A'B'C'$.

Coordinates of Triangle ABC	Coordinates of Triangle $A'B'C'$
$A(0,6)$	
$B(8,0)$	
$C(0,0)$	

d. Calculate the length of each line segment forming the sides of triangle $A'B'C'$, and record the measurements in the table.

Sides of Triangle $A'B'C'$	Lengths of Sides of Triangle $A'B'C'$ (units)
$\overline{A'B'}$	
$\overline{B'C'}$	
$\overline{A'C'}$	

e. What do you notice about the side lengths of the image and pre-image?

f. Use a protractor to measure $\angle A$, $\angle A'$, $\angle B$, and $\angle B'$. What can you conclude about the corresponding angles of triangle ABC and triangle $A'B'C'$?

In conclusion, when the leg and hypotenuse of a right triangle are congruent to the leg and hypotenuse of another right triangle, then the right triangles are congruent.

You have shown that the corresponding sides and corresponding angles of the pre-image and image are congruent. Therefore, the triangles are congruent.

Proving Three More Right Triangle Theorems

You used a two-column proof, a construction, and rigid motion to prove the Hypotenuse-Leg Congruent Theorem. There are three more right triangle congruence theorems that we are going to explore. You can prove each of them using the same methods but you'll focus on rigid motion in this lesson.

The **Leg-Leg (LL) Congruence Theorem** states: "If two legs of one right triangle are congruent to two legs of another right triangle, then the triangles are congruent."

1. Consider right triangle *ABC* with right angle *C* and points *A* (0, 5), *B* (12, 0), and *C* (0, 0).

   a. Graph right triangle *ABC*.

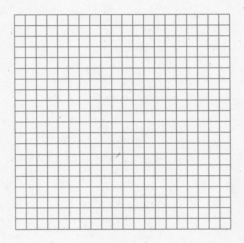

   b. Calculate the length of each line segment forming the sides of triangle *ABC,* and record the measurements in the table.

Sides of Triangle *ABC*	Lengths of Sides of Triangle *ABC* (units)
$\overline{AB}$	
$\overline{BC}$	
$\overline{AC}$	

c. Translate side *AC*, and side *BC,* to the left 3 units, and down 5 units. Then, connect points *A'*, *B'* and *C'* to form triangle *A'B'C'*. Use the table to record the image coordinates.

Coordinates of Triangle *ABC*	Coordinates of Triangle *A'B'C'*
A(0, 5)	
B(12, 0)	
C(0, 0)	

d. Calculate the length of each line segment forming the sides of triangle *A'B'C'*, and record the measurements in the table.

Sides of Triangle *A'B'C'*	Lengths of Sides of Triangle *A'B'C'* (units)
$\overline{A'B'}$	
$\overline{B'C'}$	
$\overline{A'C'}$	

e. What do you notice about the side lengths of the image and pre-image?

f. Use a protractor to measure ∠*A*, ∠*A'*, ∠*B*, and ∠*B'*. What can you conclude about the corresponding angles of triangle *ABC* and triangle *A'B'C'*?

In conclusion, when two legs of a right triangle are congruent to the two legs of another right triangle, then the right triangles are congruent.

You have shown that the corresponding sides and corresponding angles of the pre-image and image are congruent. Therefore, the triangles are congruent.

6

The **Hypotenuse-Angle (HA) Congruence Theorem** states: "If the hypotenuse and an acute angle of one right triangle are congruent to the hypotenuse and acute angle of another right triangle, then the triangles are congruent."

2. Consider right triangle ABC with right angle C and points A (0, 9), B (12, 0), and C (0, 0).

   a. Graph right triangle ABC with right ∠C, by plotting the points A (0, 9), B (12, 0), and C (0, 0).

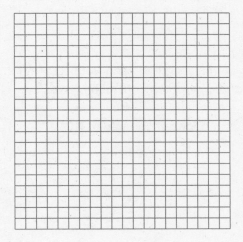

   b. Calculate the length of each line segment forming the sides of triangle ABC, and record the measurements in the table.

Sides of Triangle *ABC*	Lengths of Sides of Triangle *ABC* (units)
$\overline{AB}$	
$\overline{BC}$	
$\overline{AC}$	

6

c. Translate side AB, and $\angle A$, to the left 4 units, and down 8 units. Then, connect points A', B' and C' to form triangle $A'B'C'$. Use the table to record the image coordinates.

Coordinates of Triangle ABC	Coordinates of Triangle A'B'C'
A(0, 9)	
B(12, 0)	
C(0, 0)	

d. Calculate the length of each line segment forming the sides of triangle $A'B'C'$, and record the measurements in the table.

Sides of Triangle A'B'C'	Lengths of Sides of Triangle A'B'C' (units)
$\overline{A'B'}$	
$\overline{B'C'}$	
$\overline{A'C'}$	

e. What do you notice about the side lengths of the image and pre-image?

f. Use a protractor to measure $\angle A$, $\angle A'$, $\angle B$, and $\angle B'$. What can you conclude about the corresponding angles of triangle ABC and triangle $A'B'C'$?

In conclusion, when the hypotenuse and an acute angle of a right triangle are congruent to the hypotenuse and an acute angle of another right triangle, then the right triangles are congruent.

You have shown that the corresponding sides and corresponding angles of the pre-image and image are congruent. Therefore, the triangles are congruent.

The **Leg-Angle (LA) Congruence Theorem** states: "If a leg and an acute angle of one right triangle are congruent to a leg and an acute angle of another right triangle, then the triangles are congruent."

3. Consider right triangle *ABC* with right angle *C* and points *A* (0, 7), *B* (24, 0), and *C* (0, 0).

   a. Graph right triangle *ABC* with right ∠*C*, by plotting the points *A* (0, 7), *B* (24, 0), and *C* (0, 0).

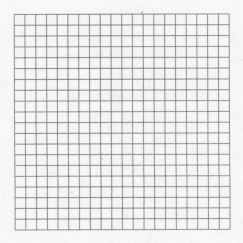

   b. Calculate the length of each line segment forming the sides of triangle *ABC,* and record the measurements in the table.

Sides of Triangle *ABC*	Lengths of Sides of Triangle *ABC* (units)
$\overline{AB}$	
$\overline{BC}$	
$\overline{AC}$	

c. Reflect side AC, and $\angle B$ over the x-axis. Then, connect points A', B' and C' to form triangle $A'B'C'$. Use the table to record the image coordinates.

Coordinates of Triangle ABC	Coordinates of Triangle $A'B'C'$
$A(0, 7)$	
$B(24, 0)$	
$C(0, 0)$	

d. Calculate the length of each line segment forming the sides of triangle $A'B'C'$, and record the measurements in the table.

Sides of Triangle $A'B'C'$	Lengths of Sides of Triangle $A'B'C'$ (units)
$\overline{A'B'}$	
$\overline{B'C'}$	
$\overline{A'C'}$	

e. What do you notice about the side lengths of the image and pre-image?

f. Use a protractor to measure $\angle A$, $\angle A'$, $\angle B$, and $\angle B'$. What can you conclude about the corresponding angles of triangle ABC and triangle $A'B'C'$?

In conclusion, when the leg and an acute angle of a right triangle are congruent to the leg and acute angle of another right triangle, then the right triangles are congruent.

You have shown that the corresponding sides and corresponding angles of the pre-image and image are congruent. Therefore, the triangles are congruent.

Determine if there is enough information to prove that the two triangles are congruent. If so, name the congruence theorem used.

1. If $\overline{CS} \perp \overline{SD}$, $\overline{WD} \perp \overline{SD}$, and P is the midpoint of $\overline{CW}$, is $\triangle CSP \cong \triangle WDP$?

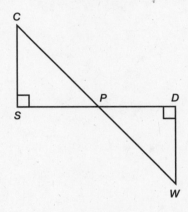

2. Pat always trips on the third step and she thinks that step may be a different size. The contractor told her that all the treads and risers are perpendicular to each other. Is that enough information to state that the steps are the same size? In other words, if $\overline{WN} \perp \overline{NZ}$ and $\overline{ZH} \perp \overline{HK}$, is $\triangle WNZ \cong \triangle ZHK$?

3. If $\overline{JA} \perp \overline{MY}$ and $\overline{JY} \cong \overline{AY}$, is $\triangle JYM \cong \triangle AYM$?

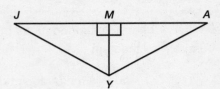

4. If $\overline{ST} \perp \overline{SR}$, $\overline{AT} \perp \overline{AR}$, and $\angle STR \cong \angle ATR$, is $\triangle STR \cong \triangle ATR$?

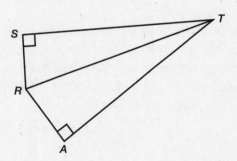

It is necessary to make a statement about the presence of right triangles when you use the Right Triangle Congruence Theorems. If you have previously identified the right angles, the reason is the definition of right triangles.

5. Create a proof of the following.

Given: $\overline{GU} \perp \overline{DB}$

$\overline{GB} \cong \overline{GD}$

Prove: $\triangle GUD \cong \triangle GUB$

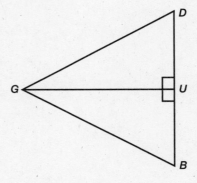

6. Create a proof of the following.

Given: $\overline{GU}$ is the ⊥ bisector of $\overline{DB}$

Prove: $\triangle GUD \cong \triangle GUB$

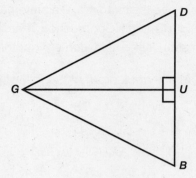

7. A friend wants to place a post in a lake 20 feet to the right of the dock. What is the minimum information you need to make sure the angle formed by the edge of the dock and the post is a right angle?

Talk the Talk

1. Which triangle congruence theorem is most closely related to the LL Congruence Theorem? Explain your reasoning.

2. Which triangle congruence theorem is most closely related to the HA Congruence Theorem? Explain your reasoning.

3. Which triangle congruence theorem is most closely related to the LA Congruence Theorem? Explain your reasoning.

4. Which triangle congruence theorem is most closely related to the HL Congruence Theorem? Explain your reasoning.

Be prepared to share your solutions and methods.

CPCTC
Corresponding Parts of Congruent Triangles are Congruent

LEARNING GOALS

In this lesson, you will:

- Identify corresponding parts of congruent triangles.
- Use corresponding parts of congruent triangles are congruent to prove angles and segments are congruent.
- Use corresponding parts of congruent triangles are congruent to prove the Isosceles Triangle Base Angle Theorem.
- Use corresponding parts of congruent triangles are congruent to prove the Isosceles Triangle Base Angle Converse Theorem.
- Apply corresponding parts of congruent triangles.

KEY TERMS

- corresponding parts of congruent triangles are congruent (CPCTC)
- Isosceles Triangle Base Angle Theorem
- Isosceles Triangle Base Angle Converse Theorem

Which of the blue lines shown is longer? Most people will answer that the line on the right appears to be longer.

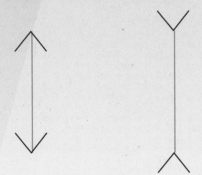

But in fact, both blue lines are the exact same length! This famous optical illusion is known as the Mueller-Lyer illusion. You can measure the lines to see for yourself. You can also draw some of your own to see how it almost always works!

If two triangles are congruent, then each part of one triangle is congruent to the corresponding part of the other triangle. **"Corresponding parts of congruent triangles are congruent,"** abbreviated as **CPCTC**, is often used as a reason in proofs. CPCTC states that corresponding angles or sides in two congruent triangles are congruent. This reason can only be used after you have proven that the triangles are congruent.

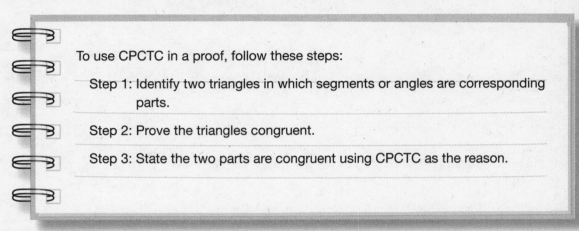

To use CPCTC in a proof, follow these steps:

Step 1: Identify two triangles in which segments or angles are corresponding parts.

Step 2: Prove the triangles congruent.

Step 3: State the two parts are congruent using CPCTC as the reason.

1. Create a proof of the following.

    Given: $\overline{CW}$ and $\overline{SD}$ bisect each other

    Prove: $\overline{CS} \cong \overline{WD}$

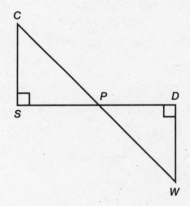

2. Create a proof of the following.

Given: $\overline{SU} \cong \overline{SK}$, $\overline{SR} \cong \overline{SH}$

Prove: $\angle U \cong \angle K$

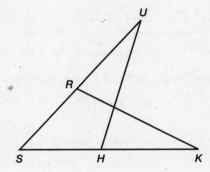

PROBLEM 2   Isosceles Triangle Base Angle Theorem and Its Converse

CPCTC makes it possible to prove other theorems.

The **Isosceles Triangle Base Angle Theorem** states: "If two sides of a triangle are congruent, then the angles opposite these sides are congruent."

To prove the Isosceles Triangle Base Angle Theorem, you need to add a line to an isosceles triangle that bisects the vertex angle as shown.

Don't forget to use congruence marks to help you.

1. Create a proof of the following.

   Given: $\overline{GB} \cong \overline{GD}$

   Prove: $\angle B \cong \angle D$

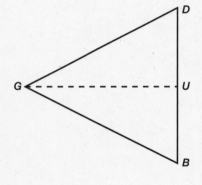

When you add a segment to a diagram, use the reason "construction".

6

The **Isosceles Triangle Base Angle Converse Theorem** states: "If two angles of a triangle are congruent, then the sides opposite these angles are congruent."

To prove the Isosceles Triangle Base Angle Converse Theorem, you need to again add a line to an isosceles triangle that bisects the vertex angle as shown.

2. Create a proof of the following.

    Given: $\angle B \cong \angle D$

    Prove: $\overline{GB} \cong \overline{GD}$

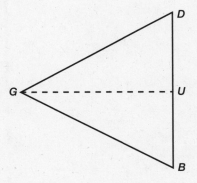

PROBLEM 3 Applications of CPCTC

1. How wide is the horse's pasture?

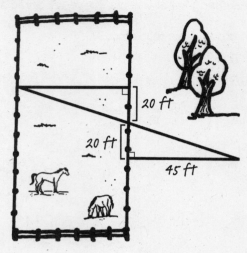

2. Calculate *AP* if the perimeter of △*AYP* is 43 cm.

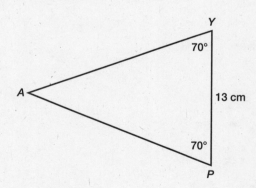

3. Lighting booms on a Ferris wheel consist of four steel beams that have cabling with light bulbs attached. These beams, along with three shorter beams, form the edges of three congruent isosceles triangles, as shown. Maintenance crews are installing new lighting along the four beams. Calculate the total length of lighting needed.

4. Calculate $m\angle T$.

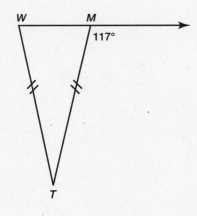

5. What is the width of the river?

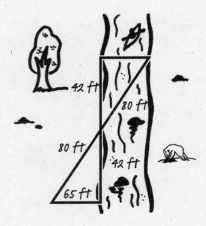

6. Given: $\overline{ST} \cong \overline{SR}$, $\overline{TA} \cong \overline{RA}$

Explain why $\angle T \cong \angle R$.

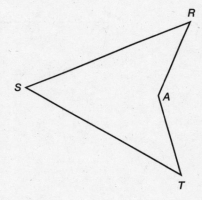

 Be prepared to share your solutions and methods.

Congruence Theorems in Action

Isosceles Triangle Theorems

You know that the measures of the three angles in a triangle equal 180°, and that no triangle can have more than one right angle or obtuse angle.

Unless, however, you're talking about a spherical triangle. A spherical triangle is a triangle formed on the surface of a sphere. The sum of the measures of the angles of this kind of triangle is always greater than 180°. Spherical triangles can have two or even three obtuse angles or right angles.

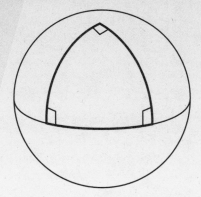

The properties of spherical triangles are important to a certain branch of science. Can you guess which one?

PROBLEM 1   Isosceles Triangle Theorems

 You will prove theorems related to isosceles triangles. These proofs involve altitudes, perpendicular bisectors, angle bisectors, and *vertex angles*. A **vertex angle of an isosceles triangle** is the angle formed by the two congruent legs in an isosceles triangle.

The **Isosceles Triangle Base Theorem** states: "The altitude to the base of an isosceles triangle bisects the base."

 1. Given: Isosceles $\triangle ABC$ with $\overline{CA} \cong \overline{CB}$.

    a. Construct altitude $\overline{CD}$ from the vertex angle to the base.

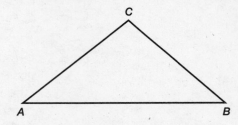

Remember, altitudes are perpendicular to bases.

2. Prove the Isosceles Triangle Base Theorem.

The **Isosceles Triangle Vertex Angle Theorem** states: "The altitude to the base of an isosceles triangle bisects the vertex angle."

3. Draw and label a diagram you can use to help you prove the Isosceles Triangle Vertex Angle Theorem. State the "Given" and "Prove" statements.

4. Prove the Isosceles Triangle Vertex Angle Theorem.

The **Isosceles Triangle Perpendicular Bisector Theorem** states: "The altitude from the vertex angle of an isosceles triangle is the perpendicular bisector of the base."

5. Draw and label a diagram you can use to help you prove the Isosceles Triangle Perpendicular Bisector Theorem. State the "Given" and "Prove" statements.

6. Prove the Isosceles Triangle Perpendicular Bisector Theorem.

PROBLEM 2 More Isosceles Triangle Theorems

The **Isosceles Triangle Altitude to Congruent Sides Theorem** states: "In an isosceles triangle, the altitudes to the congruent sides are congruent."

1. Draw and label a diagram you can use to help you prove this theorem. State the "Given" and "Prove" statements.

2. Prove the Isosceles Triangle Altitude to Congruent Sides Theorem.

The **Isosceles Triangle Angle Bisector to Congruent Sides Theorem** states:
"In an isosceles triangle, the angle bisectors to the congruent sides are congruent."

3. Draw and label a diagram you can use to help you prove this theorem. State the "Given" and "Prove" statements.

4. Prove the Isosceles Triangle Angle Bisector to Congruent Sides Theorem.

Talk the Talk

1. Solve for the width of the dog house.

   $\overline{CD} \perp \overline{AB}$

   $\overline{AC} \cong \overline{BC}$

   $CD = 12''$

   $AC = 20''$

Use the theorems you have just proven to answer each question about isosceles triangles.

2. What can you conclude about an altitude drawn from the vertex angle to the base?

3. What can you conclude about the altitudes to the congruent sides?

4. What can you conclude about the angle bisectors to the congruent sides?

Be prepared to share your solutions and methods.

6

Making Some Assumptions

Inverse, Contrapositive, Direct Proof, and Indirect Proof

The Greek philosopher Aristotle greatly influenced our understanding of physics, linguistics, politics, and science. He also had a great influence on our understanding of logic. In fact, he is often credited with the earliest study of formal logic, and he wrote six works on logic which were compiled into a collection known as the *Organon*. These works were used for many years after his death. There were a number of philosophers who believed that these works of Aristotle were so complete that there was nothing else to discuss regarding logic. These beliefs lasted until the 19th century when philosophers and mathematicians began thinking of logic in more mathematical terms.

Aristotle also wrote another book, *Metaphysics*, in which he makes the following statement: "To say of what is that it is not, or of what is not that it is, is falsehood, while to say of what is that it is, and of what is not that it is not, is truth."

What is Aristotle trying to say here, and do you agree? Can you prove or disprove this statement?

PROBLEM 1 The Inverse and Contrapositive

 Every conditional statement written in the form "If p, then q" has three additional conditional statements associated with it: the converse, the *contrapositive*, and the *inverse*. To state the **inverse**, negate the hypothesis and the conclusion. To state the **contrapositive**, negate the hypothesis and conclusion, and reverse them.

Recall that to state the converse, reverse the hypothesis and the conclusion.

Conditional Statement	If p, then q.
Converse	If q, then p.
Inverse	If not p, then not q.
Contrapositive	If not q, then not p.

 1. If a quadrilateral is a square, then the quadrilateral is a rectangle.

   a. Hypothesis p:

   b. Conclusion q:

   c. Is the conditional statement true? Explain your reasoning.

   d. Not p:

   e. Not q:

   f. Inverse:

   g. Is the inverse true? Explain your reasoning.

   h. Contrapositive:

   i. Is the contrapositive true? Explain your reasoning.

2. If an integer is even, then the integer is divisible by two.

  a. Hypothesis *p*:

  b. Conclusion *q*:

  c. Is the conditional statement true? Explain your reasoning.

  d. Not *p*:

  e. Not *q*:

  f. Inverse:

  g. Is the inverse true? Explain your reasoning.

  h. Contrapositive:

6

  i. Is the contrapositive true? Explain your reasoning.

3. If a polygon has six sides, then the polygon is a pentagon.

    a. Hypothesis p:

    b. Conclusion q:

    c. Is the conditional statement true? Explain your reasoning.

    d. Not p:

    e. Not q:

    f. Inverse:

    g. Is the inverse true? Explain your reasoning.

    h. Contrapositive:

    i. Is the contrapositive true? Explain your reasoning.

4. If two lines intersect, then the lines are perpendicular.

    a. Hypothesis p:

    b. Conclusion q:

    c. Is the conditional statement true? Explain your reasoning.

    d. Not p:

    e. Not q:

    f. Inverse:

    g. Is the inverse true? Explain your reasoning.

    h. Contrapositive:

    i. Is the contrapositive true? Explain your reasoning.

5. What do you notice about the truth value of a conditional statement and the truth value of its inverse?

6. What do you notice about the truth value of a conditional statement and the truth value of its contrapositive?

6

PROBLEM 2 Proof by Contradiction

All of the proofs up to this point were *direct proofs*. A **direct proof** begins with the given information and works to the desired conclusion directly through the use of givens, definitions, properties, postulates, and theorems.

An **indirect proof**, or **proof by contradiction**, uses the contrapositive. If you prove the contrapositive true, then the original conditional statement is true. Begin by assuming the conclusion is false, and use this assumption to show one of the given statements is false, thereby creating a contradiction.

Let's look at an example of an indirect proof.

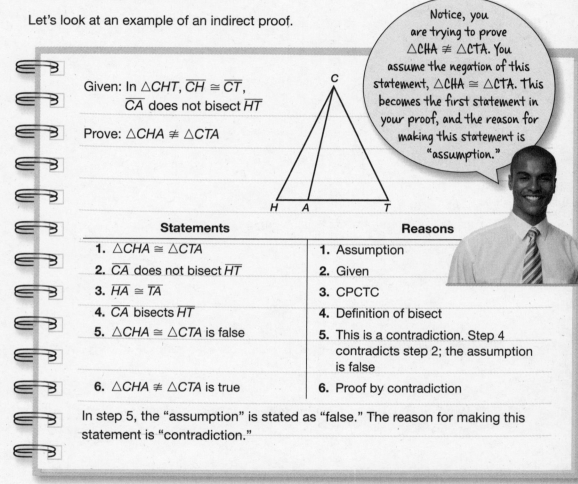

Given: In △CHT, $\overline{CH} \cong \overline{CT}$,
     $\overline{CA}$ does not bisect $\overline{HT}$

Prove: △CHA ≇ △CTA

> Notice, you are trying to prove △CHA ≇ △CTA. You assume the negation of this statement, △CHA ≅ △CTA. This becomes the first statement in your proof, and the reason for making this statement is "assumption."

Statements	Reasons
1. △CHA ≅ △CTA	1. Assumption
2. $\overline{CA}$ does not bisect $\overline{HT}$	2. Given
3. $\overline{HA} \cong \overline{TA}$	3. CPCTC
4. $\overline{CA}$ bisects $\overline{HT}$	4. Definition of bisect
5. △CHA ≅ △CTA is false	5. This is a contradiction. Step 4 contradicts step 2; the assumption is false
6. △CHA ≇ △CTA is true	6. Proof by contradiction

In step 5, the "assumption" is stated as "false." The reason for making this statement is "contradiction."

In an indirect proof:

● State the assumption; use the negation of the conclusion, or "Prove" statement.

● Write the givens.

● Write the negation of the conclusion.

● Use the assumption, in conjunction with definitions, properties, postulates, and theorems, to prove a given statement is false, thus creating a contradiction.

Hence, your assumption leads to a contradiction; therefore, the assumption must be false. This proves the contrapositive.

1. Create an indirect proof of the following.

   Given: $\overline{BR}$ bisects $\angle ABN$,

   $\angle BRA \neq \angle BRN$

   Prove: $\overline{AB} \neq \overline{NB}$

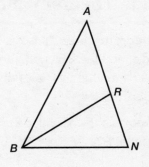

Now try one yourself!

2. Create an indirect proof to show that a triangle cannot have more than one right angle.

6

PROBLEM 3 Hinge Theorem and Its Converse

The **Hinge Theorem** states: "If two sides of one triangle are congruent to two sides of another triangle, and the included angle of the first pair is larger than the included angle of the second pair, then the third side of the first triangle is longer than the third side of the second triangle."

In the two triangles shown, notice that $RS = DE$, $ST = EF$, and $\angle S > \angle E$. The Hinge Theorem says that $RT > DF$.

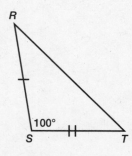
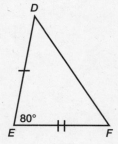

1. Use an indirect proof to prove the Hinge Theorem.

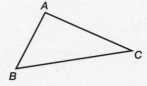
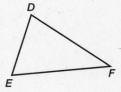

Given: $AB = DE$

$AC = DF$

$m\angle A > m\angle D$

Prove: $BC > EF$

Negating the conclusion, $BC > EF$, means that either BC is equal to EF, or BC is less than EF. Therefore, this theorem must be proven for both cases.

Case 1: $BC = EF$

Case 2: $BC < EF$

a. Write the indirect proof for Case 1, $BC = EF$.

b. Write the indirect proof for Case 2, $BC < EF$.

The **Hinge Converse Theorem** states: "If two sides of one triangle are congruent to two sides of another triangle and the third side of the first triangle is longer than the third side of the second triangle, then the included angle of the first pair of sides is larger than the included angle of the second pair of sides."

In the two triangles shown, notice that $RT = DF$, $RS = DE$, and $ST > EF$. The Hinge Converse Theorem guarantees that $m\angle R > m\angle D$.

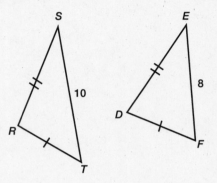

2. Create an indirect proof to prove the Hinge Converse Theorem.

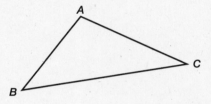

Given: $AB = DE$
   $AC = DF$
   $BC > EF$
Prove: $m\angle A > m\angle D$

This theorem must be proven for two cases.
Case 1: $m\angle A = m\angle D$
Case 2: $m\angle A < m\angle D$

a. Create an indirect proof for Case 1, $m\angle A = m\angle D$.

b. Create an indirect proof for Case 2, $m\angle A < m\angle D$.

1. Matthew and Jeremy's families are going camping for the weekend. Before heading out of town, they decide to meet at Al's Diner for breakfast. During breakfast, the boys try to decide which family will be further away from the diner "as the crow flies." "As the crow flies" is an expression based on the fact that crows, generally fly straight to the nearest food supply.

Matthew's family is driving 35 miles due north and taking an exit to travel an additional 15 miles northeast. Jeremy's family is driving 35 miles due south and taking an exit to travel an additional 15 miles southwest. Use the diagram shown to determine which family is further from the diner. Explain your reasoning.

2. Which of the following is a possible length for *AH*: 20 cm, 21 cm, or 24 cm?
   Explain your choice.

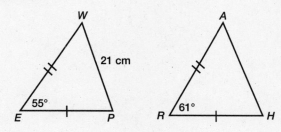

3. Which of the following is a possible angle measure for ∠*ARH*: 54°, 55° or 56°?
   Explain your choice.

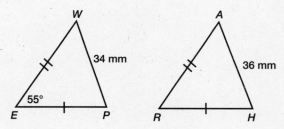

 Be prepared to share your solutions and methods.

6

KEY TERMS

- corresponding parts of congruent triangles are congruent (CPCTC) (6.2)
- vertex angle of an isosceles triangle (6.3)
- inverse (6.4)
- contrapositive (6.4)
- direct proof (6.4)
- indirect proof or proof by contradiction (6.4)

THEOREMS

- Hypotenuse-Leg (HL) Congruence Theorem (6.1)
- Leg-Leg (LL) Congruence Theorem (6.1)
- Hypotenuse-Angle (HA) Congruence Theorem (6.1)
- Leg-Angle (LA) Congruence Theorem (6.1)
- Isosceles Triangle Base Angle Theorem (6.2)
- Isosceles Triangle Base Angle Converse Theorem (6.2)
- Isosceles Triangle Base Theorem (6.3)
- Isosceles Triangle Vertex Angle Theorem (6.3)
- Isosceles Triangle Perpendicular Bisector Theorem (6.3)
- Isosceles Triangle Altitude to Congruent Sides Theorem (6.3)
- Isosceles Triangle Angle Bisector to Congruent Sides Theorem (6.3)
- Hinge Theorem (6.4)
- Hinge Converse Theorem (6.4)

6.1 Using the Hypotenuse-Leg (HL) Congruence Theorem

The Hypotenuse-Leg (HL) Congruence Theorem states: "If the hypotenuse and leg of one right triangle are congruent to the hypotenuse and leg of another right triangle, then the triangles are congruent."

Example

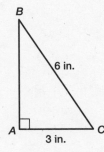
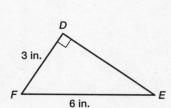

$\overline{BC} \cong \overline{EF}$, $\overline{AC} \cong \overline{DF}$, and angles A and D are right angles, so $\triangle ABC \cong \triangle DEF$.

6.1 Using the Leg-Leg (LL) Congruence Theorem

The Leg-Leg (LL) Congruence Theorem states: "If two legs of one right triangle are congruent to two legs of another right triangle, then the triangles are congruent."

Example

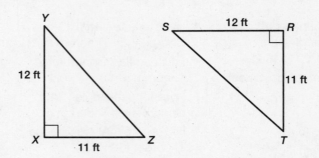

$\overline{XY} \cong \overline{RS}$, $\overline{XZ} \cong \overline{RT}$, and angles X and R are right angles, so $\triangle XYZ \cong \triangle RST$.

6.1 Using the Hypotenuse-Angle (HA) Congruence Theorem

The Hypotenuse-Angle (HA) Congruence Theorem states: "If the hypotenuse and an acute angle of one right triangle are congruent to the hypotenuse and acute angle of another right triangle, then the triangles are congruent."

Example

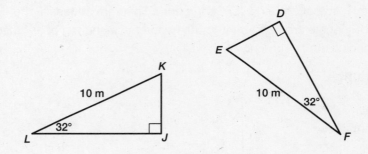

$\overline{KL} \cong \overline{EF}$, $\angle L \cong \angle F$, and angles J and D are right angles, so $\triangle JKL \cong \triangle DEF$.

6.1 Using the Leg-Angle (LA) Congruence Theorem

The Leg-Angle (LA) Congruence Theorem states: "If a leg and an acute angle of one right triangle are congruent to the leg and an acute angle of another right triangle, then the triangles are congruent."

Example

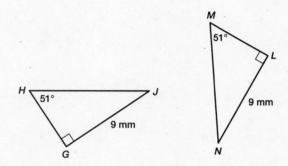

$\overline{GN} \cong \overline{LN}$, $\angle H \cong \angle M$, and angles G and L are right angles, so $\triangle GHJ \cong \triangle LMN$.

6.2 Using CPCTC to Solve a Problem

If two triangles are congruent, then each part of one triangle is congruent to the corresponding part of the other triangle. In other words, "corresponding parts of congruent triangles are congruent," which is abbreviated CPCTC. To use CPCTC, first prove that two triangles are congruent.

Example

You want to determine the distance between two docks along a river. The docks are represented as points A and B in the diagram below. You place a marker at point X, because you know that the distance between points X and B is 26 feet. Then, you walk horizontally from point X and place a marker at point Y, which is 26 feet from point X. You measure the distance between points X and A to be 18 feet, and so you walk along the river bank 18 feet and place a marker at point Z. Finally, you measure the distance between Y and Z to be 35 feet.

From the diagram, segments XY and XB are congruent and segments XA and XZ are congruent. Also, angles YXZ and BXA are congruent by the Vertical Angles Congruence Theorem. So, by the Side-Angle-Side (SAS) Congruence Postulate, $\triangle YXZ \cong \triangle BXA$. Because corresponding parts of congruent triangles are congruent (CPCTC), segment YZ must be congruent to segment BA. The length of segment YZ is 35 feet. So, the length of segment BA, or the distance between the docks, is 35 feet.

6.2 Using the Isosceles Triangle Base Angle Theorem

The Isosceles Triangle Base Angle Theorem states: "If two sides of a triangle are congruent, then the angles opposite these sides are congruent."

Example

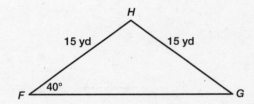

$\overline{FH} \cong \overline{GH}$, so $\angle F \cong \angle G$, and the measure of angle G is 40°.

6.2 Using the Isosceles Triangle Base Angle Converse Theorem

The Isosceles Triangle Base Angle Converse Theorem states: "If two angles of a triangle are congruent, then the sides opposite these angles are congruent."

Example

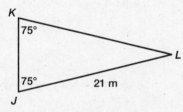

$\angle J \cong \angle K$, $\overline{JL} \cong \overline{KL}$, and the length of side KL is 21 meters.

6.3 Using the Isosceles Triangle Base Theorem

The Isosceles Triangle Base Theorem states: "The altitude to the base of an isosceles triangle bisects the base."

Example

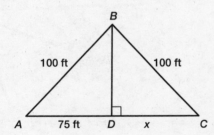

$CD = AD$, so $x = 75$ feet.

6.3 **Using the Isosceles Triangle Vertex Angle Theorem**

The Isosceles Triangle Base Theorem states: "The altitude to the base of an isosceles triangle bisects the vertex angle."

Example

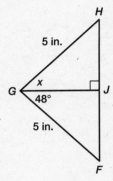

$m\angle FGJ = m\angle HGJ$, so $x = 48°$.

6.3 **Using the Isosceles Triangle Perpendicular Bisector Theorem**

The Isosceles Triangle Perpendicular Bisector Theorem states: "The altitude from the vertex angle of an isosceles triangle is the perpendicular bisector of the base."

Example

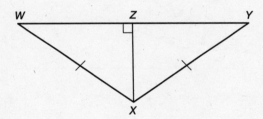

$\overline{WY} \perp \overline{XZ}$ and $WZ = YZ$

6

6.3 Using the Isosceles Triangle Altitude to Congruent Sides Theorem

The Isosceles Triangle Perpendicular Bisector Theorem states: "In an isosceles triangle, the altitudes to the congruent sides are congruent."

Example

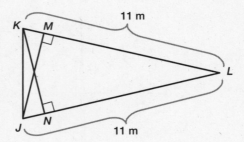

$\overline{KN} \cong \overline{JM}$

6.3 Using the Isosceles Triangle Bisector to Congruent Sides Theorem

The Isosceles Triangle Perpendicular Bisector Theorem states: "In an isosceles triangle, the angle bisectors to the congruent sides are congruent."

Example

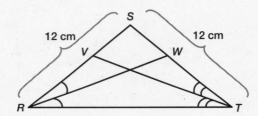

$\overline{RW} \cong \overline{TV}$

6.4 Stating the Inverse and Contrapositive of Conditional Statements

To state the inverse of a conditional statement, negate both the hypothesis and the conclusion. To state the contrapositive of a conditional statement, negate both the hypothesis and the conclusion and then reverse them.

Conditional Statement: If p, then q.

Inverse: If not p, then not q.

Contrapositive: If not q, then not p.

Example

Conditional Statement: If a triangle is equilateral, then it is isosceles.

Inverse: If a triangle is not equilateral, then it is not isosceles.

Contrapositive: If a triangle is not isosceles, then it is not equilateral.

Writing an Indirect Proof

In an indirect proof, or proof by contradiction, first write the givens. Then, write the negation of the conclusion. Then, use that assumption to prove a given statement is false, thus creating a contradiction. Hence, the assumption leads to a contradiction, therefore showing that the assumption is false. This proves the contrapositive.

Example

Given: Triangle DEF

Prove: A triangle cannot have more than one obtuse angle.

Given $\triangle DEF$, assume that $\triangle DEF$ has two obtuse angles. So, assume $m\angle D = 91°$ and $m\angle E = 91°$. By the Triangle Sum Theorem, $m\angle D + m\angle E + m\angle F = 180°$. By substitution, $91° + 91° + m\angle F = 180°$, and by subtraction, $m\angle F = -2°$. But it is not possible for a triangle to have a negative angle, so this is a contradiction. This proves that a triangle cannot have more than one obtuse angle.

Using the Hinge Theorem

The Hinge Theorem states: "If two sides of one triangle are congruent to two sides of another triangle and the included angle of the first pair is larger than the included angle of the second pair, then the third side of the first triangle is longer than the third side of the second triangle."

Example

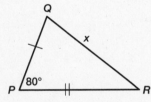
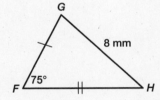

$QR > GH$, so $x > 8$ millimeters.

Using the Hinge Converse Theorem

The Hinge Converse Theorem states: "If two sides of one triangle are congruent to two sides of another triangle and the third side of the first triangle is longer than the third side of the second triangle, then the included angle of the first pair of sides is larger than the included angle of the second pair of sides."

Example

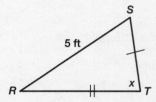
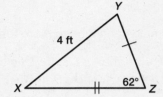

$m\angle T > m\angle Z$, so $x > 62°$.

Properties of Quadrilaterals

7

The prefix "quad" means "four." A quadrilateral has 4 sides, and a quad bike has 4 wheels. Quad bikes are all-terrain vehicles used by farmers and ranchers. People also race quad bikes—in deserts, on hills, and even on ice.

Squares and Rectangles

Properties of Squares and Rectangles

LEARNING GOALS

In this lesson, you will:

- Prove the Perpendicular/Parallel Line Theorem.
- Construct a square and a rectangle.
- Determine the properties of a square and rectangle.
- Prove the properties of a square and a rectangle.
- Solve problems using the properties of a square and a rectangle.

KEY TERM

- Perpendicular/Parallel Line Theorem

In 2010, a technology company unveiled what was billed at the time as the world's largest plasma TV. This monster of a TV measured $12\frac{2}{3}$ feet across the diagonal (152 inches long) and displayed nearly 9 million pixels in HD and, if necessary, 3D.

Just two years earlier, the same company released a 103-inch version (89.3 inches long) which you could buy for a mere $70,000.

How much would you estimate the 152-inch TV cost if the company set its prices based on the total viewing areas for their TVs?

PROBLEM 1 Know the Properties or Be Square!

A quadrilateral is a four-sided polygon. A square is a quadrilateral with four right angles and all sides congruent.

Quadrilaterals have different properties that are directly related to the measures of their interior angles and their side lengths. Perpendicular lines and right angles are useful when proving properties of certain quadrilaterals.

1. Ramira says that if two lines are perpendicular to the same line, then the two lines are parallel to each other. Is Ramira correct? If she is correct, complete the proof to justify the reasoning, or state why she is not correct.

   Given: $\ell_1 \perp \ell_3$; $\ell_2 \perp \ell_3$
   Prove: $\ell_1 \parallel \ell_2$

   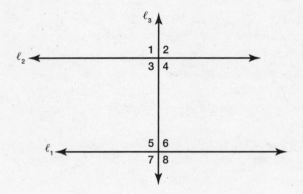

   Remember, in proofs, start with the Given statement or statements.

The **Perpendicular/Parallel Line Theorem** states: "If two lines are perpendicular to the same line, then the two lines are parallel to each other."

2. Draw a square with two diagonals. Label the vertices and the intersection of the diagonals. List all of the properties you know to be true.

A diagonal of a polygon is a line segment that connects two non-adjacent vertices.

3. Use $\overline{AB}$ to construct square *ABCD* with diagonals $\overline{AC}$ and $\overline{BD}$ intersecting at point *E*.

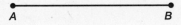

A   B

7

4. Prove the statement △DAB ≅ △CBA.

Given: Square ABCD with diagonals $\overline{AC}$ and $\overline{BD}$ intersecting at point E

Prove: △DAB ≅ △CBA

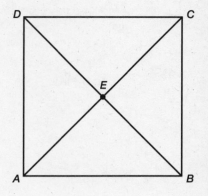

5. Do you have enough information to conclude $\overline{AC} \cong \overline{BD}$? Explain your reasoning.

You have just proven a property of a square: that its diagonals are congruent. You can now use this property as a valid reason in future proofs.

7

6. Prove the statement $\overline{DA} \parallel \overline{CB}$ and $\overline{DC} \parallel \overline{AB}$.

Given: Square $ABCD$

Prove: $\overline{DA} \parallel \overline{CB}$ and $\overline{DC} \parallel \overline{AB}$

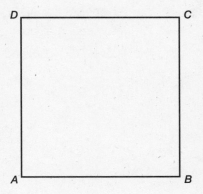

7. If a parallelogram is a quadrilateral with opposite sides parallel, do you have enough information to conclude square $ABCD$ is a parallelogram? Explain your reasoning.

You have just proven another property of a square: that its opposite sides are parallel. You can now use this property as a valid reason in future proofs.

8. Prove the statement $\overline{DE} \cong \overline{BE}$ and $\overline{CE} \cong \overline{AE}$.

Given: Square $ABCD$ with diagonals $\overline{AC}$ and $\overline{BD}$ intersecting at point E

Prove: $\overline{DE} \cong \overline{BE}$ and $\overline{CE} \cong \overline{AE}$

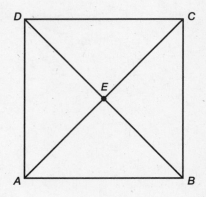

9. Do you have enough information to conclude the diagonals of a square bisect each other? Explain your reasoning.

You have just proven another property of a square: that its diagonals bisect each other. You can now use this property as a valid reason in future proofs.

10. Prove that the diagonals of a square bisect the vertex angles. Use square *ABCD* in Question 8.

 11. Prove that the diagonals of a square are perpendicular to each other. Use square *ABCD* in Question 8.

A rectangle is a quadrilateral with opposite sides congruent and all angles congruent.

1. Draw a rectangle with two diagonals. Label the vertices and the intersection of the two diagonals. List all of the properties you know to be true.

A square is also a rectangle. But, don't draw a square.

2. Use $\overline{RE}$ to construct rectangle *RECT* with diagonals $\overline{RC}$ and $\overline{ET}$ intersecting at point *A*. Do not construct a square.

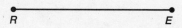

R   E

3. Prove the statement △*RCT* ≅ △*ETC*.

Given: Rectangle *RECT* with diagonals $\overline{RC}$ and $\overline{ET}$ intersecting at point *A*

Prove: △*RCT* ≅ △*ETC*

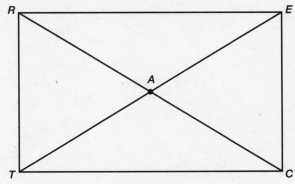

4. Do you have enough information to conclude $\overline{RT} \cong \overline{EC}$? Explain your reasoning.

7

5. Describe how you could prove the second pair of opposite sides of the rectangle are congruent.

6. Do you have enough information to conclude rectangle *RECT* is a parallelogram? Explain your reasoning.

7. Do you have enough information to conclude the diagonals of a rectangle are congruent? Explain your reasoning.

8. Do you have enough information to conclude the diagonals of a rectangle bisect each other? Explain your reasoning.

1. Ofelia is making a square mat for a picture frame. How can she make sure the mat is a square using only a ruler?

2. Gretchen is putting together a bookcase. It came with diagonal support bars that are to be screwed into the top and bottom on the back of the bookcase. Unfortunately, the instructions were lost and Gretchen does not have the directions or a measuring tool. She has a screwdriver, a marker, and a piece of string. How can Gretchen attach the supports to make certain the bookcase will be a rectangle and the shelves are parallel to the ground?

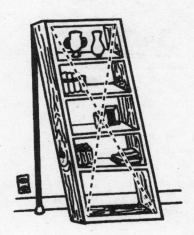

3. Matsuo knows this birdhouse has a rectangular base, but he wonders if it has a square base.

   a. What does Matsuo already know to conclude the birdhouse has a rectangular base?

   b. What does Matsuo need to know to conclude the birdhouse has a square base?

4. Consider each LED television shown.

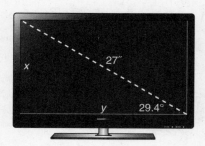 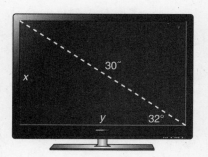

   a. Determine the dimensions of the 27″ LED TV.

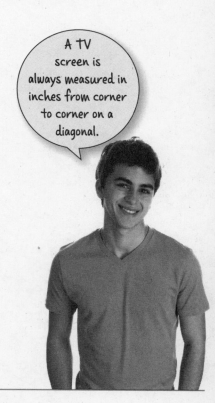

A TV screen is always measured in inches from corner to corner on a diagonal.

b. Determine the dimensions of the 30″ LED TV.

c. Compare the viewing area of each size television screen.

d. What property of a rectangle would be helpful when locating the center point of the television screen?

e. What property of a rectangle would be helpful when determining the perimeter of the television screen?

5. Sketch a square. Label the midpoint of each side of the square.

    a. Determine the polygon formed by connecting the midpoints of each side of a square and justify your conclusion.

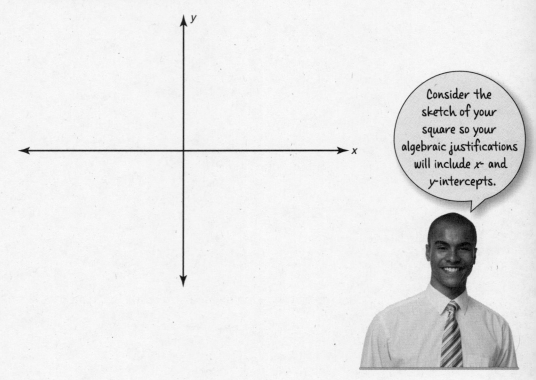

Consider the sketch of your square so your algebraic justifications will include x- and y-intercepts.

b. If the same process was repeated one more time by connecting the midpoints of each side of the polygon determined in part (a), describe the polygon that would result.

 Be prepared to share your solutions and methods.

Parallelograms and Rhombi

Properties of Parallelograms and Rhombi

LEARNING GOALS

In this lesson, you will:

- Construct a parallelogram.
- Construct a rhombus.
- Prove the properties of a parallelogram.
- Prove the properties of a rhombus.
- Solve problems using the properties of a parallelogram and a rhombus.

KEY TERM

- Parallelogram/Congruent-Parallel Side Theorem

Using a ruler, draw any quadrilateral you want. You're going to locate the midpoints of the sides of the quadrilateral, so you might want to make the sides whole-number lengths. Draw a really wacky quadrilateral. The wackier the better.

Mark the midpoints of each side and then connect these midpoints to form another quadrilateral. What quadrilateral did you create? What quadrilateral did your classmates create? Do you get the same result no matter what quadrilateral you start with?

A parallelogram is a quadrilateral with both pairs of opposite sides parallel.

 1. Draw a parallelogram with two diagonals. Label the vertices and the intersection of the diagonals. List all of the properties you know to be true.

Squares and rectangles are also parallelograms. But don't draw a square or rectangle.

2. Use $\overline{PA}$ to construct parallelogram *PARG* with diagonals $\overline{PR}$ and $\overline{AG}$ intersecting at point *M*.

P   A

3. To prove opposite sides of a parallelogram are congruent, which triangles would you prove congruent?

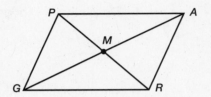

4. Use △PGR and △RAP in the parallelogram from Question 3 to prove that opposite sides of a parallelogram are congruent. Prove the statement $\overline{PG} \cong \overline{AR}$ and $\overline{GR} \cong \overline{PA}$.

Given: Parallelogram PARG with diagonals $\overline{PR}$ and $\overline{AG}$ intersecting at point M

Prove: $\overline{PG} \cong \overline{AR}$ and $\overline{GR} \cong \overline{PA}$

You have just proven a property of a parallelogram: that opposite sides of a parallelogram are congruent. You can now use this property as a valid reason in future proofs.

5. Do you have enough information to conclude ∠*PGR* ≅ ∠*RAP*? Explain your reasoning.

6. What additional angles would you need to show congruent to prove that opposite angles of a parallelogram are congruent? What two triangles do you need to prove congruent?

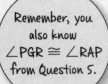

Remember, you also know ∠PGR ≅ ∠RAP from Question 5.

7. Use △*APG* and △*GRA* in the diagram from Question 3 to prove that opposite angles of a parallelogram are congruent. Create a proof of the statement ∠*GPA* ≅ ∠*ARG*.

Given: Parallelogram *PARG* with diagonals $\overline{PR}$ and $\overline{AG}$ intersecting at point *M*

Prove: ∠*GPA* ≅ ∠*ARG*

8. Prove that the diagonals of a parallelogram bisect each other. Use the parallelogram in Question 3.

9. Ray told his math teacher that he thinks a quadrilateral is a parallelogram if only one pair of opposite sides is known to be both congruent and parallel.

Is Ray correct? Use the diagram from Question 3 to either prove or disprove his conjecture.

 The **Parallelogram/Congruent-Parallel Side Theorem** states: "If one pair of opposite sides of a quadrilateral is both congruent and parallel, then the quadrilateral is a parallelogram."

7

A rhombus is a quadrilateral with all sides congruent.

1. Draw a rhombus with two diagonals. Label the vertices and the intersection of the two diagonals. List all of the properties you know to be true. (Do not draw a square.)

2. Use $\overline{RH}$ to construct rhombus *RHOM* with diagonals $\overline{RO}$ and $\overline{HM}$ intersecting at point *B*.

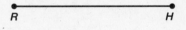

R   H

Do not construct a square.

7

3. Prove that rhombus *RHOM* is a parallelogram.

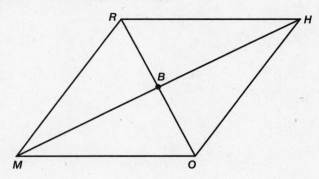

4. Since a rhombus is a parallelogram, what properties hold true for all rhombi?

7

5. Prove that the diagonals of a rhombus are perpendicular. Use the rhombus in Question 3.

6. Prove that the diagonals of a rhombus bisect the vertex angles. Use the rhombus in Question 3.

7

1. Jim tells you he is thinking of a quadrilateral that is either a square or a rhombus, but not both. He wants you to guess which quadrilateral he is thinking of and allows you to ask one question about the quadrilateral. Which question should you ask?

2. Ms. Baker told her geometry students to bring in a picture of a parallelogram for extra credit. Albert brought in a picture of the flag shown. The teacher handed Albert a ruler and told him to prove it was a parallelogram. What are two ways Albert could prove the picture is a parallelogram?

7

3. Ms. Baker held up two different lengths of rope shown and a piece of chalk. She asked her students if they could use this rope and chalk to construct a rhombus on the blackboard. Rena raised her hand and said she could construct a rhombus with the materials. Ms. Baker handed Rena the chalk and rope. What did Rena do?

First Rope

Second Rope

4. Consider the Ace of Diamonds playing card shown. The large diamond in the center of the playing card is a quadrilateral. Classify the quadrilateral based only on each piece of given information.

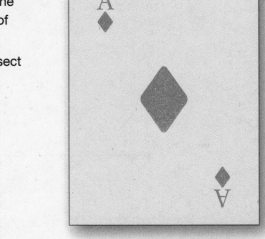

a. The diagonals of the quadrilateral bisect each other.

b. The four sides of the quadrilateral are congruent.

c. The four angles and the four sides of the quadrilateral are congruent.

d. The diagonals of the quadrilateral bisect the vertex angles.

e. The four angles of the quadrilateral are congruent.

f. The opposite sides of the quadrilateral are both congruent and parallel.

g. The opposite angles of the quadrilateral are congruent.

h. The diagonals of the quadrilateral are perpendicular to each other.

i. The diagonals of the quadrilateral are congruent.

7

5. Sketch a rhombus that is not a square. Label the midpoint of each side of the rhombus.

a. Determine the polygon formed by connecting the midpoints of each side of a rhombus and justify your conclusion.

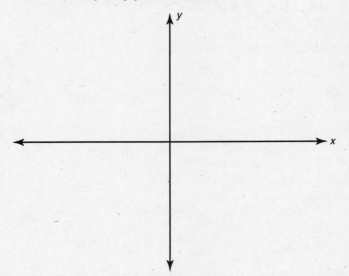

b. If the same process was repeated one more time by connecting the midpoints of each side of the polygon determined in part (a), describe the polygon that would result.

 Be prepared to share your solutions and methods.

7

7

Kites and Trapezoids
Properties of Kites and Trapezoids

Your trapezius muscles are trapezoid-shaped muscles that extend down from the base of your head to the middle of your back and out to your shoulders.

When you lift your shoulders or try to squeeze your shoulder blades together, you are using your trapezius muscles.

Competitive weightlifters make heavy use of their trapezius muscles. When lifting the barbell from the floor to their collarbones—called the "clean" phase—weightlifters develop the upper portion of their trapezius muscles, which often gives them the appearance of having no neck.

PROBLEM 1   Let's Go Fly a Kite!

A kite is a quadrilateral with two pairs of consecutive congruent sides with opposite sides that are not congruent.

1. Draw a kite with two diagonals. Label the vertices and the intersection of the two diagonals. List all of the properties you know to be true.

2. Construct kite *KITE* with diagonals $\overline{IE}$ and $\overline{KT}$ intersecting at point *S*.

3. To prove that two opposite angles of a kite are congruent, which triangles in the kite would you prove congruent? Explain your reasoning.

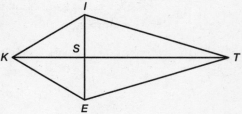

4. Prove that two opposite angles of a kite are congruent.

Given: Kite *KITE* with diagonals $\overline{KT}$ and $\overline{IE}$ intersecting at point *S*.

Prove: $\angle KIT \cong \angle KET$

You have just proven a property of a kite: two opposite angles of a kite are congruent. You are now able to use this property as a valid reason in future proofs.

5. Do you have enough information to conclude $\overline{KT}$ bisects $\angle IKE$ and $\angle ITE$? Explain your reasoning.

6. What two triangles could you use to prove $\overline{IS} \cong \overline{ES}$?

7. If $\overline{IS} \cong \overline{ES}$, is that enough information to determine that one diagonal of a kite bisects the other diagonal? Explain your reasoning.

8. Prove that the diagonals of a kite are perpendicular to each other.

Revisit Question 1 to make sure you have listed all of the properties of a kite.

A trapezoid is a quadrilateral with exactly one pair of parallel sides.

The bases of a trapezoid are its parallel sides. The **base angles of a trapezoid** are either pair of angles that share a base as a common side. The legs of a trapezoid are its non-parallel sides.

1. Draw a trapezoid. Identify the vertices, bases, base angles, and legs.

2. Use $\overline{TR}$ to construct trapezoid *TRAP*.

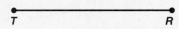

7

An **isosceles trapezoid** is a trapezoid with congruent non-parallel sides.

3. Prove that the base angles of an isosceles trapezoid are congruent.

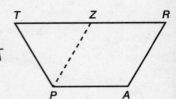

a. Given: Isosceles Trapezoid *TRAP* with $\overline{TR} \parallel \overline{PA}$, $\overline{TP} \cong \overline{RA}$

Prove: $\angle T \cong \angle R$

I can draw a line segment to help me with this proof!

b. You must also prove $\angle A \cong \angle TPA$. Prove $\angle A \cong \angle TPA$.

4. Kala insists that if a trapezoid has only one pair of congruent base angles, then the trapezoid must be isosceles. She thinks proving two pairs of base angles are congruent is not necessary. Prove the given statement to show that Kala is correct.

Given: Isosceles trapezoid *TRAP* with $\overline{TR} \parallel \overline{PA}$, $\angle T \cong \angle R$

Prove: $\overline{TP} \cong \overline{RA}$

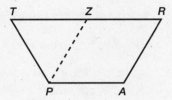

An *if and only if* statement is called a **biconditional statement** because it consists of two separate conditional statements rewritten as one statement. It is a combination of both a conditional statement and the converse of that conditional statement. A biconditional statement is true only when the conditional statement and the converse of the statement are both true.

Consider the following property of an isosceles trapezoid:

The diagonals of an isosceles trapezoid are congruent.

The property clearly states that if a trapezoid is isosceles, then the diagonals are congruent. Is the converse of this statement true? If so, then this property can be written as a biconditional statement. Rewording the property as a biconditional statement becomes:

A trapezoid is isosceles *if and only if* its diagonals are congruent.

To prove this biconditional statement is true, rewrite it as two conditional statements and prove each statement.

Statement 1: If a trapezoid is an isosceles trapezoid, then the diagonals of the trapezoid are congruent. (Original statement)

Statement 2: If the diagonals of a trapezoid are congruent, then the trapezoid is an isosceles trapezoid. (Converse of original statement)

5. Prove that the diagonals of an isosceles trapezoid are congruent.

Given: Isosceles trapezoid *TRAP* with $\overline{TP} \parallel \overline{RA}$, $\overline{TR} \cong \overline{PA}$, and diagonals $\overline{TA}$ and $\overline{PR}$.

Prove: $\overline{TA} \cong \overline{PR}$

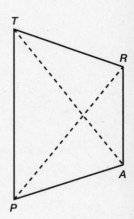

6. Prove the converse, that the trapezoid is isosceles if the diagonals are congruent.

Given: Trapezoid *TRAP* with $\overline{TP} \parallel \overline{RA}$, and diagonals $\overline{TA} \cong \overline{PR}$

Prove: Trapezoid *TRAP* is isosceles

To prove the converse, auxiliary lines must be drawn such that $\overline{RA}$ is extended to intersect a perpendicular line passing through point *T* perpendicular to $\overline{RA}$ ($\overline{TE}$) and intersect a second perpendicular line passing through point *P* perpendicular to $\overline{RA}$ ($\overline{PZ}$).

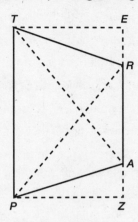

Notice that quadrilateral *TEZP* is a rectangle.

The property of an isosceles trapezoid can now be written as a biconditional statement because the conditional statement and its converse have both been proven to be true: A trapezoid is isosceles if and only if its diagonals are congruent.

7

Segment *AD* is the perimeter of an isosceles trapezoid. Follow the steps to construct the isosceles trapezoid.

A   D

1. Choose a line segment on $\overline{AD}$ for the shorter base ($\overline{AB}$).
2. Choose a line segment on $\overline{AD}$ for the longer base ($\overline{BC}$).
3. Line segment *CD* represents the sum of the length of the two legs.
4. Bisect $\overline{CD}$ to determine the length of each congruent leg. Label the midpoint *E*.
5. Copy $\overline{AB}$ onto $\overline{BC}$ (creating $\overline{BF}$) to determine the difference between the bases ($\overline{FC}$).
6. Bisect $\overline{FC}$ to determine point *G* (*FG* = *CG*).
7. Take $\overline{FG}$ (half the difference of the base lengths) and copy it onto the left end of the long base $\overline{BC}$ (creating distance $\overline{BH}$). Notice that it is already marked off on the right end of the long base ($\overline{GC}$).
8. Construct the perpendicular through point *H*. Note the distance between the two most left perpendiculars is the length of the short base.
9. Place the compass point on *B* and mark off the distance of one leg ($\overline{CE}$) on the left most perpendicular, naming the new point *I*. This forms one leg of the isosceles trapezoid.
10. Place the compass point on *C* and mark off the length of one leg ($\overline{CE}$) on the other perpendicular, naming the new point *J*. This is one leg of the isosceles trapezoid. Note that *IJ* = *AB*. *BIJC* is an isosceles trapezoid!

1. Locate four points on the coordinate plane to form a trapezoid.

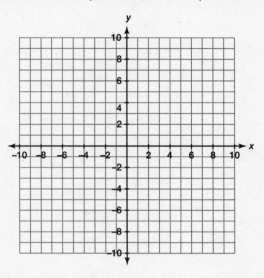

2. Identify the coordinates of the four points you chose.

3. Determine the coordinates of the midpoints of the legs of your trapezoid. Use the midpoint formula.

4. Plot and connect the midpoints of the legs. Determine the distance between the two midpoints.

7

The **midsegment** of a trapezoid is a segment formed by connecting the midpoints of the legs of the trapezoid.

5. Determine the lengths of the two bases of your trapezoid.

6. Determine the length of the midsegment of your trapezoid.

7. Compare the length of the midsegment to the sum of the lengths of the bases.

8. Is the midsegment of the trapezoid parallel to the bases of the trapezoid? Explain your reasoning.

The **Trapezoid Midsegment Theorem** states: "The midsegment of a trapezoid is parallel to each of the bases and its length is one half the sum of the lengths of the bases."

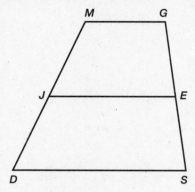

9. Prove the Trapezoid Midsegment Theorem. It will be necessary to connect points M and E to form $\overline{ME}$, and then extend $\overline{ME}$ until it intersects the extension of $\overline{DS}$ at point T.

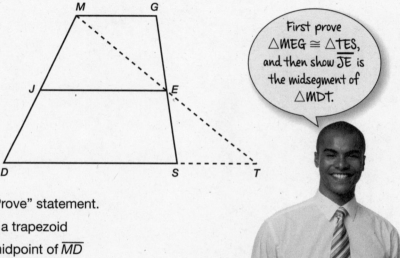

First prove $\triangle MEG \cong \triangle TES$, and then show $\overline{JE}$ is the midsegment of $\triangle MDT$.

a. Complete the "Prove" statement.

Given: $MDSG$ is a trapezoid

J is the midpoint of $\overline{MD}$

E is the midpoint of $\overline{GS}$

Prove:

7

b. Create a proof of the Trapezoid Midsegment Theorem.

1. Determine the perimeter of the kite.

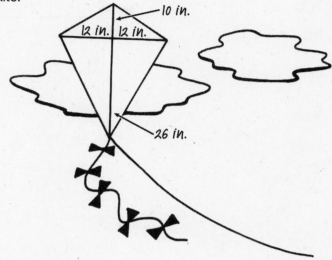

2. Could quadrilaterals 1, 2, and 3 on the kite shown be squares? Explain your reasoning.

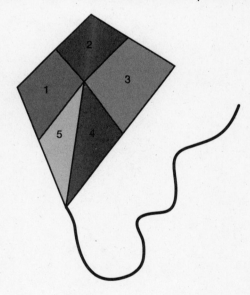

7

3. Trevor used a ruler to measure the height of each trapezoid and the length of each leg. He tells Carmen the three trapezoids must be congruent because they are all the same height and have congruent legs. What does Carmen need to do to convince Trevor that he is incorrect?

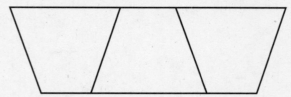

4. Mr. King said he was thinking of a quadrilateral and wanted his students to name the quadrilateral. He said he would answer a few yes-no questions to give them a hint. What questions would you ask Mr. King?

What is the fewest number of questions you could ask Mr. King to be sure you knew the correct answer?

 Be prepared to share your solutions and methods.

Interior Angles of a Polygon

Sum of the Interior Angle Measures of a Polygon

The Susan B. Anthony dollar coin was minted from 1979 to 1981 and then again in 1999. This coin was the first to show the image of a real woman.

The coin also had an unusual shape inscribed inside of it—a regular undecagon, or hendecagon, which is an 11-sided polygon. The shape was no accident, as you can see from the back of the coin which commemorates the Apollo 11 moon landing.

An **interior angle of a polygon** faces the inside of a polygon and is formed by consecutive sides of the polygon.

1. Ms. Lambert asked her class to determine the sum of the interior angle measures of a quadrilateral.

   Carson drew a quadrilateral and added one diagonal as shown. He concluded that the sum of the measures of the interior angles of a quadrilateral must be equal to 360°.

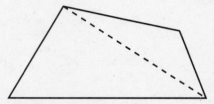

   Juno drew a quadrilateral and added two diagonals as shown. She concluded that the sum of the measures of the interior angles of a quadrilateral must be equal to 720°.

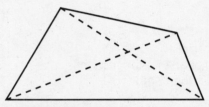

   Who is correct? Who is incorrect? Explain your reasoning.

7

The Triangle Sum Theorem states that the sum of the three interior angles of any triangle is equal to 180°. You can use this information to calculate the sum of the interior angles of other polygons.

1. Calculate the sum of the interior angle measures of a quadrilateral by completing each step.

   a. Draw a quadrilateral. Draw a diagonal using only one vertex of the quadrilateral.

A diagonal is a line segment connecting non-adjacent vertices.

   b. How many triangles are formed when the diagonal divides the quadrilateral?

   c. If the sum of the interior angle measures of each triangle is 180°, what is the sum of all the interior angle measures of the triangles formed by the diagonal?

2. Calculate the sum of the interior angle measures of a pentagon by completing each step.

   a. Draw a pentagon. Draw all possible diagonals using only one vertex of the pentagon.

   b. How many triangles are formed when the diagonal(s) divide the pentagon?

   c. If the sum of the interior angle measures of each triangle is 180°, what is the sum of all the interior angle measures of the triangles formed by the diagonal(s)?

3. Calculate the sum of the interior angle measures of a hexagon by completing each step.

   a. Draw a hexagon. Draw all possible diagonals using one vertex of the hexagon.

   b. How many triangles are formed when the diagonal(s) divide the hexagon?

   c. If the sum of the interior angle measures of each triangle is 180°, what is the sum of all the interior angle measures of the triangles formed by the diagonal(s)?

4. Complete the table shown.

Number of Sides of the Polygon	3	4	5	6
Number of Diagonals Drawn				
Number of Triangles Formed				
Sum of the Measures of the Interior Angles				

5. What pattern do you notice between the number of possible diagonals drawn from one vertex of the polygon, and the number of triangles formed by those diagonals?

6. Compare the number of sides of the polygon to the number of possible diagonals drawn from one vertex. What do you notice?

7. Compare the number of sides of the polygon to the number of triangles formed by drawing all possible diagonals from one vertex. What do you notice?

8. What pattern do you notice about the sum of the interior angle measures of a polygon as the number of sides of each polygon increases by 1?

9. Predict the number of possible diagonals drawn from one vertex and the number of triangles formed for a seven-sided polygon using the table you completed.

10. Predict the sum of all the interior angle measures of a seven-sided polygon using the table your completed.

7

11. Continue the pattern to complete the table.

Number of Sides of the Polygon	7	8	9	16
Number of Diagonals Drawn				
Number of Triangles Formed				
Sum of the Measures of the Interior Angles				

12. When you calculated the number of triangles formed in the 16-sided polygon, did you need to know how many triangles were formed in a 15-sided polygon first? Explain your reasoning.

13. If a polygon has 100 sides, how many triangles are formed by drawing all possible diagonals from one vertex? Explain your reasoning.

14. What is the sum of all the interior angle measures of a 100-sided polygon? Explain your reasoning.

15. If a polygon has *n* sides, how many triangles are formed by drawing all diagonals from one vertex? Explain your reasoning.

16. What is the sum of all the interior angle measures of an *n*-sided polygon? Explain your reasoning.

17. Use the formula to calculate the sum of all the interior angle measures of a polygon with 32 sides.

18. If the sum of all the interior angle measures of a polygon is 9540°, how many sides does the polygon have? Explain your reasoning.

7

1. Use the formula developed in Problem 2, Question 16 to calculate the sum of all the interior angle measures of a decagon.

2. Calculate each interior angle measure of a decagon if each interior angle is congruent. How did you calculate your answer?

3. Complete the table.

Number of Sides of Regular Polygon	3	4	5	6	7	8
Sum of Measures of Interior Angles						
Measure of Each Interior Angle						

4. If a regular polygon has *n* sides, write a formula to calculate the measure of each interior angle.

5. Use the formula to calculate each interior angle measure of a regular 100-sided polygon.

6. If each interior angle measure of a regular polygon is equal to 150°, determine the number of sides. How did you calculate your answer?

1. *PENTA* is a regular pentagon. Solve for *x*.

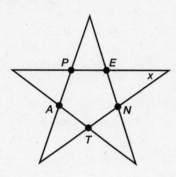

2. The Susan B. Anthony dollar coin minted in 1999 features a regular 11-gon, or hendecagon, inside a circle on both sides of the coin.

What is the measure of each interior angle of the regular hendecagon?

7

3. The high school pep squad is preparing a halftime performance for the next basketball game. Six students will hold banners to form a regular hexagon as shown with the school mascot in the very center. Each of the banners is exactly 4 feet long.

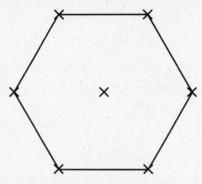

a. What angle does each student form with his or her banners? Explain your reasoning.

b. What is the distance from each student on the regular hexagon to the school mascot in the center? Show your work and explain your reasoning.

7

4. Yael and Brynn wanted to calculate how much space the halftime show would take up.

Yael

To determine the height of the hexagon, I first drew $\overline{AC}$. Then, I drew $\overline{BD}$ to create two right triangles. Finally, I used trigonometry to solve for the lengths AD and DC.

I already know the distance across the hexagon.

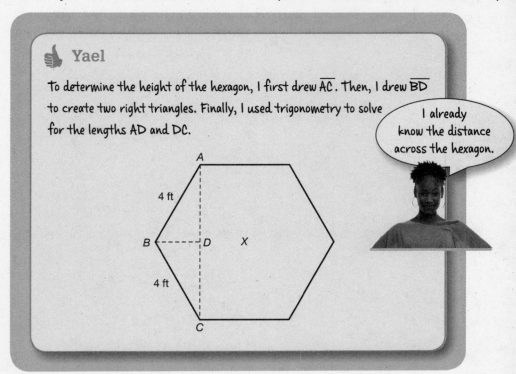

Brynn

To determine the height of the hexagon, I first drew line segments XY and XZ to create triangle XYZ. Then, I drew $\overline{XW}$ perpendicular to $\overline{YZ}$ to create two right triangles. Finally, I used trigonometry to solve for the height.

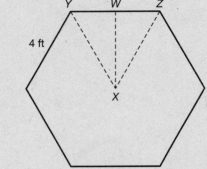

a. Verify that both Yael's method and Brynn's method result in the same height.

b. Calculate how much rectangular space the students need for the halftime show. Show your work and explain your reasoning.

c. About how much space would the halftime show take up if 8 students formed a regular octagon with 4-foot banners? Show your work.

 Be prepared to share your methods and solutions.

Exterior and Interior Angle Measurement Interactions

Sum of the Exterior Angle Measures of a Polygon

LEARNING GOALS

In this lesson, you will:

- Write a formula for the sum of the exterior angles of any polygon.
- Calculate the sum of the exterior angles of any polygon, given the number of sides.
- Write a formula for the measure of each exterior angle of any regular polygon.
- Calculate the measure of an exterior angle of a regular polygon, given the number of sides.
- Calculate the number of sides of a regular polygon, given the measure of each exterior angle.

KEY TERM

- exterior angle of a polygon

On April 5, 1968, Jane Elliott decided to try what is now a famous "experiment" with her third grade class in Riceville, Iowa. The purpose of her experiment was to allow her young students to feel what it was like to be in the "in group" and to be in the "out group."

She divided the class into blue-eyed students and brown-eyed students and informed the class that the blue-eyed students were the "superior group," who received special privileges at school. Elliott also encouraged students to only talk and play with other members of their in group or out group.

The results were shocking and immediate. Students in the out group began to do more poorly academically, while those in the in group did better. The in group students also began acting arrogant and bossy, while those in the out group became quiet and timid.

All of this happened, even though the students knew they were part of an experiment.

PROBLEM 1 Is There a Formula?

Previously, you wrote a formula for the sum of all the interior angle measures of a polygon. In this lesson, you will write a formula for the sum of all the exterior angle measures of a polygon.

Each interior angle of a polygon can be paired with an exterior angle. An **exterior angle of a polygon** is formed adjacent to each interior angle by extending one side of each vertex of the polygon as shown in the triangle.

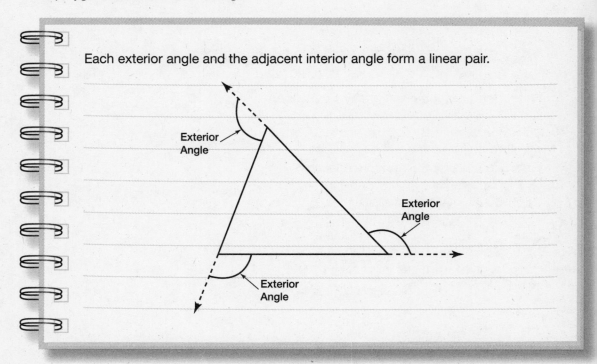

Each exterior angle and the adjacent interior angle form a linear pair.

Exterior Angle

Exterior Angle

Exterior Angle

1. Use the formula for the sum of interior angle measures of a polygon and the Linear Pair Postulate to calculate the sum of the exterior angle measures of a triangle.

Let's explore the sum of the exterior angle measures of other polygons.

2. Calculate the sum of the exterior angle measures of a quadrilateral by completing each step.

   a. Draw a quadrilateral and extend each side to locate an exterior angle at each vertex.

   b. Use the formula for the sum of interior angle measures of a polygon and the Linear Pair Postulate to calculate the sum of the exterior angle measures of a quadrilateral.

3. Calculate the sum of the exterior angle measures of a pentagon by completing each step.

   a. Draw a pentagon and extend each side to locate an exterior angle at each vertex.

b. Use the formula for the sum of the interior angle measures of a polygon and the Linear Pair Postulate to calculate the sum of the exterior angle measures of a pentagon.

4. Calculate the sum of the exterior angle measures of a hexagon by completing each step.

   a. Without drawing a hexagon, how many linear pairs are formed by each interior and adjacent exterior angle? How do you know?

   b. What is the relationship between the number of sides of a polygon and the number of linear pairs formed by each interior angle and its adjacent exterior angle?

   c. Use the formula for the sum of the interior angle measures of a polygon and the Linear Pair Postulate to calculate the sum of the measures of the exterior angles of a hexagon.

5. Complete the table.

Number of Sides of the Polygon	3	4	5	6	7	15
Number of Linear Pairs Formed						
Sum of Measures of Linear Pairs						
Sum of Measures of Interior Angles						
Sum of Measures of Exterior Angles						

6. When you calculated the sum of the exterior angle measures in the 15-sided polygon, did you need to know anything about the number of linear pairs, the sum of the linear pair measures, or the sum of the interior angle measures of the 15-sided polygon? Explain your reasoning.

7. If a polygon has 100 sides, calculate the sum of the exterior angle measures. Explain how you calculated your answer.

8. What is the sum of the exterior angle measures of an *n*-sided polygon?

9. If the sum of the exterior angle measures of a polygon is 360°, how many sides does the polygon have? Explain your reasoning.

7

10. Explain why the sum of the exterior angle measures of any polygon is always equal to 360°.

Regular Polygons

1. Calculate the measure of each exterior angle of an equilateral triangle. Explain your reasoning.

2. Calculate the measure of each exterior angle of a square. Explain your reasoning.

3. Calculate the measure of each exterior angle of a regular pentagon. Explain your reasoning.

4. Calculate the measure of each exterior angle of a regular hexagon. Explain your reasoning.

---

5. Complete the table shown to look for a pattern.

Number of Sides of a Regular Polygon	3	4	5	6	7	15
Sum of Measures of Exterior Angles						
Measure of Each Interior Angle						
Measure of Each Exterior Angle						

6. When you calculated the measure of each exterior angle in the 15-sided regular polygon, did you need to know anything about the measure of each interior angle? Explain your reasoning.

7. If a regular polygon has 100 sides, calculate the measure of each exterior angle. Explain how you calculated your answer.

8. What is the measure of each exterior angle of an *n*-sided regular polygon?

9. If the measure of each exterior angle of a regular polygon is 18°, how many sides does the polygon have? Explain how you calculated your answer.

7

10. Simon installed a custom-built pool in his backyard in the shape of a regular nonagon. The pool has a perimeter of 180 feet. Simon wants to install decking around the pool as shown. Each trapezoid section of deck will be congruent and have a width of 5 feet.

Think about exterior angles or angles formed by parallel lines cut by a transversal.

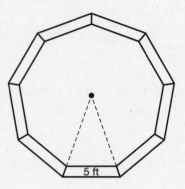

5 ft

a. What are the interior angle measures of each section of deck? Show your work and explain your reasoning.

7

b. What are the dimensions of each section of deck? Show your work and explain your reasoning.

c. What is the total sitting area of the entire deck?

Two sisters, Molly and Lily, were arguing about who was better at using a compass and a straightedge.

1. Molly challenged Lily to construct a regular hexagon. Undaunted by the challenge, Lily took the compass and went to work. What did Lily do?

2. Lily then challenged Molly to construct a square. Molly grabbed her compass with gusto and began the construction. What did Molly do?

3. Both sisters were now glaring at each other and their
mother, a math teacher, walked into the room. Determined
to end this dispute, she gave her daughters a challenge.
She told them the only way to settle the argument was to
see who could be the first to come up with a construction
for a regular pentagon. Give it a try!

Hint: There
are only six steps.
The first two steps are
to draw a starter line and
to construct a
perpendicular line.

Be prepared to share your solutions and methods.

Quadrilateral Family

Categorizing Quadrilaterals Based on Their Properties

In this lesson, you will:

- List the properties of quadrilaterals.
- Categorize quadrilaterals based upon their properties.
- Construct quadrilaterals given a diagonal.

Okay, maybe the trapezoid is a kind of oddball of quadrilaterals, but did you know that its area formula, $\frac{1}{2}(b_1 + b_2)h$, can be used to determine the area of other polygons?

Take a parallelogram, for example. Since its bases are the same length, you can just use b to describe the length of each base.

$A = \frac{1}{2}(b + b)h$

$ = \frac{1}{2}(2b)h$

$ = bh$

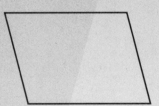

The square, too. All three measurements (b_1, b_2, and h) are the same. So, change all the variables to, say, s.

$A = \frac{1}{2}(s + s)s$

$ = \frac{1}{2}(2s)s$

$ = \frac{1}{2} \cdot 2s^2$

$ = s^2$

Even the triangle's area can be represented using the trapezoid area formula. Can you figure out how?

PROBLEM 1 Characteristics of Quadrilaterals

Complete the table by placing a checkmark in the appropriate row and column to associate each figure with its properties.

Characteristic	Quadrilateral	Trapezoid	Parallelogram	Kite	Rhombus	Rectangle	Square
No parallel sides							
Exactly one pair of parallel sides							
Two pairs of parallel sides							
One pair of sides are both congruent and parallel							
Two pairs of opposite sides are congruent							
Exactly one pair of opposite angles are congruent							
Two pairs of opposite angles are congruent							
Consecutive angles are supplementary							
Diagonals bisect each other							
All sides are congruent							
Diagonals are perpendicular to each other							
Diagonals bisect the vertex angles							
All angles are congruent							
Diagonals are congruent							

7

PROBLEM 2   Now I Can See the Relationships!

1. Create a Venn diagram that describes the relationships between all of the quadrilaterals listed. Number each region and name the figure located in each region.

2. Write a description for each region.

Trapezoids	Kites
Rhombi	Rectangles
Parallelograms	Squares
Quadrilaterals	

7

Determine whether each statement is true or false. If it is false, explain why.

1. A square is also a rectangle.

2. A rectangle is also a square.

3. The base angles of a trapezoid are congruent.

4. A parallelogram is also a trapezoid.

5. A square is a rectangle with all sides congruent.

6. The diagonals of a trapezoid are congruent.

7. A kite is also a parallelogram.

8. The diagonals of a rhombus bisect each other.

7

Joe is thinking of a specific polygon. He has listed six hints. As you read each hint, use deductive reasoning to try and guess Joe's polygon. By the last hint you should be able to read Joe's mind.

1. The polygon has four sides.

2. The polygon has at least one pair of parallel sides.

3. The diagonals of the polygon bisect each other.

4. The polygon has opposite sides congruent.

5. The diagonals of the polygon are perpendicular to each other.

6. The polygon does not have four congruent angles.

Knowing certain properties of each quadrilateral makes it possible to construct the quadrilateral given only a single diagonal.

1. Describe how you could construct parallelogram *WXYZ* given only diagonal $\overline{WY}$.

2. Describe how you could construct rhombus *RHOM* given only diagonal $\overline{RO}$.

3. Describe how you could construct kite *KITE* given only diagonal $\overline{KT}$.

Be prepared to share your solutions and methods.

Chapter 7 Summary

7.1 Using the Perpendicular/Parallel Line Theorem

The Perpendicular/Parallel Line Theorem states: "If two lines are perpendicular to the same line, then the two lines are parallel to each other."

Example

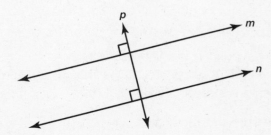

Because line *p* is perpendicular to line *m* and line *p* is perpendicular to line *n*, lines *m* and *n* are parallel.

7.1 Determining Properties of Squares

A square is a quadrilateral with four right angles and all sides congruent. You can use the Perpendicular/Parallel Line Theorem and congruent triangles to determine the following properties of squares.

- The diagonals of a square are congruent.

- Opposite sides of a square are parallel.

- The diagonals of a square bisect each other.

- The diagonals of a square bisect the vertex angles.

- The diagonals of a square are perpendicular to each other.

Example

For square *PQRS*, the following statements are true:

- $\overline{PR} \cong \overline{QS}$

- $\overline{PQ} \parallel \overline{RS}$ and $\overline{PS} \parallel \overline{QR}$

- $\overline{PT} \cong \overline{RT}$ and $\overline{QT} \cong \overline{ST}$

- $\angle PQS \cong \angle RQS$, $\angle QRP \cong \angle SRP$, $\angle RSQ \cong \angle PSQ$, and $\angle SPR \cong \angle QPR$

- $\overline{PR} \perp \overline{QS}$

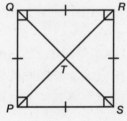

7.1 Determining Properties of Rectangles

A rectangle is a quadrilateral with opposite sides congruent and with four right angles. You can use the Perpendicular/Parallel Line Theorem and congruent triangles to determine the following properties of rectangles.

- Opposite sides of a rectangle are congruent.

- Opposite sides of a rectangle are parallel.

- The diagonals of a rectangle are congruent.

- The diagonals of a rectangle bisect each other.

Example

For rectangle *FGHJ*, the following statements are true.

- $\overline{FG} \cong \overline{HJ}$ and $\overline{FJ} \cong \overline{GH}$

- $\overline{FG} \parallel \overline{HJ}$ and $\overline{FJ} \parallel \overline{GH}$

- $\overline{FH} \cong \overline{GJ}$

- $\overline{GK} \cong \overline{JK}$ and $\overline{FK} \cong \overline{HK}$

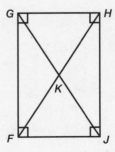

7.2 Determining Properties of Parallelograms

A parallelogram is a quadrilateral with both pairs of opposite sides parallel. You can use congruent triangles to determine the following properties of parallelograms.

- Opposite sides of a parallelogram are congruent.

- Opposite angles of a parallelogram are congruent.

- The diagonals of a parallelogram bisect each other.

Example

For parallelogram WXYZ, the following statements are true.

- $\overline{WX} \cong \overline{YZ}$ and $\overline{WZ} \cong \overline{XY}$

- $\angle WXY \cong \angle WZY$ and $\angle XYZ \cong \angle XWZ$

- $\overline{WV} \cong \overline{YV}$ and $\overline{XV} \cong \overline{ZV}$

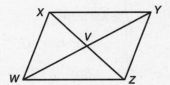

7.2 Using the Parallelogram/Congruent-Parallel Side Theorem

The Parallelogram/Congruent-Parallel Side Theorem states: "If one pair of opposite sides of a quadrilateral is both congruent and parallel, then the quadrilateral is a parallelogram."

Example

In quadrilateral ABCD, $\overline{AB} \cong \overline{CD}$ and $\overline{AB} \parallel \overline{CD}$. So, quadrilateral ABCD is a parallelogram, and thus has all of the properties of a parallelogram.

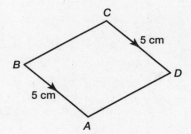

7

7.2 Determining Properties of Rhombi

A rhombus is a quadrilateral with all sides congruent. You can use congruent triangles to determine the following properties of rhombi.

- Opposite angles of a rhombus are congruent.

- Opposite sides of a rhombus are parallel.

- The diagonals of a rhombus are perpendicular to each other.

- The diagonals of a rhombus bisect each other.

- The diagonals of a rhombus bisect the vertex angles.

Example

For rhombus *ABCD*, the following statements are true:

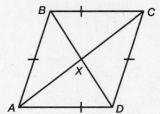

- $\angle ABC \cong \angle CDA$ and $\angle BCD \cong \angle DAB$

- $\overline{AB} \parallel \overline{CD}$ and $\overline{BC} \parallel \overline{DA}$

- $\overline{AC} \perp \overline{BD}$

- $\overline{AX} \cong \overline{CX}$ and $\overline{BX} \cong \overline{DX}$

- $\angle BAC \cong \angle DAC$, $\angle ABD \cong \angle CBD$, $\angle BCA \cong \angle DCA$, and $\angle CDB \cong \angle ADB$

7.3 Determining Properties of Kites

A kite is a quadrilateral with two pairs of consecutive congruent sides with opposite sides that are not congruent. You can use congruent triangles to determine the following properties of kites.

- One pair of opposite angles of a kite is congruent.

- The diagonals of a kite are perpendicular to each other.

- The diagonal that connects the opposite vertex angles that are not congruent bisects the diagonal that connects the opposite vertex angles that are congruent.

- The diagonal that connects the opposite vertex angles that are not congruent bisects the vertex angles.

Example

For kite *KLMN*, the following statements are true:

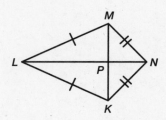

- $\angle LMN \cong \angle LKN$

- $\overline{KM} \perp \overline{LN}$

- $\overline{KP} \cong \overline{MP}$

- $\angle KLN \cong \angle MLN$ and $\angle KNL \cong \angle MNL$

Determining Properties of Trapezoids

A trapezoid is a quadrilateral with exactly one pair of parallel sides. An isosceles trapezoid is a trapezoid with congruent non-parallel sides. You can use congruent triangles to determine the following properties of isosceles trapezoids:

- The base angles of a trapezoid are congruent.

- The diagonals of a trapezoid are congruent.

Example

For isosceles trapezoid *PQRS*, the following statements are true:

- $\angle QPS \cong \angle RSP$

- $\overline{PR} \cong \overline{QS}$

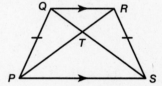

Determining the Sum of the Interior Angle Measures of Polygons

You can calculate the sum of the interior angle measures of a polygon by using the formula $180°(n - 2)$, where n is the number of sides of the polygon. You can calculate the measure of each interior angle of a regular polygon by dividing the formula by n, the number of sides of the regular polygon.

Examples

The sum of the interior angle measures of a pentagon is $180°(5 - 2) = 540°$.

Each interior angle of a regular pentagon measures $\frac{540°}{5} = 108°$.

The sum of the interior angle measures of a hexagon is $180°(6 - 2) = 720°$.

Each interior angle of a regular hexagon measures $\frac{720°}{6} = 120°$.

The sum of the interior angle measures of a decagon is $180°(10 - 2) = 1440°$.

Each interior angle of a regular decagon measures $\frac{1440°}{10} = 144°$.

The sum of the interior angle measures of an 18-gon is $180°(18 - 2) = 2880°$.

Each interior angle of a regular 18-gon measures $\frac{2880°}{18} = 160°$.

Determining the Sum of the Exterior Angle Measures of Polygons

You can use the formula for the sum of the interior angle measures of a polygon and the Linear Pair Postulate to determine that the sum of the exterior angle measures of any polygon is 360°.

Examples

You can use the formula for the sum of the interior angle measures of a polygon to determine that the interior angle measures of the hexagon is 720°. Then, you can use the Linear Pair Postulate to determine that the sum of the angle measures formed by six linear pairs is 6(180°) = 1080°. Next, subtract the sum of the interior angle measures from the sum of the linear pair measures to get the sum of the exterior angle measures: 1080° − 720° = 360°.

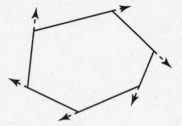

You can use the formula for the sum of the interior angle measures of a polygon to determine that the interior angle measures of the nonagon is 1260°. Then, you can use the Linear Pair Postulate to determine that the sum of the angle measures formed by nine linear pairs is 9(180°) = 1620°. Next, subtract the sum of the interior angle measures from the sum of the linear pair measures to get the sum of the exterior angle measures: 1620° − 1260° = 360°.

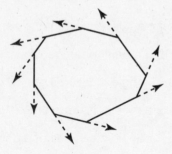

Identifying Characteristics of Quadrilaterals

The table shows the characteristics of special types of quadrilaterals.

	Trapezoid	Parallelogram	Kite	Rhombus	Rectangle	Square
No parallel sides			•			
Exactly one pair of parallel sides	•					
Two pairs of parallel sides		•		•	•	•
One pair of sides are both congruent and parallel		•		•	•	•
Two pairs of opposite sides are congruent		•		•	•	•
Exactly one pair of opposite angles are congruent			•			
Two pairs of opposite angles are congruent		•		•	•	•
Consecutive angles are supplementary		•		•	•	•
Diagonals bisect each other		•		•	•	•
All sides are congruent				•		•
Diagonals are perpendicular to each other			•	•		•
Diagonals bisect the vertex angles				•		•
All angles are congruent					•	•
Diagonals are congruent					•	•

Trigonometry

> These are just the right triangles for the job. Trusses are wooden frames that are used to support the roofs of houses. They are often in the shape of right triangles.

Three Angle Measure

Introduction to Trigonometry

LEARNING GOALS

In this lesson, you will:

- Explore trigonometric ratios as measurement conversions.
- Analyze the properties of similar right triangles.

KEY TERMS

- reference angle
- opposite side
- adjacent side

" I've been workin' on the railroad, all the live long day." Can you hear that tune in your head? Can you sing the first two notes? Those two notes are separated by an interval called a perfect fourth. The two notes of a perfect fourth vibrate at different frequencies, and these frequencies are always in the ratio 4 : 3. That is, the higher note of a perfect fourth vibrates about 1.33 times faster than the lower note.

What about the first two notes of "Frosty the Snowman"? Can you sing those? The interval between these notes is called a minor third. The ratio of the higher note frequency to lower note frequency in a minor third is 6 : 5.

All of the intervals in a musical scale are constructed according to specific frequency ratios.

PROBLEM 1 Convert to Trigonometry!

You know that to convert between measurements you can multiply by a conversion ratio. For example, to determine the number of centimeters that is equivalent to 30 millimeters, you can multiply by $\frac{1 \text{ cm}}{10 \text{ mm}}$ because there are 10 millimeters in each centimeter:

$$30 \text{ mm} \times \frac{1 \text{ cm}}{10 \text{ mm}} = \frac{30 \text{ cm}}{10}$$
$$= 3 \text{ cm}$$

In trigonometry, you use conversion ratios too. These ratios apply to right triangles.

Triangle *ABC* shown is a 45°-45°-90° triangle.

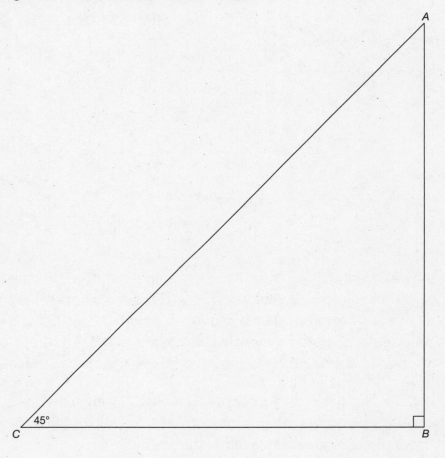

1. Draw a vertical line segment, $\overline{DE}$, connecting the hypotenuse of triangle *ABC* with side $\overline{BC}$. Label the endpoint of the vertical line segment along the hypotenuse as point *D*. Label the other endpoint as point *E*.

2. Explain how you know that triangle *ABC* is similar to triangle *DEC*.

3. Measure each of the sides of triangles *ABC* and *DEC* in millimeters. Record the approximate measurements.

I know some things about 45°-45°-90° right triangles I can use to verify that these are the right measurements.

You know that the hypotenuse of a right triangle is the side that is opposite the right angle. In trigonometry, the legs of a right triangle are often referred to as the *opposite side* and the *adjacent side*. These references are based on the angle of the triangle that you are looking at, which is called the **reference angle**. The **opposite side** is the side opposite the reference angle. The **adjacent side** is the side adjacent to the reference angle that is *not* the hypotenuse.

4. For triangles *ABC* and *DEC*, identify the opposite side, adjacent side, and hypotenuse, using angle *C* as the reference angle.

5. Determine each side length ratio for triangles *ABC* and *DEC*, using angle *C* as the reference angle. Write your answers as decimals rounded to the nearest thousandth.

a. $\dfrac{\text{side opposite } \angle C}{\text{hypotenuse}}$

b. $\dfrac{\text{side adjacent to } \angle C}{\text{hypotenuse}}$

c. $\dfrac{\text{side opposite } \angle C}{\text{side adjacent to } \angle C}$

6. Draw two more vertical line segments, $\overline{FG}$ and $\overline{HJ}$, connecting the hypotenuse of triangle ABC with side $\overline{BC}$. Label the endpoints of the vertical line segments along the hypotenuse as points F and H. Label the other endpoints as points G and J.

a. Explain how you know that triangles ABC, DEC, FGC, and HJC are all similar.

b. Measure each of the sides of the two new triangles you created. Record the side length measurements for all four triangles in the table.

Triangle Name	Length of Side Opposite Angle C	Length of Side Adjacent to Angle C	Length of Hypotenuse
Triangle *ABC*			
Triangle *DEC*			
Triangle *FGC*			
Triangle *HJC*			

c. Determine each side length ratio for all four triangles using angle C as the reference angle.

Triangle Name	$\dfrac{\text{side opposite } \angle C}{\text{hypotenuse}}$	$\dfrac{\text{side adjacent to } \angle C}{\text{hypotenuse}}$	$\dfrac{\text{side opposite } \angle C}{\text{side adjacent to } \angle C}$
Triangle *ABC*			
Triangle *DEC*			
Triangle *FGC*			
Triangle *HJC*			

7. Compare the side length ratios of all four triangles in the table. What do you notice?

8. Compare your measurements and ratios with those of your classmates. What do you notice?

9. Calculate the slope of the hypotenuse in each of the four triangles. Explain how you determined your answers.

Given the same reference angle measure, are each of the ratios you studied constant in similar right triangles? You can investigate this question by analyzing similar right triangles without side measurements.

Consider triangles *ABC* and *DEC* shown. They are both 45°-45°-90° triangles.

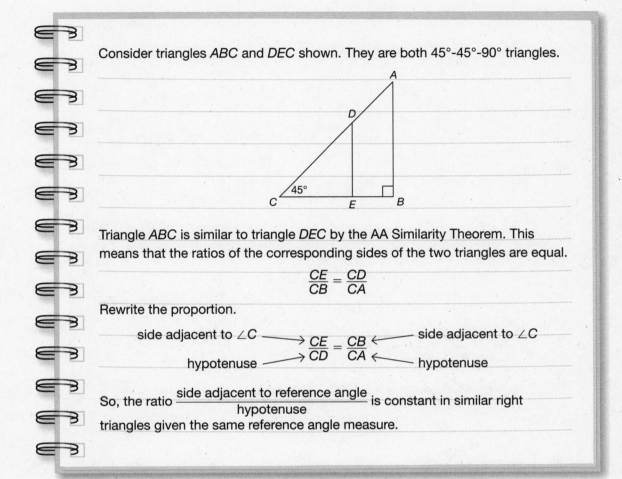

Triangle *ABC* is similar to triangle *DEC* by the AA Similarity Theorem. This means that the ratios of the corresponding sides of the two triangles are equal.

$$\frac{CE}{CB} = \frac{CD}{CA}$$

Rewrite the proportion.

side adjacent to $\angle C$ ——→ $\dfrac{CE}{CD} = \dfrac{CB}{CA}$ ←—— side adjacent to $\angle C$

hypotenuse ——→ $\phantom{\dfrac{CE}{CD} = \dfrac{CB}{CA}}$ ←—— hypotenuse

So, the ratio $\dfrac{\text{side adjacent to reference angle}}{\text{hypotenuse}}$ is constant in similar right triangles given the same reference angle measure.

10. Use triangle *ABC* in the worked example with reference angle *C* to verify that the ratios $\dfrac{\text{side opposite reference angle}}{\text{hypotenuse}}$ and $\dfrac{\text{side opposite reference angle}}{\text{side adjacent to reference angle}}$ are constant in similar right triangles. Show your work.

PROBLEM 2   30°-60°-90°

Triangle *PQR* shown is a 30°-60°-90° triangle.

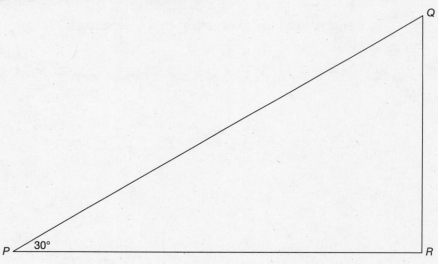

1. Draw three vertical line segments, $\overline{AB}$, $\overline{CD}$, and $\overline{EF}$, connecting the hypotenuse of triangle *PQR* with side $\overline{PR}$. Label the endpoints of the vertical line segments along the hypotenuse as points *A*, *C*, and *E*. Label the other endpoints as points *B*, *D*, and *F*.

2. Measure each of the sides of the four similar right triangles in millimeters. Record the side length measurements in the table.

Triangle Name	Length of Side Opposite Angle P	Length of Side Adjacent to Angle P	Length of Hypotenuse
Triangle PQR			
Triangle PEF			
Triangle PCD			
Triangle PAB			

3. Determine each side length ratio for all four triangles using angle P as the reference angle.

Triangle Name	$\dfrac{\text{side opposite } \angle P}{\text{hypotenuse}}$	$\dfrac{\text{side adjacent to } \angle P}{\text{hypotenuse}}$	$\dfrac{\text{side opposite } \angle P}{\text{side adjacent to } \angle P}$
Triangle PQR			
Triangle PEF			
Triangle PCD			
Triangle PAB			

4. Compare the side length ratios of all four triangles in the table. What do you notice?

5. What conclusions can you draw from Problem 1 and Problem 2 about the three ratios you studied in 45°-45°-90° triangles and 30°-60°-90° triangles?

6. Is each of the three ratios you studied in this lesson the same for any right triangles with congruent reference angles? Explain your reasoning.

7. Explain why Alicia is incorrect.

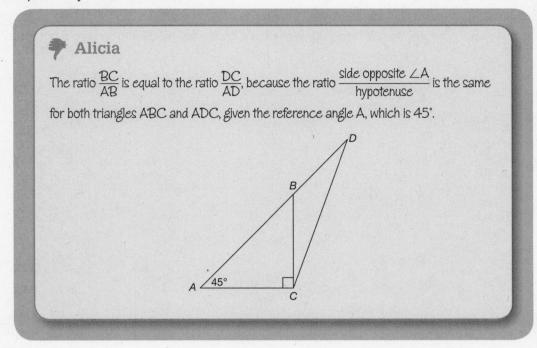

Alicia

The ratio $\frac{BC}{AB}$ is equal to the ratio $\frac{DC}{AD}$, because the ratio $\frac{\text{side opposite } \angle A}{\text{hypotenuse}}$ is the same for both triangles ABC and ADC, given the reference angle A, which is 45°.

8. Is each of the three ratios you studied in this lesson the same for any triangles with congruent reference angles? Explain your reasoning.

The three ratios you worked with in this lesson are very important to trigonometry and have special names and properties. You will learn more about these ratios in the next several lessons.

Talk the Talk

1. As the reference angle measure increases, what happens to each ratio? Explain your reasoning.

a. $\dfrac{\text{opposite}}{\text{hypotenuse}}$

b. $\dfrac{\text{adjacent}}{\text{hypotenuse}}$

c. $\dfrac{\text{opposite}}{\text{adjacent}}$

Be prepared to share your solutions and methods.

The Tangent Ratio

Tangent Ratio, Cotangent Ratio, and Inverse Tangent

When we talk about "going off on a tangent" in everyday life, we are talking about touching on a topic and then veering off to talk about something completely unrelated.

"Tangent" in mathematics has a similar meaning—a tangent line is a straight line that touches a curve at just one point. In this lesson, though, you will see that tangent is a special kind of ratio in trigonometry.

It's one you've already learned about!

PROBLEM 1 **Wheelchair Ramps**

The maximum incline for a safe wheelchair ramp should not exceed a ratio of 1 : 12. This means that every 1 unit of vertical rise requires 12 units of horizontal run. The maximum rise for any run is 30 inches. The ability to manage the incline of the ramp is related to both its steepness and its length.

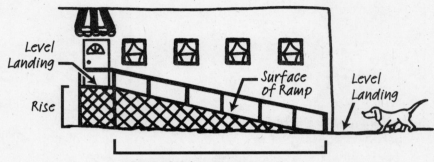

Troy decides to build 2 ramps, each with the ratio 1 : 12.

1. The first ramp extends from the front yard to the front porch. The vertical rise from the yard to the porch is 2.5 feet.

   a. Draw a diagram of the ramp. Include the measurements for the vertical rise and horizontal run of the ramp.

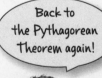

Back to the Pythagorean Theorem again!

   b. Calculate the length of the surface of the ramp.

2. The second ramp extends from the deck on the back of the house to the backyard. The vertical rise from the yard to the deck is 18 inches.

    a. Draw a diagram of the ramp. Include the measurements for the vertical rise and horizontal run of the ramp.

    b. Calculate the length of the surface of the ramp.

3. Compare the two ramps. Are the triangles similar? Explain your reasoning.

4. Compare and describe the angles of inclination of the two ramps.

PROBLEM 2 **Slope and Right Triangles**

In the wheelchair ramp problem, Troy used 1 : 12 as the ratio of the rise of each ramp to the run of each ramp.

1. Describe the shape of each wheelchair ramp.

2. What does the ratio of the rise of the ramp to the run of the ramp represent?

3. Analyze the triangles shown.

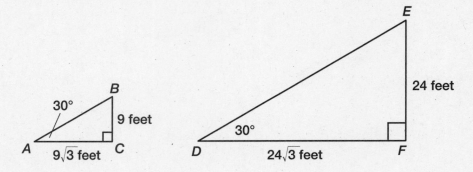

a. Verify the triangles are similar. Explain your reasoning.

b. Calculate the ratio of the rise to the run for each triangle. How do the ratios compare?

A standard mathematical convention is to write fractions so that there are no irrational numbers in the denominator. **Rationalizing the denominator** is the process of rewriting a fraction so that no irrational numbers are in the denominator.

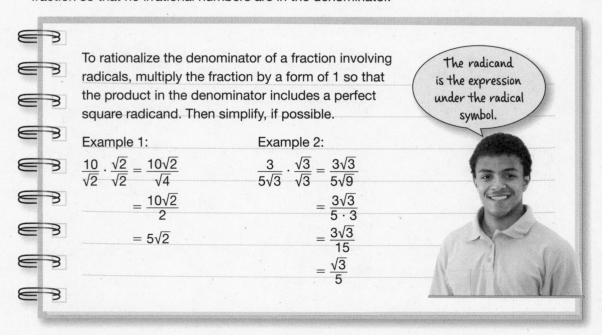

To rationalize the denominator of a fraction involving radicals, multiply the fraction by a form of 1 so that the product in the denominator includes a perfect square radicand. Then simplify, if possible.

The radicand is the expression under the radical symbol.

Example 1:

$$\frac{10}{\sqrt{2}} \cdot \frac{\sqrt{2}}{\sqrt{2}} = \frac{10\sqrt{2}}{\sqrt{4}}$$

$$= \frac{10\sqrt{2}}{2}$$

$$= 5\sqrt{2}$$

Example 2:

$$\frac{3}{5\sqrt{3}} \cdot \frac{\sqrt{3}}{\sqrt{3}} = \frac{3\sqrt{3}}{5\sqrt{9}}$$

$$= \frac{3\sqrt{3}}{5 \cdot 3}$$

$$= \frac{3\sqrt{3}}{15}$$

$$= \frac{\sqrt{3}}{5}$$

4. Rewrite your answers in Question 3, part (b), by rationalizing the denominators. Show your work.

5. Analyze the triangles shown.

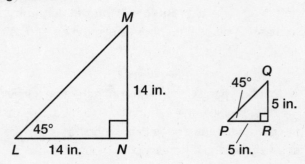

a. Verify the triangles are similar. Explain your reasoning.

b. Calculate the ratio of the rise to the run for each triangle. How do the ratios compare?

6. What can you conclude about the ratios of the rise to the run in similar right triangles?

The **tangent (tan)** of an acute angle in a right triangle is the ratio of the length of the side that is opposite the reference angle to the length of the side that is adjacent to the reference angle. The expression "tan A" means "the tangent of ∠A."

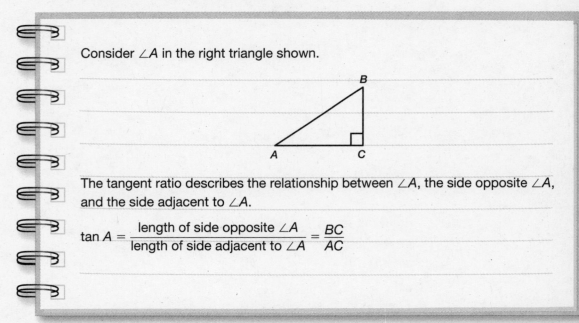

Consider ∠A in the right triangle shown.

The tangent ratio describes the relationship between ∠A, the side opposite ∠A, and the side adjacent to ∠A.

$$\tan A = \frac{\text{length of side opposite } \angle A}{\text{length of side adjacent to } \angle A} = \frac{BC}{AC}$$

7. Complete the ratio that represents the tangent of ∠B.

$$\tan B = \frac{\text{length of side opposite } \angle B}{\text{length of side adjacent to } \angle B} = \frac{\rule{2cm}{0pt}}{\rule{2cm}{0pt}}$$

8. Determine the tangent values of all the acute angles in the right triangles from Questions 3 and 5.

9. What can you conclude about the tangent values of congruent angles in similar triangles?

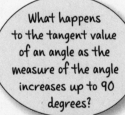

What happens to the tangent value of an angle as the measure of the angle increases up to 90 degrees?

10. Consider the tangent values in Question 8. In each triangle, compare tan 30° to tan 60°. What do you notice? Why do you think this happens?

11. A proposed wheelchair ramp is shown.

4°
24 inches

a. What information about the ramp is required to show that the ramp meets the safety rules?

b. Write a decimal that represents the greatest value of the slope of a safe ramp.

Check the "mode" on your calculator, make sure it is set on "degrees."

c. If you calculate the value of tan 4°, how can you use this value to determine whether the ramp meets the safety rules?

d. Use a calculator to determine the value of tan 4°. Round your answer to the nearest hundredth.

e. What is the ratio of the rise of the proposed ramp to its run? Is the ramp safe?

12. Another proposed wheelchair ramp is shown. What is the run of the ramp? If necessary, round your answer to the nearest inch.

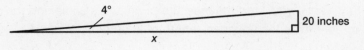

4°

20 inches

x

How do I know these ramps are safe?

13. Another proposed wheelchair ramp is shown. What is the rise of this ramp? If necessary, round your answer to the nearest inch.

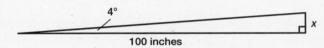

4°

x

100 inches

14. If other ramps that have a 4° angle with different side measurements are drawn by extending or shortening the rise and run, will the tangent ratios always be equivalent? Explain your reasoning.

PROBLEM **3** **Generally Speaking . . .**

In the previous problems, you used the measure of an acute angle and the length of a side in a right triangle to determine the unknown length of another side.

Consider a right triangle with acute angles of unknown measures and sides of unknown lengths. Do you think the same relationships will be valid?

1. If one acute angle of a right triangle has a measure of x degrees, what algebraic expression represents the measure of the second acute angle? Label this angle and explain your reasoning.

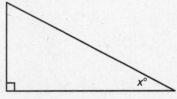

2. Suppose two right triangles are similar and each triangle contains an acute angle that measures $x°$, as shown.

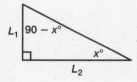

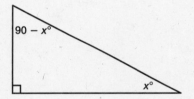

   a. If the side opposite the acute angle measuring $x°$ in the first triangle is of length L_1, what algebraic expression represents the length of the side opposite the acute angle measuring $x°$ in the second triangle?

   b. If the side opposite the acute angle measuring $90 - x°$ in the first triangle is of length L_2, what algebraic expression represents the length of the side opposite the acute angle measuring $90 - x°$ in the second triangle?

3. Write an expression to represent the tangent of the angle measuring $x°$ in the first triangle.

4. Write an expression to represent the tangent of the angle measuring $x°$ in the second triangle.

5. Write a proportion to represent the relationship between the two triangles in terms of the tangents of the angle measuring $x°$.

PROBLEM 4 Cotangent Ratio

The **cotangent (cot)** of an acute angle in a right triangle is the ratio of the length of the side that is adjacent to the angle to the length of the side that is opposite the angle. The expression "cot A" means "the cotangent of $\angle A$."

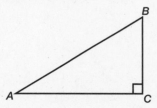

1. Complete the ratio that represents the cotangent of $\angle A$.

$$\cot A = \frac{\text{length of side adjacent to } \angle A}{\text{length of side opposite } \angle A} = \frac{\boxed{}}{\boxed{}}$$

What can I do if there is no cotangent button on my calculator?

2. Prove algebraically that the cotangent of $A = \dfrac{1}{\tan A}$.

3. As the measure of an acute angle increases, the tangent value of the acute angle increases. Explain the behavior of the cotangent value of an acute angle as the measure of the acute angle increases.

4. A ski slope at Snowy Valley has an average angle of elevation of 21°.

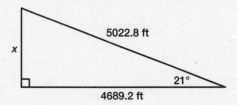

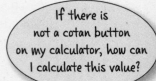

If there is not a cotan button on my calculator, how can I calculate this value?

a. Calculate the vertical height of the ski slope x using the cotangent ratio.

b. Calculate the vertical height of the ski slope x using the tangent ratio.

c. Which ratio did you prefer to use when calculating the value of x? Explain your reasoning.

5. Are all right triangles that contain a 21° angle similar? Why or why not?

6. If other right triangles containing a 21° angle with different side measurements are drawn by extending or shortening the rise and run, will the cotangent ratios always be equivalent?

PROBLEM 5 Inverse Tangent

The **inverse tangent** (or arc tangent) of x is defined as the measure of an acute angle whose tangent is x. If you know the length of any two sides of a right triangle, it is possible to compute the measure of either acute angle by using the inverse tangent, or the $\tan^{-1}$ button on a graphing calculator.

In right triangle ABC, if $\tan A = x$, then $\tan^{-1} x = m\angle A$.

1. Consider triangle ABC shown.

   a. If $\tan A = \dfrac{15}{10}$, then calculate $\tan^{-1}\left(\dfrac{15}{10}\right)$ to determine $m\angle A$.

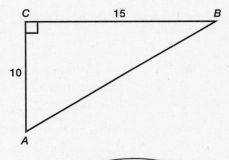

   b. Determine the ratio for $\tan B$, and then use $\tan^{-1}(\tan B)$ to calculate $m\angle B$.

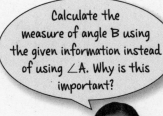

Calculate the measure of angle B using the given information instead of using ∠A. Why is this important?

c. Add $m\angle A$ and $m\angle B$. Does your sum make sense in terms of the angle measures of a triangle?

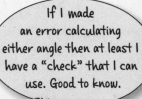

If I made an error calculating either angle then at least I have a "check" that I can use. Good to know.

2. Calculate $m\angle E$.

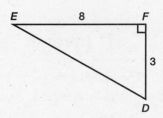

3. Movable bridges are designed to open waterways for large boats and barges. When the bridge moves, all vehicle traffic stops.

The maximum height of the open bridge deck of the movable bridge shown is 37 feet above the water surface. The waterway width is 85 feet. Calculate the angle measure formed by the movement of the bridge.

Many mountainous areas have road signs like this sign that refer to the percentage grade for the road. An 8% grade, for example, means that the altitude changes by 8 feet for each 100 feet of horizontal distance.

1. To determine the percentage grade that should be put on a road sign where the angle of elevation of the road is 9°, what function would be most helpful?

2. To determine the angle of elevation of a road with a percentage grade of 7%, what function would be most helpful?

3. Determine the angle of elevation of a road with a percentage grade of 6%.

4. Determine the percentage road grade that should be put on a road sign where the angle of elevation is 10°.

5. Does the image in the sign accurately represent an 8% grade? Explain how you can determine the answer.

6. What is the approximate angle of elevation that is actually shown in the sign?

Be prepared to share your solutions and methods.

The Sine Ratio

Sine Ratio, Cosecant Ratio, and Inverse Sine

LEARNING GOALS

In this lesson, you will:

- Use the sine ratio in a right triangle to solve for unknown side lengths.
- Use the cosecant ratio in a right triangle to solve for unknown side lengths.
- Relate the sine ratio to the cosecant ratio.
- Use the inverse sine in a right triangle to solve for unknown angle measures.

KEY TERMS

- sine (sin)
- cosecant (csc)
- inverse sine

Measuring angles on paper is easy when you have a protractor. But what about measuring angles in the real world? You can build an astrolabe (pronounced uh-STRAW-luh-bee) to help you.

Copy and cut out the astrolabe shown (without the straw). You will probably want to glue the astrolabe to cardboard or heavy paper before cutting it out.

Cut a drinking straw to match the length of the one shown. Tape the straw to the edge labeled "Place straw on this side" so that it rests on the astrolabe as shown.

Poke a hole through the black dot shown and pass a string through this hole. Knot the string or tape it so that it stays in place.

Finally, tie a weight to the end of the string. You're ready to go!

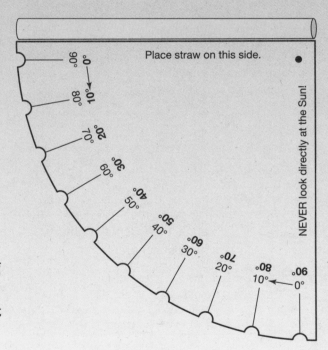

595

PROBLEM 1 **Fore!**

Each golf club in a set of clubs is designed to cause the ball to travel different distances and different heights. One design element of a golf club is the angle of the club face.

Club Face Angle

You can draw a right triangle that is formed by the club face angle. The right triangles formed by different club face angles are shown.

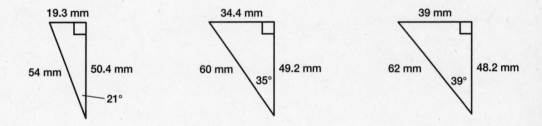

19.3 mm	34.4 mm	39 mm
54 mm	50.4 mm	60 mm	49.2 mm	62 mm	48.2 mm
21°	35°	39°

1. How do you think the club face angle affects the path of the ball?

2. For each club face angle, write the ratio of the side length opposite the given acute angle to the length of the hypotenuse. Write your answers as decimals rounded to the nearest hundredth.

3. What happens to this ratio as the angle measure gets larger?

The **sine (sin)** of an acute angle in a right triangle is the ratio of the length of the side that is opposite the angle to the length of the hypotenuse. The expression "sin *A*" means "the sine of ∠*A*."

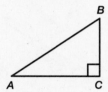

4. Complete the ratio that represents the sine of ∠*A*.

$$\sin A = \frac{\text{length of side opposite } \angle A}{\text{length of hypotenuse}} = \frac{\boxed{}}{\boxed{}}$$

5. For each triangle in Problem 1, calculate the sine value of the club face angle. Then calculate the sine value of the other acute angle. Round your answers to the nearest hundredth.

6. What do the sine values of the angles in Question 5 all have in common?

7. Jun says that the sine value of every acute angle is less than 1. Is Jun correct? Explain your reasoning.

8. What happens to the sine values of an angle as the measure of the angle increases?

9. Use the right triangles shown to calculate the values of sin 30°, sin 45°, and sin 60°.

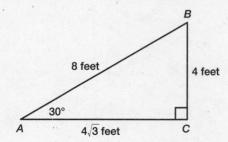

10. A golf club has a club face angle A for which sin $A \approx 0.45$. Estimate the measure of $\angle A$. Use a calculator to verify your answer.

The **cosecant (csc)** of an acute angle in a right triangle is the ratio of the length of the hypotenuse to the length of the side that is opposite the angle. The expression "csc A" means "the cosecant of ∠A."

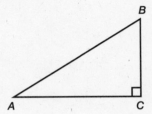

What do I do if there's no cosecant button on my calculator?

1. Complete the ratio that represents the cosecant of ∠A.

$$\csc A = \frac{\text{length of hypotenuse}}{\text{length of side opposite } \angle A} = \frac{\boxed{}}{\boxed{}}$$

2. Prove algebraically that the cosecant of $A = \dfrac{1}{\sin A}$.

3. As the measure of an acute angle increases, the sine value of the acute angle increases. Explain the behavior of the cosecant value of an acute angle as the measure of the acute angle increases.

PROBLEM 3 **Inverse Sine**

The **inverse sine** (or arc sine) of x is defined as the measure of an acute angle whose sine is x. If you know the length of any two sides of a right triangle, it is possible to calculate the measure of either acute angle by using the inverse sine, or $\sin^{-1}$ button on a graphing calculator.

In right triangle ABC, if sin A = x, then $\sin^{-1} x = m\angle A$.

1. In right triangle ABC, if $\sin A = \frac{2}{5}$, calculate $\sin^{-1}\left(\frac{2}{5}\right)$ to determine $m\angle A$.

2. Determine the ratio for sin B, and then use $\sin^{-1}(\sin B)$ to calculate $m\angle B$.

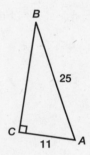

3. Calculate $m\angle B$.

4. The movable bridge shown is called a double-leaf Bascule bridge. It has a counterweight that continuously balances the bridge deck, or "leaf," throughout the entire upward swing, providing an open waterway for boat traffic. The counterweights on double-leaf bridges are usually located below the bridge decks.

The length of one leaf, or deck, is 42 feet. The maximum height of an open leaf is 30 feet. Calculate the measure of the angle formed by the movement of the bridge.

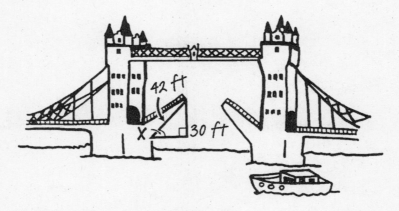

5. The Leaning Tower of Pisa is a tourist attraction in Italy. It was built on unstable land and, as a result, it really does lean!

The height of the tower is approximately 55.86 meters from the ground on the low side and 56.7 meters from the ground on the high side. The top of the tower is displaced horizontally 3.9 meters as shown.

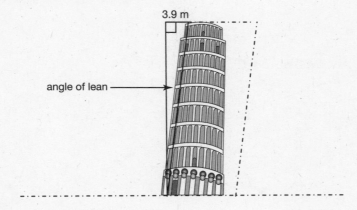

Determine the angle at which the tower leans.

Talk the Talk

Match each diagram with the appropriate situation and identify the trigonometric function that would be most helpful in answering each question. Then calculate the unknown measurement.

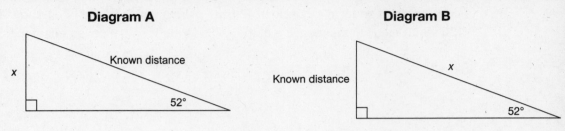

Diagram A

x

Known distance

52°

Diagram B

Known distance

x

52°

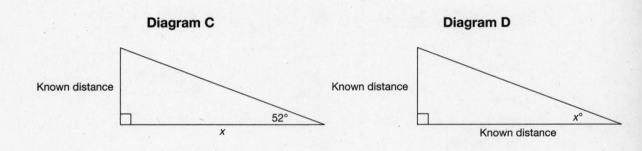

Diagram C

Known distance

52°

x

Diagram D

Known distance

Known distance

x°

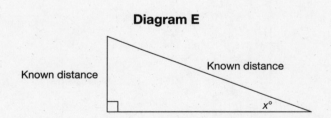

Diagram E

Known distance

Known distance

x°

1. A building is 80 feet high. An observer stands an unknown distance away from the building and, looking up to the top of the building, notes that the angle of elevation is 52°. Determine the distance from the base of the building to the observer.

2. A building is 80 feet high. An observer stands 62.5 feet away from the building and looking up to the top of the building he ponders the measure of the angle of elevation. Determine the measure of the angle of elevation.

3. An observer stands an unknown distance away from a building and looking up to the top of the building notes that the angle of elevation is 52°. He also knows the distance from where he is standing to the top of the building is 101.52 feet. Determine the height of the building.

4. A building is 80 feet high. An observer stands an unknown distance away from the building and looking up to the top of the building he ponders the measure of the angle of elevation. He also knows the distance from where he is standing to the top of the building is 101.52 feet. Determine the measure of the angle of elevation.

5. A building is 80 feet high. An observer stands an unknown distance away from the building and looking up to the top of the building notes that the angle of elevation is 52°. Determine the distance from the observer to the top of the building.

 Be prepared to share your solutions and methods.

The Cosine Ratio

Cosine Ratio, Secant Ratio, and Inverse Cosine

The applications of trigonometry are tremendous. Engineering, acoustics, architecture, physics . . . you name it, they probably use it.

One important application of trigonometry can be found in finding things—specifically, where you are in the world using GPS, or the Global Positioning System. This system employs about two dozen satellites communicating with a receiver on Earth. The receiver talks to 4 satellites at the same time, uses trigonometry to calculate the information received, and then tells you where on Earth you are.

A "guy wire" is used to provide stability to tall structures like radio towers. Guy wires are attached near the top of a tower and are attached to the ground.

A guy wire and its tower form a right triangle. It is important that all guy wires form congruent triangles so that the tension on each wire is the same.

1. Each triangle shown represents the triangle formed by a tower and guy wire. The angle formed by the wire and the ground is given in each triangle.

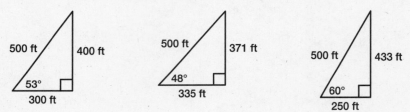

For each acute angle formed by the wire and the ground, write the ratio of the length of the side adjacent to the angle to the length of the hypotenuse. Write your answers as decimals rounded to the nearest hundredth if necessary.

The **cosine (cos)** of an acute angle in a right triangle is the ratio of the length of the side that is adjacent to the angle to the length of the hypotenuse. The expression "cos A" means "the cosine of $\angle A$."

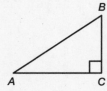

2. Complete the ratio to represent the cosine of $\angle A$.

$$\cos A = \frac{\text{length of side adjacent to } \angle A}{\text{length of hypotenuse}} = \frac{}{}$$

3. For each triangle in Question 1, calculate the cosine value of the angle made by the guy wire and the ground. Then calculate the cosine value of the other acute angle. Round your answers to the nearest hundredth if necessary.

4. What do the cosine values of the angles in Question 3 all have in common?

5. Is the cosine value of every acute angle less than 1? Explain your reasoning.

6. What happens to the cosine value of an angle as the measure of the angle increases?

7. Use the right triangles shown to calculate the values of cos 30°, cos 45°, and cos 60°. Show all your work.

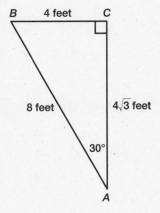

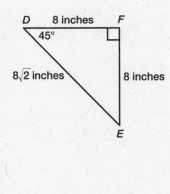

---

8. A guy wire is 600 feet long and forms a 55° angle with the ground. First, draw a diagram of this situation. Then, calculate the number of feet from the tower's base to where the wire is attached to the ground.

9. Firemen are climbing a 65′ ladder to the top of a 56′ building. Calculate the distance from the bottom of the ladder to the base of the building, and use the cosine ratio to compute the measure of the angle formed where the ladder touches the top of the building.

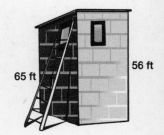

65 ft

56 ft

10. For the triangle shown, calculate the values of sin 30°, cos 30°, and tan 30°.

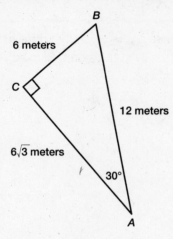

6 meters

C

12 meters

$6\sqrt{3}$ meters

30°

A

B

11. Calculate the value of $\dfrac{\sin 30°}{\cos 30°}$.

12. What do you notice about the value of $\dfrac{\sin 30°}{\cos 30°}$?

13. Do you think that the relationship between the sine, cosine, and tangent values of an angle is true for any angle? Explain your reasoning.

PROBLEM **2** **Secant Ratio**

The **secant (sec)** of an acute angle in a right triangle is the ratio of the length of the hypotenuse to the length of the side that is adjacent to the angle. The expression "sec A" means "the secant of ∠A."

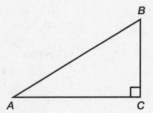

1. Complete the ratio to represent the secant of ∠A.

$$\sec A = \frac{\text{length of hypotenuse}}{\text{length of side adjacent to } \angle A} = \boxed{}$$

2. Prove algebraically that the secant of $A = \dfrac{1}{\cos A}$.

3. As the measure of an acute angle increases, the cosine value of the acute angle decreases. Explain the behavior of the secant value of an acute angle as the acute angle increases.

4. If there is no "sec" button on your graphing calculator, how can you compute the secant?

5. The diagram shows the measurements for the ski slope in the first lesson.

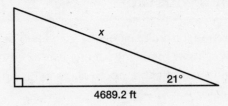

a. Use the cosine function to determine the length of the slope.

b. Use the secant function to determine the length of the slope.

PROBLEM 3 Inverse Cosine

The **inverse cosine** (or arc cosine) of x is defined as the measure of an acute angle whose cosine is x. If you know the length of any two sides of a right triangle, it is possible to compute the measure of either acute angle by using the inverse cosine, or $\cos^{-1}$ button on a graphing calculator.

In right triangle ABC, if $\cos A = x$, then $\cos^{-1} x = m\angle A$.

1. In right triangle ABC, if $\cos A = \frac{2}{7}$, calculate $\cos^{-1}\left(\frac{2}{7}\right)$ to determine $m\angle A$.

2. Determine the ratio for $\cos B$, and then use $\cos^{-1}(\cos B)$ to calculate $m\angle B$.

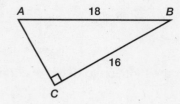

3. Calculate $m\angle B$.

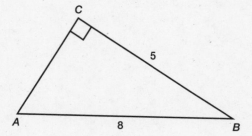

4. A typical cable-stayed bridge is a continuous girder with one or more towers erected above piers in the middle of the span. From these towers, cables stretch down diagonally (usually to both sides) and support the girder. Tension and compression are calculated into the design of this type of suspension bridge.

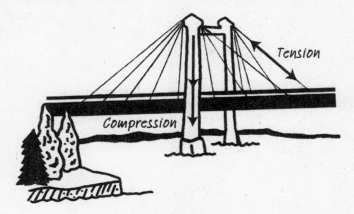

One cable is 95 feet. The span on the deck of the bridge from that cable to the girder is 80 feet. Calculate the angle formed by the deck and the cable.

5. Diane is training for a charity bicycle marathon. She leaves her house at noon and heads due west, biking at an average rate of 4 miles per hour. At 3 PM she changes course to N 65°W as shown. Determine the bike's distance from Diane's home at 5 PM.

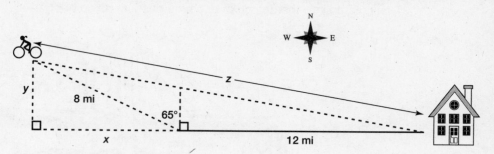

Talk the Talk

1. Match each trigonometric function with the appropriate abbreviation.

1.	Sine	A.	$\cos^{-1}$
2.	Cosine	B.	cot
3.	Tangent	C.	csc
4.	Cosecant	D.	$\tan^{-1}$
5.	Secant	E.	$\sin^{-1}$
6.	Cotangent	F.	cos
7.	Arc tan	G.	sin
8.	Arc sin	H.	tan
9.	Arc cos	I.	sec

2. Match each trigonometric function with the appropriate description.

1.	Sin	A.	$\dfrac{hypotenuse}{opposite}$
2.	Cos	B.	$\dfrac{hypotenuse}{adjacent}$
3.	Tan	C.	$\dfrac{opposite}{hypotenuse}$
4.	Csc	D.	$\dfrac{opposite}{adjacent}$
5.	Sec	E.	$\dfrac{adjacent}{opposite}$
6.	Cot	F.	$\dfrac{adjacent}{hypotenuse}$

3. Given the known information and the solution requirement, determine which function can be used to solve each situation.

Known Information	Solution Requirement	Function Used
• Hypotenuse • Opposite	Measure of reference angle	
• Opposite • Acute angle measure	Hypotenuse	
• Hypotenuse • Acute angle measure	Adjacent	
• Opposite • Adjacent	Measure of reference angle	
• Hypotenuse • Acute angle measure	Opposite	
• Hypotenuse • Adjacent	Measure of reference angle	

Sometimes it is helpful to use a mnemonic device to transform information into a form that you can easily remember. Can you come up with a mnemonic for the trig ratios?

 Be prepared to share your solutions and methods.

We Complement Each Other!

Complement Angle Relationships

You've worked with complements before, remember? Two angles whose measures add up to 90 degrees are called complements.

In right triangles, complements are pretty easy to locate. The two angles whose measures are *not* 90 degrees must be complements. In trigonometry, complements are easy to identify by name, too. The prefix "co-" in front of trigonometric ratio names stands for "complement."

PROBLEM 1 **Angles Are Very Complementary!**

Consider triangle *ABC* with right angle *C*. Angles *A* and *B* are complementary angles because the sum of their measures is equal to 90 degrees. The trigonometric ratios also have complementary relationships.

1. Use triangle *ABC* to answer each question.

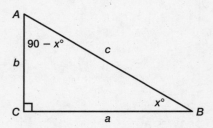

a. Compare the ratios that represent sin ∠*A* and cos ∠*B*.

b. Compare the ratios that represent sin ∠*B* and cos ∠*A*.

c. Compare the ratios that represent csc ∠*A* and sec ∠*B*.

d. Compare the ratios that represent tan ∠*A* and cot ∠*B*.

2. Which two functions are described by the ratio $\frac{c}{b}$?

3. Which two functions are described by the ratio $\frac{b}{a}$?

4. Use your answers to Questions 1 through 3 to complete the table.

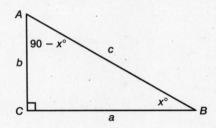

Reference Angle	sin	cos	tan	csc	sec	cot
A						
B						

5. Summarize the relationship between the trigonometric functions of complementary angles.

PROBLEM 2 Using Complements

1. Given: sin 30° = 0.5

Use the Pythagorean Theorem and your
knowledge of complementary functions
to complete the chart. Include both a
ratio and its decimal equivalent for
each function.

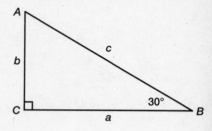

Reference Angle	sin	cos	tan	csc	sec	cot
30°						
60°						

2. Given: sin 45° = 0.707

Use the Pythagorean Theorem and your knowledge
of complementary functions to complete the chart.
Include both a ratio and its decimal equivalence for
each function.

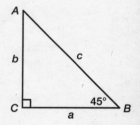

Reference Angle	sin	cos	tan	csc	sec	cot
45°						

3. Trafalgar Square is a tourist attraction located in London, England, United Kingdom. The name commemorates the Battle of Trafalgar (1805), a British naval victory of the Napoleonic Wars over France.

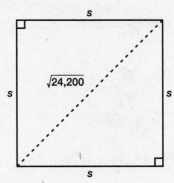

a. Use a trigonometric function to solve for the dimensions of Trafalgar Square.

b. Use the Pythagorean Theorem to solve for the dimensions of Trafalgar Square.

PROBLEM **3**   **Hot Air Balloons, The Grand Canyon, and Radar**

1. At an altitude of 1,000 feet, a balloonist measures the angle of depression from the balloon to the landing zone. The measure of that angle is 15°. How far is the balloon from the landing zone?

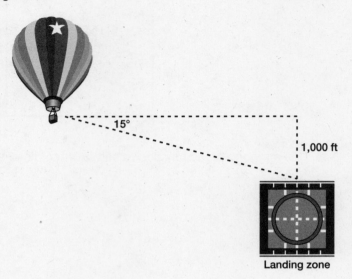

15°

1,000 ft

Landing zone

2. To measure the width of the Grand Canyon, a surveyor stands at a point on the North Rim of the canyon and measures the angle of depression to a point directly across on the South Rim of the canyon.

At the surveyor's position on the North Rim, the Grand Canyon is 7,256 feet above sea level. The point on the South Rim, directly across, is 6,159 feet above sea level. Sketch a diagram of the situation and determine the width of the Grand Canyon at the surveyor's position.

3. An aircraft uses radar to spot another aircraft 8,000 feet away at a 12° angle of depression. Sketch the situation and determine the vertical and horizontal separation between the two aircraft.

4. When a space shuttle returns from a mission, the angle of its descent to the ground from the final 10,000 feet above the ground is between 17° and 19° with the horizontal. Sketch a diagram of the situation and determine the maximum and minimum horizontal distances between the landing site and where the descent begins.

Be prepared to share your solutions and methods.

Time to Derive!

Deriving the Triangle Area Formula, the Law of Sines, and the Law of Cosines

LEARNING GOALS

In this lesson, you will:

- Derive the formula for the area of a triangle using the sine function.
- Derive the Law of Sines.
- Derive the Law of Cosines.

KEY TERMS

- Law of Sines
- Law of Cosines

Suppose you want to measure the height of a tree. You are 100 feet from the tree, and the angle from your feet to the top of the tree is 33 degrees. However, the tree isn't growing straight up from the ground. It leans a little bit toward you. The tree is actually growing out of the ground at an 83 degree angle. How tall is the tree?

Once you finish this lesson, see if you can answer this question.

PROBLEM 1   Deriving Another Version of the Area Formula

Whether you are determining the area of a right triangle, solving for the unknown side lengths of a right triangle, or solving for the unknown angle measurements in a right triangle, the solution paths are fairly straightforward. You can use what you learned previously, such as the area formula for a triangle, the Pythagorean Theorem, and the Triangle Sum Theorem.

Solving for unknown measurements of sides or angles of a triangle becomes more involved if the given triangle is not a right triangle.

Consider triangle *ABC* as shown.

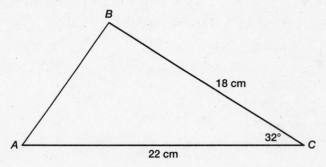

Use of the area formula requires the height of the triangle, which is not given.

Use of the Pythagorean Theorem requires the triangle to be a right triangle, which it is not. Use of the Triangle Sum Theorem requires the measures of two angles of the triangle, which are not given.

In this lesson, you will explore how trigonometric ratios are useful when determining the area of *any* triangle, solving for unknown lengths of sides of *any* triangle, and solving for unknown measures of angles in *any* triangle.

1. Analyze triangle *ABC*.

   a. Write the formula for the area of triangle *ABC* in terms of *b* and *h*.

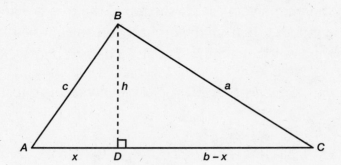

b. Write the ratio that represents sin *C* and solve for the height, *h*.

c. Rewrite the formula you wrote for the area of triangle *ABC* in Question 1 by substituting the expression for the value of *h* in Question 2.

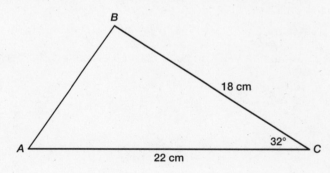

Congratulations! You have just derived the formula for the area of any triangle using a trigonometric ratio.

The area formula, $A = \frac{1}{2}ab \sin C$, can be used to determine the area of any triangle if you know the lengths of two sides and the measure of the included angle.

2. Use a trigonometric ratio to determine the area of the triangle.

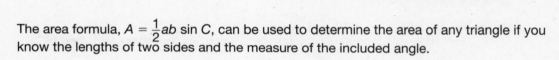

PROBLEM 2 Deriving the Law of Sines

You have used the trigonometric ratios to solve for unknown side length and angle measures in right triangles. Let's explore relationships between side lengths and angle measures in any triangle.

1. Analyze triangle ABC.

    a. Write a ratio to represent sin A, and then solve for the height, h.

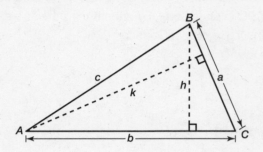

    b. Write a ratio that represents sin C, and then solve for the height, h.

    c. What can you conclude about the relationship between $c \cdot \sin A$ and $a \cdot \sin C$?

    d. Express $c \cdot \sin A = a \cdot \sin C$ as a proportion.

    e. Write a ratio that represents sin B, and then solve for the height, k.

    f. Write a ratio that represents sin C, and then solve for the height, k.

g. What can you conclude about the relationship between $c \cdot \sin B$ and $b \cdot \sin C$?

h. Express $c \cdot \sin B = b \cdot \sin C$ as a proportion.

i. Derive the *Law of Sines* by combining the proportions formed in parts (d) and (h).

The **Law of Sines**, or $\frac{\sin A}{a} = \frac{\sin B}{b} = \frac{\sin C}{c}$, can be used to determine the unknown side lengths or the unknown angle measures in *any* triangle.

2. Use the Law of Sines to determine the measure of $\angle B$.

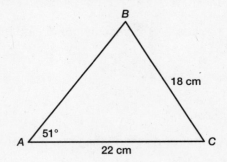

The Law of Sines is one relationship between the side lengths and angle measures of any triangle. Another relationship is called the *Law of Cosines*.

1. Analyze triangle *ABC*.

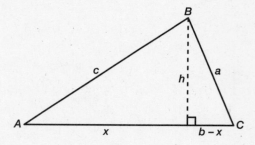

a. Write a ratio that represents sin *A*, and then solve for the height, *h*.

b. Write a ratio that represents cos *A*, and then solve for *x*.

c. Solve for a^2 using the Pythagorean Theorem.

d. Substitute the expressions for *h* and *x* into the equation in part (c).

e. Use the equation you wrote in part (d) to solve for a^2.

Think about the identity $\sin^2 A + \cos^2 A = 1$

2. Repeat the steps in Question 1 to solve for b^2.

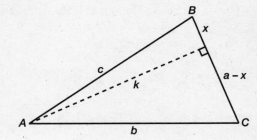

3. Repeat the steps in Question 1 to solve for c^2.

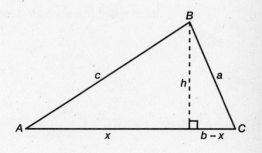

The **Law of Cosines**, or

$$a^2 = c^2 + b^2 - 2bc \cdot \cos A$$

$$b^2 = a^2 + c^2 - 2ac \cdot \cos B$$

$$c^2 = a^2 + b^2 - 2ab \cdot \cos C$$

can be used to determine the unknown lengths of sides or the unknown measures of angles in *any* triangle.

Congratulations! You have just derived the Law of Cosines.

4. Why is the Pythagorean Theorem considered to be a special case of the Law of Cosines?

PROBLEM 4 **Applying Yourself!**

A surveyor was hired to determine the approximate length of a proposed tunnel which, will be necessary to complete a new highway. A mountain stretches from point *A* to point *B* as shown. The surveyor stands at point *C* and measures the distance from where she is standing to both points *A* and *B*, then measures the angle formed between these two distances.

1. Use the surveyor's measurements to determine the length of the proposed tunnel.

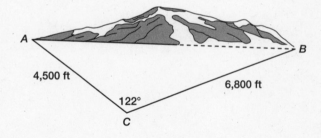

2. A nature lover decides to use geometry to determine if she can swim across a river. She locates two points, *A* and *B*, along one side of the river and determines the distance between these points is 250 meters. She then spots a point *C* on the other side of the river and measures the angles formed using point *C* to point *A* and then point *C* to point *B*. She determines the measure of the angle whose vertex is located at point *A* to be 35° and the angle whose vertex is located at point *B* to be 127° as shown.

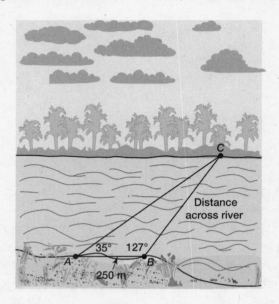

How did she determine the distance across the river from point *B* to point *C* and what is that distance?

3. A typical direct flight from Pittsburgh, Pennsylvania, to New York City is approximately 368 miles. A pilot alters the course of his aircraft 33° for 85 miles to avoid a storm and then turns the aircraft heading straight for New York City, as shown.

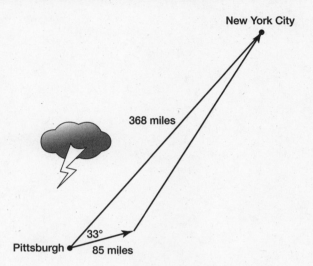

a. How many additional miles did the aircraft travel to avoid the storm?

b. If a commercial jet burns an average of 11.875 liters per kilometer, and the cost of jet fuel is $3.16 per gallon, this alteration in route due to the storm cost the airline company how much money?

Talk the Talk

1. When is it appropriate to use the Law of Sines?

2. When is it appropriate to use the Law of Cosines?

Be prepared to share your solutions and methods.

KEY TERMS

- reference angle (8.1)
- opposite side (8.1)
- adjacent side (8.1)
- rationalizing the denominator (8.2)
- tangent (tan) (8.2)

- cotangent (cot) (8.2)
- inverse tangent (8.2)
- sine (sin) (8.3)
- cosecant (csc) (8.3)
- inverse sine (8.3)
- cosine (cos) (8.4)

- secant (sec) (8.4)
- inverse cosine (8.4)
- Law of Sines (8.6)
- Law of Cosines (8.6)

8.1 Analyzing the Properties of Similar Right Triangles

In similar triangles, the ratio $\dfrac{\text{opposite}}{\text{hypotenuse}}$ is equal for corresponding reference angles.

In similar triangles, the ratio $\dfrac{\text{adjacent}}{\text{hypotenuse}}$ is equal for corresponding reference angles.

In similar triangles, the ratio $\dfrac{\text{opposite}}{\text{adjacent}}$ is equal for corresponding reference angles.

Example

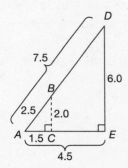

Right triangles *ABC* and *ADE* are similar. Consider angle *A* as the reference angle.

$\dfrac{\text{opposite}}{\text{hypotenuse}}$ ratios:

$\quad$ triangle *ABC*: $\dfrac{2.0}{2.5} = 0.8$

$\quad$ triangle *ADE*: $\dfrac{6.0}{7.5} = 0.8$

$\dfrac{\text{adjacent}}{\text{hypotenuse}}$ ratios:

$\quad$ triangle *ABC*: $\dfrac{1.5}{2.5} = 0.6$

$\quad$ triangle *ADE*: $\dfrac{4.5}{7.5} = 0.6$

$\dfrac{\text{opposite}}{\text{adjacent}}$ ratios:

$\quad$ triangle *ABC*: $\dfrac{0.8}{0.6} \approx 1.33$

$\quad$ triangle *ADE*: $\dfrac{0.8}{0.6} \approx 1.33$

8.2 Using the Tangent Ratio

The tangent (tan) of an acute angle in a right triangle is the ratio of the length of the side that is opposite the angle to the length of the side that is adjacent to the angle. You can use the tangent of an angle to determine the length of a leg in a right triangle when you know the measure of an acute angle and the length of the other leg.

Example

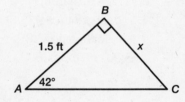

$$\tan 42° = \frac{x}{1.5}$$

$$1.5(\tan 42°) = x$$

$$x \approx 1.35 \text{ ft}$$

8.2 Using the Cotangent Ratio

The cotangent (cot) of an acute angle in a right triangle is the ratio of the length of the side that is adjacent to the angle to the length of the side that is opposite the angle. You can use the cotangent of an angle to determine the length of a leg in a right triangle when you know the measure of an acute angle and the length of the other leg.

Example

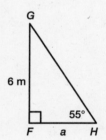

$$\cot 55° = \frac{a}{6}$$

$$6(\cot 55°) = a$$

$$6\left(\frac{1}{\tan 55°}\right) = a$$

$$a \approx 4.20 \text{ m}$$

8.2 Using the Inverse Tangent

The inverse tangent, or arc tangent, of x is defined as the measure of an acute angle whose tangent is x. You can use the inverse tangent to calculate the measure of either acute angle in a right triangle when you know the lengths of both legs.

Example

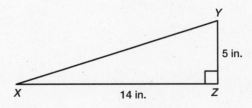

$$m\angle X = \tan^{-1}\left(\frac{5}{14}\right) \approx 19.65°$$

$$m\angle Y = \tan^{-1}\left(\frac{14}{5}\right) \approx 70.35°$$

8.2 Solving Problems Using the Tangent Ratio

An angle of elevation is the angle above a horizontal. You can use trigonometric ratios to solve problems involving angles of elevation.

Example

Mitchell is standing on the ground 14 feet from a building and he is looking up at the top of the building. The angle of elevation that his line of sight makes with the horizontal is 65°. His eyes are 5.2 feet from the ground. To calculate the height of the building, first draw a diagram of the situation. Then write and solve an equation involving a trigonometric ratio.

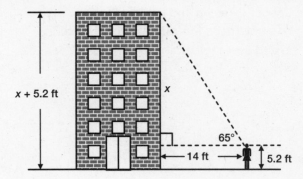

$$\tan 65° = \frac{x}{14}$$

$$14(\tan 65°) = x$$

$$x \approx 30 \text{ ft}$$

$$x + 5.2 = 30 + 5.2 = 35.2 \text{ ft}$$

The building is about 35.2 feet tall.

8.3 Using the Sine Ratio

The sine (sin) of an acute angle in a right triangle is the ratio of the length of the side that is opposite the angle to the length of the hypotenuse. You can use the sine of an angle to determine the length of a leg in a right triangle when you know the measure of the angle opposite the leg and the length of the hypotenuse. You can also use the sine of an angle to determine the length of the hypotenuse when you know the measure of an acute angle and the length of the leg opposite the angle.

Example

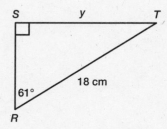

$$\sin 61° = \frac{y}{18}$$

$$18(\sin 61°) = y$$

$$x \approx 15.74 \text{ cm}$$

8.3 Using the Cosecant Ratio

The cosecant (csc) of an acute angle in a right triangle is the ratio of the length of the hypotenuse to the length of the side that is opposite the angle. You can use the cosecant of an angle to determine the length of a leg in a right triangle when you know the measure of the angle opposite the leg and the length of the hypotenuse. You can also use the cosecant of an angle to determine the length of the hypotenuse when you know the measure of an acute angle and the length of the leg opposite the angle.

Example

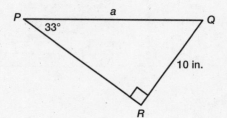

$$\csc 33° = \frac{a}{10}$$

$$10(\csc 33°) = a$$

$$10\left(\frac{1}{\sin 33°}\right) = a$$

$$a \approx 18.36 \text{ in.}$$

8.3 Using the Inverse Sine

The inverse sine, or arc sine, of x is defined as the measure of an acute angle whose sine is x. You can use the inverse sine to calculate the measure of an acute angle in a right triangle when you know the length of the leg opposite the angle and the length of the hypotenuse.

Example

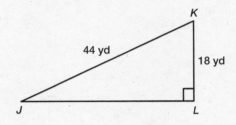

$$m\angle J = \sin^{-1}\left(\frac{18}{44}\right) \approx 24.15°$$

8.4 Using the Cosine Ratio

The cosine (cos) of an acute angle in a right triangle is the ratio of the length of the side that is adjacent to the angle to the length of the hypotenuse. You can use the cosine of an angle to determine the length of a leg in a right triangle when you know the measure of the angle adjacent to the leg and the length of the hypotenuse. You can also use the cosine of an angle to determine the length of the hypotenuse when you know the measure of an acute angle and the length of the leg adjacent to the angle.

Example

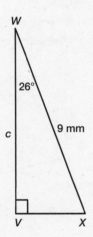

$$\cos 26° = \frac{c}{9}$$
$$9(\cos 26°) = c$$
$$c \approx 8.09 \text{ mm}$$

8.4 ## Using the Secant Ratio

The secant (sec) of an acute angle in a right triangle is the ratio of the length of the hypotenuse to the length of the side that is adjacent to the angle. You can use the secant of an angle to determine the length of a leg in a right triangle when you know the measure of the angle adjacent to the leg and the length of the hypotenuse. You can also use the secant of an angle to determine the length of the hypotenuse when you know the measure of an acute angle and the length of the leg adjacent to the angle.

Example

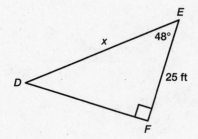

$$\sec 48° = \frac{x}{25}$$

$$25(\sec 48°) = x$$

$$25\left(\frac{1}{\cos 48°}\right) = x$$

$$x \approx 37.36 \text{ ft}$$

8.4 ## Using the Inverse Cosine

The inverse cosine, or arc cosine, of x is defined as the measure of an acute angle whose cosine is x. You can use the inverse cosine to calculate the measure of an acute angle in a right triangle when you know the length of the leg adjacent to the angle and the length of the hypotenuse.

Example

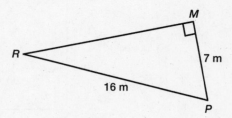

$$m\angle P = \cos^{-1}\left(\frac{7}{16}\right) \approx 64.06°$$

Exploring Complementary Angle Relationships in a Right Triangle

The two acute angles of a right triangle are complementary angles because the sum of their measures is 90 degrees. The trigonometric ratios also have complementary relationships:

The sine of an acute angle is equal to the cosine of its complement.

The tangent of an acute angle is equal to the cotangent of its complement.

The secant of an acute angle is equal to the cosecant of its complement.

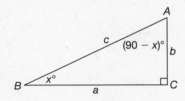

Example

Angle A and angle B are complementary angles.

$\sin \angle A = \dfrac{a}{c}$

$\cos \angle B = \dfrac{a}{c}$

$\sin \angle A$ and $\cos \angle B$ are the same ratio.

$\sin \angle B = \dfrac{b}{c}$

$\cos \angle A = \dfrac{b}{c}$

$\sin \angle B$ and $\cos \angle A$ are the same ratio.

$\tan \angle A = \dfrac{a}{b}$

$\cot \angle B = \dfrac{a}{b}$

$\tan \angle A$ and $\cot \angle B$ are the same ratio.

$\tan \angle B = \dfrac{b}{a}$

$\cot \angle A = \dfrac{b}{a}$

$\tan \angle B$ and $\cot \angle A$ are the same ratio.

$\sec \angle A = \dfrac{c}{b}$

$\csc \angle B = \dfrac{c}{b}$

$\sec \angle A$ and $\csc \angle B$ are the same ratio.

$\sec \angle B = \dfrac{c}{a}$

$\csc \angle A = \dfrac{c}{a}$

$\sec \angle B$ and $\csc \angle A$ are the same ratio.

Solving Problems Using Complementary Angle Relationships

An angle of elevation is the angle below a horizontal. You can use trigonometric ratios to solve problems involving angles of depression.

Example

You are standing on a cliff and you see a house below you. You are 50 feet above the house. The angle of depression that your line of sight makes with the horizontal is 33°. To calculate the horizontal distance x you are from the house, first draw a diagram of the situation. Then write and solve an equation involving a trigonometric ratio.

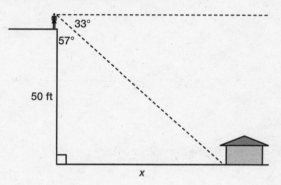

$$\tan 57° = \frac{x}{50}$$

$$50(\tan 57°) = x$$

$$x \approx 77 \text{ ft}$$

You are about 77 feet from the house.

Deriving and Using a Formula for the Area of a Triangle

You can calculate the area of any triangle if you know the lengths of two sides and the measure of the included angle.

Area formula:

For any triangle ABC, $A = \frac{1}{2}ab(\sin C)$.

Example

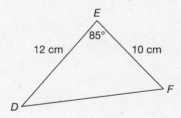

$$A = \frac{1}{2}df(\sin E)$$

$$A = \frac{1}{2}(10)(12)(\sin 85°)$$

$$A \approx 59.8 \text{ square centimeters}$$

8.6 Deriving and Using the Law of Sines

You can use the Law of Sines when

- you know the lengths of two sides of a triangle and the measure of an angle opposite one of those sides, and you want to know the measure of the angle opposite the other known side.

or

- you know the measures of two angles of a triangle and the length of a side opposite one of those angles, and you want to know the length of the side opposite the other known angle.

Law of Sines:

$$\text{For any triangle } ABC, \frac{\sin A}{a} = \frac{\sin B}{b} = \frac{\sin C}{c}.$$

Example

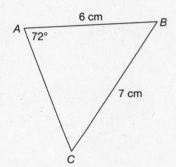

$$\frac{\sin A}{a} = \frac{\sin B}{b} = \frac{\sin C}{c}$$

$$\frac{\sin A}{a} = \frac{\sin C}{c}$$

$$\frac{\sin 72°}{7} = \frac{\sin C}{6}$$

$$6 \sin 72° = 7 \sin C$$

$$\sin C = \frac{6 \sin 72°}{7} \approx 0.815$$

$$C \approx 54.6°$$

8.6 Deriving and Using the Law of Cosines

You can use the Law of Cosines when

- You know the lengths of all three sides of a triangle and you want to solve for the measure of any of the angles

or

- You know the lengths of two sides of a triangle and the measure of the included angle, and you want to solve for the length of the third side.

Law of Cosines

For any triangle ABC,

$$a^2 = b^2 + c^2 - 2bc \cos A$$

$$b^2 = a^2 + c^2 - 2ac \cos B$$

$$c^2 = a^2 + b^2 - 2ab \cos C.$$

Example

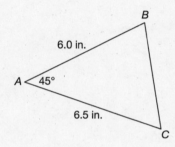

$a^2 = b^2 + c^2 - 2bc \cos A$

$a^2 = 6.5^2 + 6.0^2 - 2(6.5)(6.0)(\cos 45°)$

$a^2 = 42.25 + 36 - 78(\cos 45°)$

$a^2 \approx 23.10$

$a \approx 4.8$ inches

Circles

9

That's no moon. It's a picture of a solar eclipse in the making. A solar eclipse occurs when the Moon passes between the Earth and the Sun. Scientists can predict when solar eclipses will happen years into the future.

Riding a Ferris Wheel
Introduction to Circles

LEARNING GOALS

In this lesson, you will:

- Review the definition of line segments related to a circle such as chord, diameter, secant, and tangent.
- Review definitions of points related to a circle such as center and point of tangency.
- Review the definitions of angles related to a circle such as central angle and inscribed angle.
- Review the definitions of arcs related to a circle such as major arc, minor arc, and semicircle.
- Prove all circles are similar using rigid motion.

KEY TERMS

- center of a circle
- radius
- chord
- diameter
- secant of a circle
- tangent of a circle
- point of tangency
- central angle
- inscribed angle
- arc
- major arc
- minor arc
- semicircle

Amusement parks are a very popular destination. Many people like rides that go fast, like roller coasters. Others prefer more relaxing rides. One of the most popular rides is the Ferris wheel.

The invention of the Ferris wheel is credited to George Washington Gale Ferris, Jr., who debuted his new ride at the World's Columbian Exposition in Chicago, Illinois in 1893. It was 264 feet tall, had a capacity of 2160 people, took 10 minutes to complete a revolution, and cost 50 cents to ride. Of course 50 cents was quite a bit of money at the time.

The well-known London Eye in England is the tallest Ferris wheel in the Western Hemisphere. The Singapore Flyer, located near the Singapore River, is currently the tallest in the world. It is more than a third of a mile high!

A Ferris wheel is in the shape of a circle.

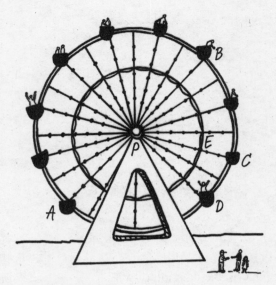

Recall that a circle is the set of all points in a plane that are equidistant from a given point, which is called the **center of the circle**. The distance from a point on the circle to the center is the **radius** of the circle. A circle is named by its center. For example, the circle seen in the Ferris wheel is circle *P*.

1. Use the circle to answer each question.

   a. Name the circle.

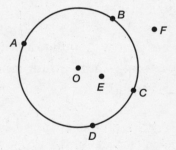

   b. Use a straightedge to draw $\overline{OB}$, a radius of circle *O*. Where are the endpoints located with respect to the circle?

c. How many radii does a circle have? Explain your reasoning.

Remember, *radii* is the plural of radius.

d. Use a straightedge to draw $\overline{AC}$. Then, use a straightedge to draw $\overline{BD}$. How are the line segments different? How are they the same?

Both line segments *AC* and *BD* are *chords* of the circle. A **chord** is a line segment with each endpoint on the circle. Line segment *AC* is called a *diameter* of the circle. A **diameter** is a chord that passes through the center of the circle.

e. Why is $\overline{BD}$ not considered a diameter?

f. How does the length of the diameter of a circle relate to the length of the radius?

g. Are all radii of the same circle, or of congruent circles, always, sometimes, or never congruent? Explain your reasoning.

A **secant of a circle** is a line that intersects a circle at exactly two points.

2. Draw a secant using the circle shown.

3. Maribel says that a chord is part of a secant. David says that a chord is different from a secant. Explain why Maribel and David are both correct.

4. What is the longest chord in a circle?

A **tangent of a circle** is a line that intersects a circle at exactly one point. The point of intersection is called the **point of tangency**.

5. Draw a tangent using circle Z shown.

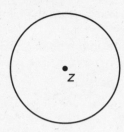

Try to draw different tangent lines through the point you chose.

6. Choose another point on the circle. How many tangent lines can you draw through this point?

7. Explain the difference between a secant and a tangent.

8. Check the appropriate term(s) associated with each characteristic in the table shown.

Characteristic	Chord	Secant	Diameter	Radius	Tangent
A line					
A line segment					
A line segment having both endpoints on the circle					
A line segment having one endpoint on the circle					
A line segment passing through the center of the circle					
A line intersecting a circle at exactly two points					
A line intersecting a circle at exactly one point					

A **central angle** is an angle whose vertex is the center of the circle.

An **inscribed angle** is an angle whose vertex is on the circle.

1. Four friends are riding a Ferris wheel in the positions shown.

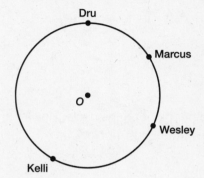

a. Draw a central angle where Dru and Marcus are located on the sides of the angle.

b. Draw an inscribed angle where Kelli is the vertex and Dru and Marcus are located on the sides of the angle.

c. Draw an inscribed angle where Wesley is the vertex and Dru and Marcus are located on the sides of the angle.

d. Compare and contrast these three angles.

An **arc** of a circle is any unbroken part of the circumference of a circle. An arc is named using its two endpoints. The symbol used to describe arc AB is $\overset{\frown}{AB}$.

A **major arc** of a circle is the largest arc formed by a secant and a circle. It goes more than halfway around a circle.

A **minor arc** of a circle is the smallest arc formed by a secant and a circle. It goes less than halfway around a circle.

A **semicircle** is exactly half of a circle.

To avoid confusion, three points are used to name semicircles and major arcs. The first point is an endpoint of the arc, the second point is any point at which the arc passes through and the third point is the other endpoint of the arc.

2. Use the same Ferris wheel from Question 1 to answer each question.

Use the ⌢ symbol to name arcs.

a. Label the location of each person with the first letter of his or her name.

b. Identify two different arcs and name them.

c. Draw a diameter on the circle shown so that point *D* is an endpoint. Label the second endpoint as point *Z*. The diameter divided the circle into two semicircles.

d. Name each semicircle.

e. Name all minor arcs.

f. Name all major arcs.

Recall that two figures are similar if there is a set of transformations that will move one figure exactly covering the other. To prove any two circles are similar, only a translation (slide) and a dilation (enlargement or reduction) are necessary. In this problem, you will use a point that is not on a circle as the center of dilation and a given scale factor to show any two circles are similar.

Step 1: Draw circle A.

Step 2: Locate point B not on circle A as the center of dilation.

Step 3: Dilate circle A by a scale factor of 3, locating points A' and C' such that $BA' = 3 \cdot BA$ and $BC' = 3 \cdot BC$

Step 4: Using radius $A'C'$, draw circle A'.

Read through the steps and plan your drawing before you start. Will circle A' be smaller or larger than circle A?

The ratio of the radii of circles A and A' are equal to the absolute value of the scale factor.

1. Given any two circles, do you think you can always identify a dilation that maps one circle onto another?

2. The scale factor is the ratio of $C'B$ to CB. Will this be true for any two circles?

3. Can you conclude any two circles are always similar? Explain your reasoning.

Talk the Talk

Use the diagram shown to answer Questions 1 through 7.

1. Name a diameter.

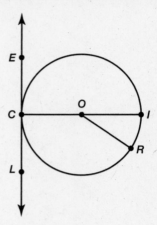

2. Name a radius.

3. Name a central angle.

4. Name an inscribed angle.

5. Name a minor arc.

6. Name a major arc.

7. Name a semicircle.

  Be prepared to share your solutions and methods.

Take the Wheel

Central Angles, Inscribed Angles, and Intercepted Arcs

Before airbags were installed in car steering wheels, the recommended position for holding the steering wheel was the 10–2 position. Now, one of the recommended positions is the 9–3 position to account for the airbags. The numbers 10, 2, 9, and 3 refer to the numbers on a clock. So, the 10–2 position means that one hand is at 10 o'clock and the other hand is at 2 o'clock.

PROBLEM 1 Keep Both Hands on the Wheel

Recall that the degree measure of a circle is 360°.

Each minor arc of a circle is associated with and determined by a specific central angle. The **degree measure** of a minor arc is the same as the degree measure of its central angle. For example, if the measure of central angle *PRQ* is 30°, then the degree measure of its minor arc *PQ* is equal to 30°. Using symbols, this can be expressed as follows: If ∠*PRQ* is a central angle and *m*∠*PRQ* = 30°, then *m*$\widehat{PQ}$ = 30°.

1. The circles shown represent steering wheels, and the points on the circles represent the positions of a person's hands.

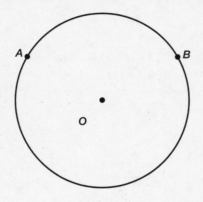

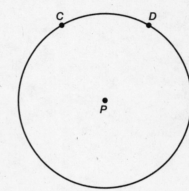

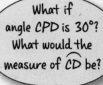

> What if angle *CPD* is 30°? What would the measure of $\widehat{CD}$ be?

For each circle, use the given points to draw a central angle. The hand position on the left is 10–2 and the hand position on the right is 11–1.

a. What are the names of the central angles?

b. Without using a protractor, determine the central angle measures. Explain your reasoning.

c. How do the measures of these angles compare?

d. Why do you think the hand position represented by the circle on the left is recommended and the hand position represented on the right is not recommended?

e. Describe the measures of the minor arcs.

What is the measure of a semicircle?

f. Plot and label point *Z* on each circle so that it does not lie between the endpoints of the minor arcs. Determine the measures of the major arcs that have the same endpoints as the minor arcs.

2. If the measures of two central angles of the same circle (or congruent circles) are equal, are their corresponding minor arcs congruent? Explain your reasoning.

3. If the measures of two minor arcs of the same circle (or congruent circles) are equal, are their corresponding central angles congruent? Explain your reasoning.

9

9.2 Central Angles, Inscribed Angles, and Intercepted Arcs ■ 663

Adjacent arcs are two arcs of the same circle sharing a common endpoint.

4. Draw and label two adjacent arcs on circle O shown.

The **Arc Addition Postulate** states: "The measure of an arc formed by two adjacent arcs is the sum of the measures of the two arcs."

5. Apply the Arc Addition Postulate to the adjacent arcs you created.

An *intercepted arc* is an arc associated with and determined by angles of the circle. An **intercepted arc** is a portion of the circumference of the circle located on the interior of the angle whose endpoints lie on the sides of an angle.

6. Consider circle O.

    a. Draw inscribed ∠PSR on circle O.

    b. Name the intercepted arc associated with ∠PSR.

7. Consider the central angle shown.

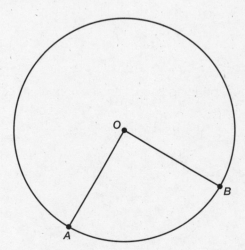

    a. Use a straightedge to draw an inscribed angle that contains points A and B on its sides. Name the vertex of your angle point P. What do the angles have in common?

b. Use your protractor to measure the central angle and the inscribed angle. How is the measure of the inscribed angle related to the measure of the central angle and the measure of $\overset{\frown}{AB}$?

c. Use a straightedge to draw a different inscribed angle that contains points A and B on its sides. Name its vertex point Q. Measure the inscribed angle. How is the measure of the inscribed angle related to the measure of the central angle and the measure of $\overset{\frown}{AB}$?

d. Use a straightedge to draw one more inscribed angle that contains points A and B on its sides. Name its vertex point R. Measure the inscribed angle. How is the measure of the inscribed angle related to the measure of the central angle and the measure of $\overset{\frown}{AB}$?

8. What can you conclude about inscribed angles that have the same intercepted arc?

9. Dalia says that the measure of an inscribed angle is half the measure of the central angle that intercepts the same arc. Nate says that it is twice the measure. Sandy says that the inscribed angle is the same measure. Who is correct? Explain your reasoning.

10. Inscribed angles formed by two chords can be drawn three different ways with respect to the center of the circle.

Case 1: Use circle *O* shown to draw and label inscribed ∠*MPT* such that the center point lies on one side of the inscribed angle.

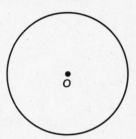

Case 2: Use circle *O* shown to draw and label inscribed ∠*MPT* such that the center point lies on the interior of the inscribed angle.

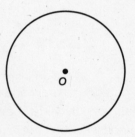

Case 3: Use circle *O* shown to draw and label inscribed ∠*MPT* such that the center point lies on the exterior of the inscribed angle.

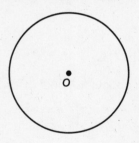

Do these three cases cover all the possible ways inscribed angles can be drawn?

11. To prove your Inscribed Angle Conjecture, you must prove each case in Question 10.

Case 1:

Given: $\angle MPT$ is inscribed in circle O.

$m\angle MPT = x$

Point O lies on diameter $\overline{PM}$.

Prove: $m\angle MPT = \frac{1}{2}m\widehat{MT}$

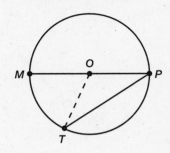

Statements	Reasons
1. $\angle MPT$ is inscribed in circle O. $m\angle MPT = x$ Point O lies on diameter $\overline{PM}$.	1. Given
2. Connect points O and T to form radius $\overline{OT}$.	2. Construction

Case 2:

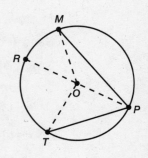

Given: ∠MPT is inscribed in circle O.

Point O is in the interior of ∠MPT.

$m\angle MPO = x$

$m\angle TPO = y$

Prove: $m\angle MPT = \frac{1}{2}m\widehat{MT}$

Statements	Reasons
1. ∠MPT is inscribed in circle O. Point O is in the interior of ∠MPT. $m\angle MPO = x$ $m\angle TPO = y$	**1.** Given
2. Construct diameter $\overline{PR}$. Connect points O and T to form radius $\overline{OT}$. Connect points O and M to form radius $\overline{OM}$.	**2.** Construction

Case 3:

Given: ∠MPT is inscribed in circle O.

Point O is in the exterior of ∠MPT.

Prove: $m\angle MPT = \frac{1}{2}m\overset{\frown}{MT}$

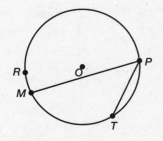

Statements	Reasons
1. ∠MPT is inscribed in circle O. Point O is in the exterior of ∠MPT.	1. Given
2. Construct diameter $\overline{PR}$. Connect points O and T to form radius $\overline{OT}$. Connect points O and M to form radius $\overline{OM}$.	2. Construction

You will need to construct a diameter through point P and construct radii OM and OT.

You've just proved the Inscribed Angle Conjecture, which you can now call the Inscribed Angle Theorem. Nice effort!

 The **Inscribed Angle Theorem** states: "The measure of an inscribed angle is half the measure of its intercepted arc."

12. Aubrey wants to take a family picture. Her camera has a 70° field of view, but to include the entire family in the picture, she needs to cover a 140° arc. Explain what Aubrey needs to do to fit the entire family in the picture. Use the diagram to draw the solution.

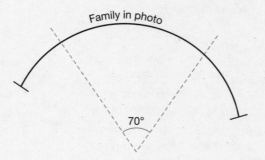

Family in photo

70°

PROBLEM 2 Parallel Lines Intersecting a Circle

Do parallel lines intersecting a circle intercept congruent arcs on the circle?

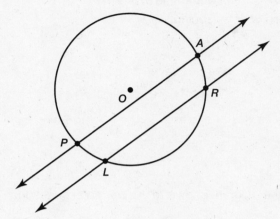

1. Create a proof for this conjecture.

   Given:

   Prove:

You have just proven the Parallel Lines–Congruent Arcs Conjecture. It is now known as the Parallel Lines–Congruent Arcs Theorem which states that parallel lines intercept congruent arcs on a circle.

Talk the Talk

1. $\overline{MP}$ is a diameter of circle O.
   If $m\overparen{MT} = 124°$, determine $m\angle TPW$.
   Explain your reasoning.

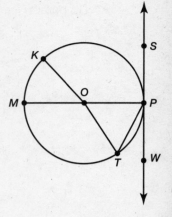

2. Use the diagram shown to answer each question.

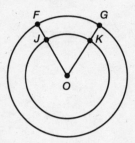

   a. Are radii $\overline{OJ}$, $\overline{OK}$, $\overline{OF}$, and $\overline{OG}$ all congruent? Explain your reasoning.

   b. Is $m\overparen{FG}$ greater than $m\overparen{JK}$? Explain your reasoning.

   c. If $m\angle FOG = 57°$, determine $m\overparen{JK}$ and $m\overparen{FG}$. Explain your reasoning.

3. DeJaun told Thomas there was not enough information to determine whether circle *A* was congruent to circle *B*. He said they would have to know the length of a radius in each circle to determine whether the circles were congruent. Thomas explained to DeJaun why he was incorrect. What did Thomas say to DeJaun?

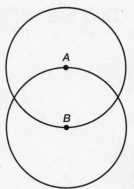

 Be prepared to share your solutions and methods.

9

Manhole Covers
Measuring Angles Inside and Outside of Circles

Manhole covers are heavy removable plates that are used to cover maintenance holes in the ground. Most manhole covers are circular and can be found all over the world. The tops of these covers can be plain or have beautiful designs cast into their tops.

PROBLEM 1 Inside the Circle

The vertex of an angle can be located inside of a circle, outside of a circle, or on a circle. In this lesson, you will explore these locations and prove theorems related to each situation.

1. Circle O shows a simple manhole cover design.

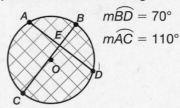

$m\overset{\frown}{BD} = 70°$

$m\overset{\frown}{AC} = 110°$

a. Consider $\angle BED$. How is this angle different from the angles that you have seen so far in this chapter? How is this angle the same?

b. Can you determine the measure of $\angle BED$ with the information you have so far? If so, how? Explain your reasoning.

c. Draw chord CD. Use the information given in the figure to name the measures of any angles that you do know. Explain your reasoning.

d. How does $\angle BED$ relate to $\triangle CED$?

e. Write a statement showing the relationship between $m\angle BED$, $m\angle EDC$, and $m\angle ECD$.

f. What is the measure of $\angle BED$?

It appears that the measure of an interior angle in a circle is equal to half of the sum of the measures of the arcs intercepted by the angle and its vertical angle. This observation can be stated as a theorem and proven.

2. Prove the Interior Angles of a Circle Theorem.

Given: Chords EK and GH intersect at point F in circle O.

Prove: $m\angle KFH = \frac{1}{2}(m\overset{\frown}{HK} + m\overset{\frown}{EG})$

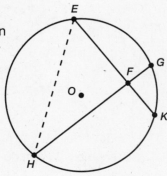

Congratulations! You have just proved the Interior Angles of a Circle Theorem. You can use this theorem as a valid reason in proofs.

The **Interior Angles of a Circle Theorem** states: "If an angle is formed by two intersecting chords or secants of a circle such that the vertex of the angle is in the interior of the circle, then the measure of the angle is half of the sum of the measures of the arcs intercepted by the angle and its vertical angle."

9

1. Circle *T* shows another simple manhole cover design.

$m\widehat{KM} = 80°$
$m\widehat{LN} = 30°$

a. Consider $\overline{KL}$ and $\overline{MN}$. Use a straightedge to draw secants that coincide with each line segment. Where do the secants intersect? Label this point as point *P* on the figure.

b. Draw chord $\overline{KN}$. Can you determine the measure of $\angle KPM$ with the information you have so far? If so, how? Explain your reasoning.

c. Use the information given in the figure to name the measures of any angles that you do know. Explain how you determined your answers.

d. How does $\angle KPN$ relate to $\triangle KPN$?

e. Write a statement showing the relationship between $m\angle KPN$, $m\angle NKP$, and $m\angle KNM$.

f. What is the measure of $\angle KPN$?

g. Describe the measure of $\angle KPM$ in terms of the measures of both arcs intercepted by $\angle KPM$.

It appears that the measure of an exterior angle of a circle is equal to half of the difference of the arc measures that are intercepted by the angle. This observation can be stated as a theorem and proved.

2. An angle with a vertex located in the exterior of a circle can be formed by a secant and a tangent, two secants, or two tangents.

   a. **Case 1:** Use circle O shown to draw and label an exterior angle formed by a secant and a tangent.

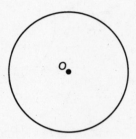

   b. **Case 2:** Use circle O shown to draw and label an exterior angle formed by two secants.

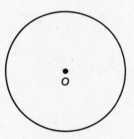

   c. **Case 3:** Use circle O shown to draw and label an exterior angle formed by two tangents.

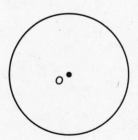

To prove the Exterior Angles of a Circle Conjecture previously stated, you must prove each of the three cases.

3. Prove each case of the Exterior Angles of a Circle Conjecture.

   a. **Case 1**

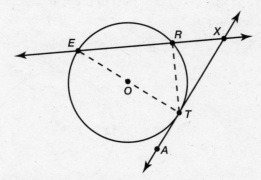

Given: Secant *EX* and tangent *TX* intersect at point *X*.

Prove: $m\angle EXT = \frac{1}{2}(m\widehat{ET} - m\widehat{RT})$

Statements	Reasons
1. Secant *EX* and tangent *TX* intersect at point *X*.	1. Given
2. Connect points *E* and *T* to form chord *ET*. Connect points *R* and *T* to form chord *RT*.	2. Construction

b. Case 2

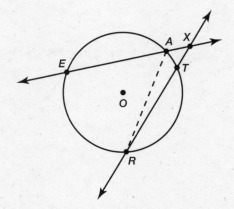

Given: Secants *EX* and *RX* intersect at point *X*.

Prove: $m\angle EXR = \frac{1}{2}(m\widehat{ER} - m\widehat{AT})$

Statements	Reasons
1. Secants *EX* and *RX* intersect at point *X*.	**1.** Given
2. Connect points *A* and *R* to form chord *AR*.	**2.** Construction

c. Case 3

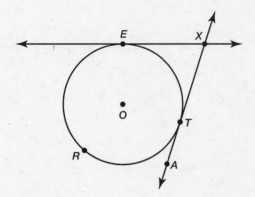

Given: Tangents *EX* and *AX* intersect at point *X*.

Prove: $m\angle EXT = \frac{1}{2}(m\widehat{ERT} - m\widehat{ET})$

Statements	Reasons
1. Tangents *EX* and *AX* intersect at point *X*.	**1.** Given

 The **Exterior Angles of a Circle Theorem** states: "If an angle is formed by two intersecting chords or secants of a circle such that the vertex of the angle is in the exterior of the circle, then the measure of the angle is half of the difference of the measures of the arcs intercepted by the angle."

1. Consider ∠*UTV* with vertex located on circle *C*. Line *VW* is drawn tangent to circle *C* at point *T*.

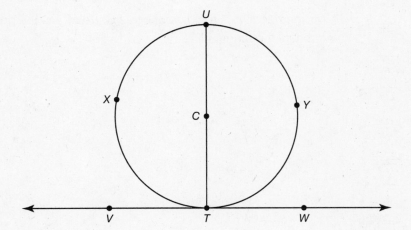

a. Determine $m\overset{\frown}{UXT}$ and $m\overset{\frown}{UYT}$. Explain your reasoning.

Recall that an inscribed angle is an angle whose vertex lies on the circle and whose measure is half the measure of its intercepted arc.

b. Determine $m\angle UTV$ and $m\angle UTW$. Explain your reasoning.

It appears that when a line is drawn tangent to a circle, the angles formed at the point of tangency are right angles and therefore the radius drawn to the point of tangency is perpendicular to the tangent line.

This observation can be proved and stated as a theorem.

The proof of this theorem is done by contradiction. Recall that a proof by contradiction begins with an assumption. Using the assumption and its implications, we arrive at a contradiction. When this happens, the proof is complete.

Line segment *CA* is a radius of circle *C*. Point *A* is the point at which the radius intersects the tangent line.

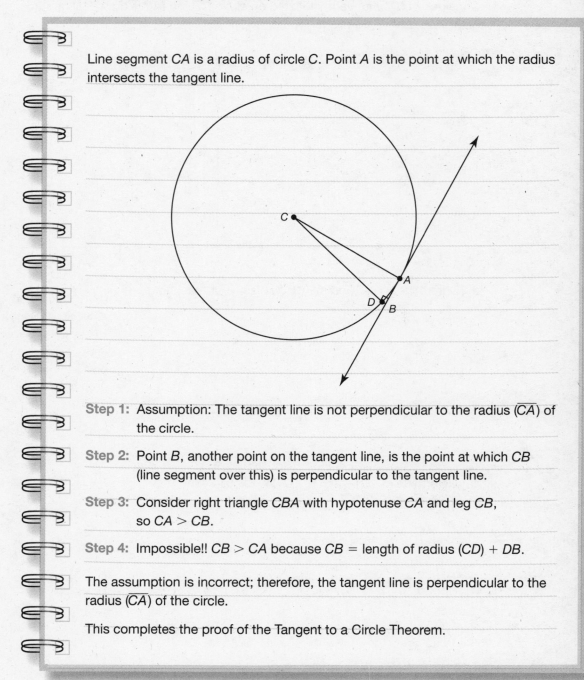

Step 1: Assumption: The tangent line is not perpendicular to the radius ($\overline{CA}$) of the circle.

Step 2: Point *B*, another point on the tangent line, is the point at which *CB* (line segment over this) is perpendicular to the tangent line.

Step 3: Consider right triangle *CBA* with hypotenuse *CA* and leg *CB*, so *CA* > *CB*.

Step 4: Impossible!! *CB* > *CA* because *CB* = length of radius (*CD*) + *DB*.

The assumption is incorrect; therefore, the tangent line is perpendicular to the radius ($\overline{CA}$) of the circle.

This completes the proof of the Tangent to a Circle Theorem.

The **Tangent to a Circle Theorem** states: "A line drawn tangent to a circle is perpendicular to a radius of the circle drawn to the point of tangency."

2. Molly is standing at the top of Mount Everest, which has an elevation of 29,029 feet. Her eyes are 5 feet above ground level. The radius of Earth is approximately 3960 miles. How far can Molly see on the horizon?

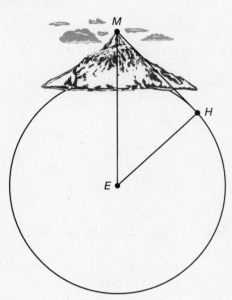

3. When you are able to see past buildings and hills or mountains—when you can look all the way to the horizon, how far is that? You can use the Pythagorean Theorem to help you tell.

Imagine you are standing on the surface of the Earth and you have a height of *h*. The distance to the horizon is given by *d* in the diagram shown, and *R* is the radius of Earth.

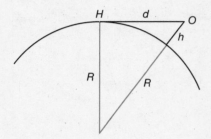

Using your height, create a formula you can use to determine how far away the horizon is.

PROBLEM 4 Determine the Measures

1. Use the diagrams shown to determine the measures of each.

    a. Determine $m\widehat{RT}$.

        $m\widehat{FG} = 86°$

        $m\widehat{HP} = 21°$

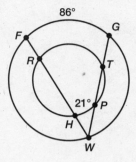

    b. Using the given information, what additional information can you determine about the diagram?

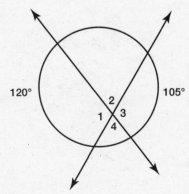

c. Determine $m\widehat{CD}$.

$m\widehat{AB} = 88°$

$m\angle AED = 80°$

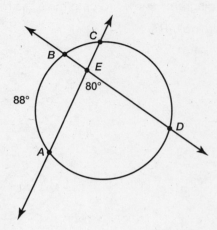

d. Explain how knowing $m\angle ERT$ can help you determine $m\angle EXT$.

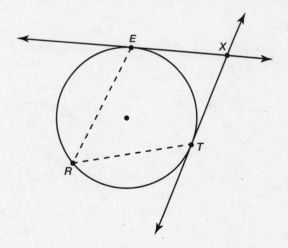

 Be prepared to share your solutions and methods.

Color Theory
Chords

LEARNING GOALS

In this lesson, you will:

- Determine the relationships between a chord and a diameter of a circle.
- Determine the relationships between congruent chords and their minor arcs.
- Prove the Diameter–Chord Theorem.
- Prove the Equidistant Chord Theorem.
- Prove the Equidistant Chord Converse Theorem.
- Prove the Congruent Chord–Congruent Arc Theorem.
- Prove the Congruent Chord–Congruent Arc Converse Theorem.
- Prove the Segment–Chord Theorem.

KEY TERMS

- Diameter–Chord Theorem
- Equidistant Chord Theorem
- Equidistant Chord Converse Theorem
- Congruent Chord–Congruent Arc Theorem
- Congruent Chord–Congruent Arc Converse Theorem
- segments of a chord
- Segment–Chord Theorem

Color theory is a set of rules that is used to create color combinations. A color wheel is a visual representation of color theory.

The color wheel is made of three different kinds of colors: primary, secondary, and tertiary. Primary colors (red, blue, and yellow) are the colors you start with. Secondary colors (orange, green, and purple) are created by mixing two primary colors. Tertiary colors (red-orange, yellow-orange, yellow-green, blue-green, blue-purple, red-purple) are created by mixing a primary color with a secondary color.

PROBLEM 1 Chords and Diameters

Chords and their perpendicular bisectors lead to several interesting conclusions. In this lesson, we will prove theorems to identify these special relationships.

1. Consider circle C with points B, Y, and R.

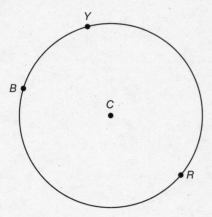

a. Draw chord $\overline{YR}$.

b. Construct the perpendicular bisector of chord YR.

c. Draw chord $\overline{BR}$.

d. Construct the perpendicular bisector of chord BR.

e. Draw chord $\overline{BY}$.

f. Construct the perpendicular bisector of chord BY.

g. What do you notice about the relationship between the perpendicular bisectors of a chord and the center point of the circle?

The perpendicular bisector of a chord appears to also bisect the chord's intercepted arc. This observation can be proved and stated as a theorem.

2. Prove the Diameter–Chord Conjecture.

Given: $\overline{MI}$ is a diameter of circle O.

$\overline{MI} \perp \overline{DA}$

Prove: $\overline{MI}$ bisects $\overline{DA}$.

$\overline{MI}$ bisects $\overparen{DA}$.

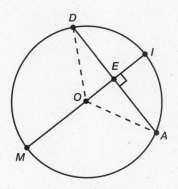

Statements	Reasons
1. $\overline{MI}$ is a diameter of circle O. $\overline{MI} \perp \overline{DA}$	**1.** Given
2. Connect points O and D to form chord $\overline{OD}$. Connect points O and A to form chord $\overline{OA}$.	**2.** Construction

Sweet!
We just proved
the Diameter–Chord
Conjecture!

The **Diameter–Chord Theorem** states: "If a circle's diameter is perpendicular to a chord, then the diameter bisects the chord and bisects the arc determined by the chord."

3. Use circle *T* to draw two congruent chords that are not parallel to each other and do not pass through the center point of the circle.

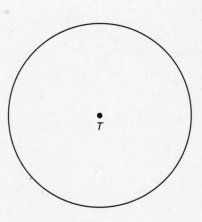

a. Construct the perpendicular bisector of each chord.

b. Use your compass to compare the distance each chord is from the center point of the circle.

Congruent chords appear to be equidistant from the center point of the circle. This observation can be proved and stated as a theorem.

4. Prove the Equidistant Chord Conjecture.

Given: $\overline{CH} \cong \overline{DR}$

$\overline{OE} \perp \overline{CH}$

$\overline{OI} \perp \overline{DR}$

Prove: $\overline{CH}$ and $\overline{DR}$ are equidistant from the center point.

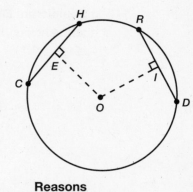

Here's a hint. You need to get OE = OI.

Statements	Reasons
1. $\overline{CH} \cong \overline{DR}$ $\overline{OE} \perp \overline{CH}$ $\overline{OI} \perp \overline{DR}$	1. Given
2. Connect points O and H, O and C, O and D, O and R to form radii OH, OC, OD, and OR, respectively.	2. Construction

All that work pays off. You have just proved the Equidistant Chord Conjecture . . . I mean, Equidistant Chord Theorem.

The **Equidistant Chord Theorem** states:
"If two chords of the same circle or congruent circles are congruent, then they are equidistant from the center of the circle."

The **Equidistant Chord Converse Theorem** states: "If two chords of the same circle or congruent circles are equidistant from the center of the circle, then the chords are congruent."

5. Prove the Equidistant Chord Converse Theorem.

Given: $OE = OI$ ($\overline{CH}$ and $\overline{DR}$ are equidistant from the center point.)

$\overline{OE} \perp \overline{CH}$

$\overline{OI} \perp \overline{DR}$

Prove: $\overline{CH} \cong \overline{DR}$

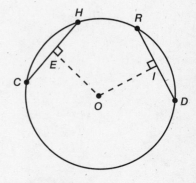

Statements	Reasons
1. $OE = OI$ $\overline{OE} \perp \overline{CH}$ $\overline{OI} \perp \overline{DR}$	1. Given
2. Connect points O and H, O and C, O and D, O and R to form radii $\overline{OH}$, $\overline{OC}$, $\overline{OD}$, and $\overline{OR}$, respectively.	2. Construction

6. Write the Equidistant Chord Theorem and the Equidistant Chord Converse Theorem as a biconditional statement.

A neighbor gave you a plate of cookies as a housewarming present. Before you could eat a single cookie, the cat jumped onto the kitchen counter and knocked the cookie plate onto the floor, shattering it into many pieces. The cookie plate will need to be replaced and returned to the neighbor. Unfortunately, cookie plates come in various sizes and you need to know the exact diameter of the broken plate. It would be impossible to reassemble all of the broken pieces, but one large chunk has remained intact as shown.

You think that there has to be an easy way to determine the diameter of the broken plate. As you sit staring at the large piece of the broken plate, your sister Sarah comes home from school. You update her on the latest crisis, and she begins to smile. Sarah tells you not to worry because she learned how to solve for the diameter of the plate in geometry class today. She gets a piece of paper, a compass, a straightedge, a ruler, and a marker out of her backpack and says, "Watch this!"

What does Sarah do? Describe how she can determine the diameter of the plate with the broken piece. Then, show your work on the broken plate shown.

PROBLEM 3 Chords and Arcs

1. Consider circle *C* shown.

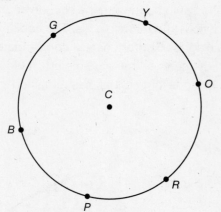

a. Draw two congruent chords.

b. Draw four radii by connecting the endpoints of each chord with the center point of the circle.

The two central angles formed by each pair of radii appear to be congruent; therefore, the minor arcs associated with each central angle are also congruent.

This observation can be proved and stated as a theorem.

2. Prove the Congruent Chord–Congruent Arc Theorem.

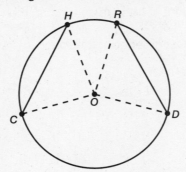

Given: $\overline{CH} \cong \overline{DR}$

Prove: $\overparen{CH} \cong \overparen{DR}$

Fantastic! You've just proved the Congruent Chord–Congruent Arc Conjecture. Now it's a theorem!

The **Congruent Chord–Congruent Arc Theorem** states: "If two chords of the same circle or congruent circles are congruent, then their corresponding arcs are congruent."

The **Congruent Chord–Congruent Arc Converse Theorem** states: "If two arcs of the same circle or congruent circles are congruent, then their corresponding chords are congruent."

3. Prove the Congruent Chord–Congruent Arc Converse Theorem.

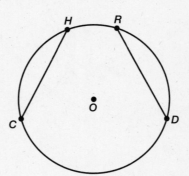

Given: $\overparen{CH} \cong \overparen{DR}$

Prove: $\overline{CH} \cong \overline{DR}$

Statements	Reasons
1. $\overparen{CH} \cong \overparen{DR}$	1. Given
2. Connect points O and H, O and C, O and D, and O and R to form radii OH, OC, OD, and OR, respectively.	2. Construction

4. Write the Congruent Chord–Congruent Arc Theorem and the Congruent Chord-Congruent Arc Converse Theorem as a biconditional statement.

Segments of a chord are the segments formed on a chord when two chords of a circle intersect.

1. Consider circle *C*.

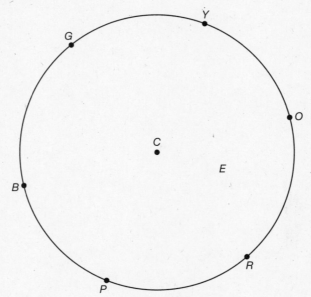

a. Draw two intersecting chords such that one chord connects two primary colors and the second chord connects to secondary colors.

b. Label the point at which the two chords intersect point *E*.

c. Use a ruler to measure the length of each segment on the two chords.

The product of the lengths of the segments on the first chord appears to be equal to the product of the lengths of the segments on the second chord.

This observation can be proved and stated as a theorem.

2. Prove the Segment-Chord Conjecture.

Given: Chords *HD* and *RC* intersect at point *E* in circle *O*.

Prove: $EH \cdot ED = ER \cdot EC$

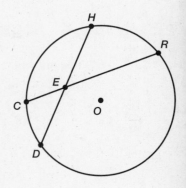

Connect points C and D, and points H and R. Show the triangles are similar.

Congrats! You've proved the Segment–Chord Theorem. Nice work! Now you can use this theorem as a valid reason in proofs.

The **Segment–Chord Theorem** states that "if two chords in a circle intersect, then the product of the lengths of the segments of one chord is equal to the product of the lengths of the segments of the second chord."

Be prepared to share your solutions and methods.

Solar Eclipses
Tangents and Secants

LEARNING GOALS

In this lesson, you will:

- Determine the relationship between a tangent line and a radius.
- Determine the relationship between congruent tangent segments.
- Prove the Tangent Segment Theorem.
- Prove the Secant Segment Theorem.
- Prove the Secant Tangent Theorem.

KEY TERMS

- tangent segment
- Tangent Segment Theorem
- secant segment
- external secant segment
- Secant Segment Theorem
- Secant Tangent Theorem

Total solar eclipses occur when the moon passes between Earth and the sun. The position of the moon creates a shadow on the surface of Earth.

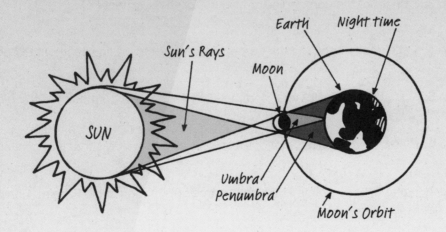

A pair of tangent lines forms the boundaries of the umbra, the lighter part of the shadow. Another pair of tangent lines forms the boundaries of the penumbra, the darker part of the shadow.

Constructing a Line Tangent to a Circle

9

Previously, you proved that when a tangent line is drawn to a circle, a radius of the circle drawn to the point of tangency is perpendicular to the tangent line. This lesson focuses on tangent lines drawn to a circle from a point outside the circle.

Follow these steps to construct a tangent line to a circle through a point outside of the circle.

Step 1: Draw a circle with center point C and locate point P outside of the circle.

Step 2: Draw line segment PC.

Step 3: Construct the perpendicular bisector of line segment PC.

Step 4: Label the midpoint of the perpendicular bisector of line segment PC point M.

Step 5: Adjust the radius of your compass to the distance from point M to point C.

Step 6: Place the compass point on point M, and cut two arcs that intersect circle C.

Step 7: Label the two points at which the arcs cut through circle C point A and point B.

Step 8: Connect point P and A to form tangent line PA and connect point P and B to form tangent line PB.

Line PA and line PB are tangent to circle C.

For the purposes of the problem situation, the Moon, the Sun, and Earth are represented by circles of different sizes.

Consider point *P* located outside of the Moon, Earth, and the Sun. Lines *AF* and *BE* are drawn tangent to the Moon, Earth, and the Sun as shown.

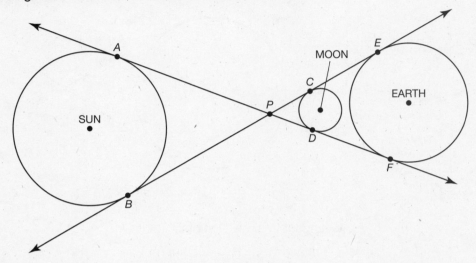

A **tangent segment** is a line segment formed by connecting a point outside of the circle to a point of tangency.

1. Identify the two tangent segments drawn from point *P* associated with the Sun. Then, use a compass to compare the length of the two segments.

The figure is not drawn to scale because the sun is actually over 100 times larger than the Earth.

2. Identify the tangent segments drawn from point *P* associated with the Moon. Then, use a compass to compare the length of the two line segments.

3. Identify the tangent segments drawn from point *P* associated with the Earth. Then, use a compass to compare the length of the two line segments.

It appears that two tangent segments drawn to the same circle from the same point outside of the circle are congruent.

This observation can be proved and stated as a theorem.

4. Prove the Tangent Segment Conjecture.

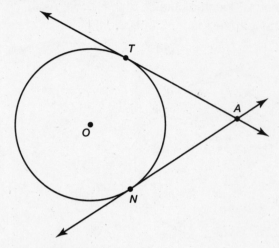

Given: $\overleftrightarrow{AT}$ is tangent to circle O at point T.

$\overleftrightarrow{AN}$ is tangent to circle O at point N.

Prove: $\overline{AT} \cong \overline{AN}$

Woot! The Tangent Segment Theorem. I can call it that now because I just proved it.

The **Tangent Segment Theorem** states: "If two tangent segments are drawn from the same point on the exterior of a circle, then the tangent segments are congruent."

5. In the figure, $\overleftrightarrow{KP}$ and $\overleftrightarrow{KS}$ are tangent to circle W and $m\angle PKS = 46°$. Calculate $m\angle KPS$. Explain your reasoning.

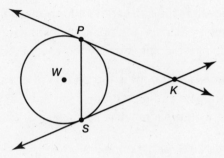

6. In the figure, $\overleftrightarrow{PS}$ is tangent to circle M and $m\angle SMO = 119°$. Calculate $m\angle MPS$. Explain your reasoning.

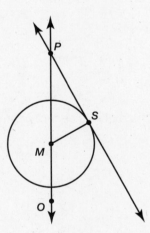

PROBLEM 3 Secant Segments

A **secant segment** is the line segment formed when two secants intersect outside a circle. A secant segment begins at the point at which the two secants intersect, continues into the circle, and ends at the point at which the secant exits the circle.

An **external secant segment** is the portion of each secant segment that lies on the outside of the circle. It begins at the point at which the two secants intersect and ends at the point where the secant enters the circle.

9

1. Consider circle C with the measurements as shown.

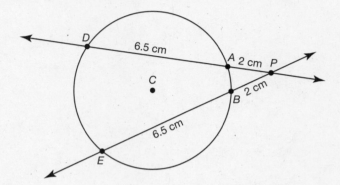

The vertex of ∠DPE is located outside of circle C. Because this angle is formed by the intersection of two secants, each secant line contains a secant segment and an external secant segment.

a. Identify the two secant segments.

b. Identify the two external secant segments.

It appears that the product of the lengths of the segment and its external secant segment is equal to the product of the lengths of the second secant segment and its external secant segment.

This observation can be proved and stated as a theorem.

2. Prove the Secant Segment Conjecture.

Given: Secants CS and CN intersect at point C in the exterior of circle O.

Prove: $CS \cdot CE = CN \cdot CA$

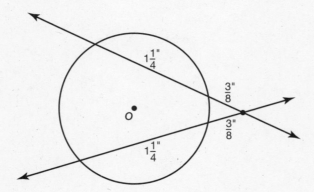

It may be helpful to connect points A and S, and points E and N.

The **Secant Segment Theorem** states: "If two secants intersect in the exterior of a circle, then the product of the lengths of the secant segment and its external secant segment is equal to the product of the lengths of the second secant segment and its external secant segment."

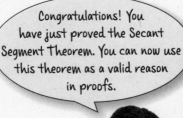

Congratulations! You have just proved the Secant Segment Theorem. You can now use this theorem as a valid reason in proofs.

3. Consider circle *C* with the measurements as shown.

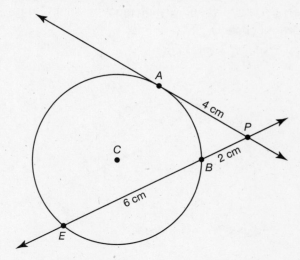

The vertex of ∠*APE* is located outside of circle *C*. Because this angle is formed by the intersection of a secant and a tangent, the secant line contains a secant segment and an external secant segment whereas the tangent line contains a tangent segment.

a. Identify the secant segment.

b. Identify the external secant segment.

c. Identify the tangent segment.

It appears that the product of the lengths of the segment and its external secant segment is equal to the square of the length of the tangent segment.

This observation can be proved and stated as a theorem.

4. Prove the Secant Tangent Conjecture.

Given: Tangent AT and secant AG intersect at point A in the exterior of circle O.

Prove: $(AT)^2 = AG \cdot AN$

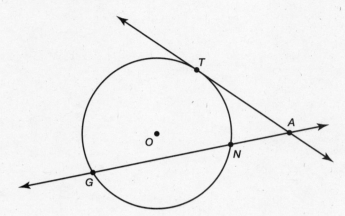

The **Secant Tangent Theorem** states: "If a tangent and a secant intersect in the exterior of a circle, then the product of the lengths of the secant segment and its external secant segment is equal to the square of the length of the tangent segment."

Be prepared to share your solutions and methods.

9

Chapter 9 Summary

- center of a circle (9.1)
- radius (9.1)
- chord (9.1)
- diameter (9.1)
- secant of a circle (9.1)
- tangent of a circle (9.1)
- point of tangency (9.1)
- central angle (9.1)
- inscribed angle (9.1)
- arc (9.1)
- major arc (9.1)
- minor arc (9.1)
- semicircle (9.1)
- degree measure of an arc (9.2)
- adjacent arcs (9.2)
- intercepted arc (9.2)
- segments of a chord (9.4)
- tangent segment (9.5)
- secant segment (9.5)
- external secant segment (9.5)

- Arc Addition Postulate (9.2)
- Inscribed Angle Theorem (9.2)
- Parallel Lines-Congruent Arcs Theorem (9.2)
- Interior Angles of a Circle Theorem (9.3)
- Exterior Angles of a Circle Theorem (9.3)
- Tangent to a Circle Theorem (9.3)
- Diameter-Chord Theorem (9.4)
- Equidistant Chord Theorem (9.4)
- Equidistant Chord Converse Theorem (9.4)
- Congruent Chord-Congruent Arc Theorem (9.4)
- Congruent Chord-Congruent Arc Converse Theorem (9.4)
- Segment-Chord Theorem (9.4)
- Tangent Segment Theorem (9.5)
- Secant Segment Theorem (9.5)
- Secant Tangent Theorem (9.5)

9

Identifying Parts of a Circle

A circle is the set of all points in a plane that are equidistant from a given point. The following are parts of a circle.

- The center of a circle is a point inside the circle that is equidistant from every point on the circle.

- A radius of a circle is a line segment that is the distance from a point on the circle to the center of the circle.

- A chord is a segment whose endpoints are on a circle.

- A diameter of a circle is a chord across a circle that passes through the center.

- A secant is a line that intersects a circle at exactly two points.

- A tangent is a line that intersects a circle at exactly one point, and this point is called the point of tangency.

- A central angle is an angle of a circle whose vertex is the center of the circle.

- An inscribed angle is an angle of a circle whose vertex is on the circle.

- A major arc of a circle is the largest arc formed by a secant and a circle.

- A minor arc of a circle is the smallest arc formed by a secant and a circle.

- A semicircle is exactly half a circle.

Examples

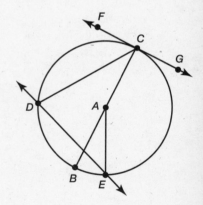

- Point *A* is the center of circle *A*.

- Segments *AB*, *AC*, and *AE* are radii of circle *A*.

- Segment *BC* is a diameter of circle *A*.

- Segments *BC*, *DC*, and *DE* are chords of circle *A*.

- Line *DE* is a secant of circle *A*.

- Line *FG* is a tangent of circle *A*, and point *C* is a point of tangency.

- Angle *BAE* and angle *CAE* are central angles.

- Angle *BCD* and angle *CDE* are inscribed angles.

- Arcs *BDE*, *CDE*, *CED*, *DCE*, and *DCB* are major arcs.

- Arcs *BD*, *BE*, *CD*, *CE*, and *DE* are minor arcs.

- Arc *BDC* and arc *BEC* are semicircles.

9.2 Determining Measures of Arcs

The degree measure of a minor arc is the same as the degree measure of its central angle.

Example

In circle Z, $\angle XZY$ is a central angle measuring 120°. So, $m\overarc{XY} = 120°$.

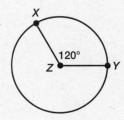

9.2 Using the Arc Addition Postulate

Adjacent arcs are two arcs of the same circle sharing a common endpoint. The Arc Addition Postulate states: "The measure of an arc formed by two adjacent arcs is equal to the sum of the measures of the two arcs."

Example

In circle A, arcs BC and CD are adjacent arcs. So, $m\overarc{BCD} = m\overarc{BC} + m\overarc{CD} = 180° + 35° = 215°$.

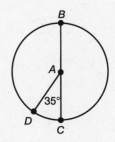

9.2 **Using the Inscribed Angle Theorem**

The Inscribed Angle Theorem states: "The measure of an inscribed angle is one half the measure of its intercepted arc."

Example

In circle M, $\angle JKL$ is an inscribed angle whose intercepted arc JL measures 66°.

So, $m\angle JKL = \frac{1}{2}(m\widehat{JL}) = \frac{1}{2}(66°) = 33°$.

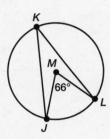

9.2 **Using the Parallel Lines–Congruent Arcs Theorem**

The Parallel Lines-Congruent Arcs Theorem states: "Parallel lines intercept congruent arcs on a circle."

Example

Lines AB and CD are parallel lines on circle Q and $m\widehat{AC} = 60°$. So, $m\widehat{AC} = m\widehat{BD}$, and $m\widehat{BD} = 60°$.

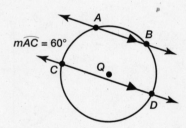

9.3 Using the Interior Angles of a Circle Theorem

The Interior Angles of a Circle Theorem states: "If an angle is formed by two intersecting chords or secants such that the vertex of the angle is in the interior of the circle, then the measure of the angle is half the sum of the measures of the arcs intercepted by the angle and its vertical angle."

Example

In circle P, chords QR and ST intersect to form vertex angle TVR and its vertical angle QVS. So, $m\angle TVR = \frac{1}{2}(m\overarc{TR} + m\overarc{QS}) = \frac{1}{2}(110° + 38°) = \frac{1}{2}(148°) = 74°$.

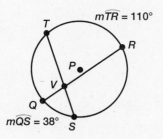

$m\overarc{TR} = 110°$

$m\overarc{QS} = 38°$

9.3 Using the Exterior Angles of a Circle Theorem

The Exterior Angles of a Circle Theorem states: "If an angle is formed by two intersecting secants, two intersecting tangents, or an intersecting tangent and secant such that the vertex of the angle is in the exterior of the circle, then the measure of the angle is half the difference of the measures of the arc(s) intercepted by the angle."

Example

In circle C, secant FH and tangent FG intersect to form vertex angle GFH.

So, $m\angle GFH = \frac{1}{2}(m\overarc{GH} - m\overarc{JG}) = \frac{1}{2}(148° - 45°) = \frac{1}{2}(103°) = 51.5°$.

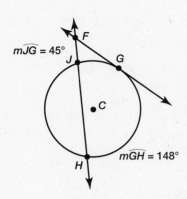

$m\overarc{JG} = 45°$

$m\overarc{GH} = 148°$

9.3 Using the Tangent to a Circle Theorem

The Tangent to a Circle Theorem states: "A line drawn tangent to a circle is perpendicular to a radius of the circle drawn to the point of tangency."

Example

Radius $\overline{OP}$ is perpendicular to the tangent line s.

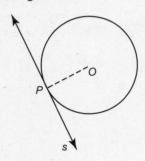

9.4 Using the Diameter-Chord Theorem

The Diameter-Chord Theorem states: "If a circle's diameter is perpendicular to a chord, then the diameter bisects the chord and bisects the arc determined by the chord."

Example

In circle K, diameter $\overline{ST}$ is perpendicular to chord $\overline{FG}$. So $FR = GR$ and $m\overset{\frown}{FT} = m\overset{\frown}{GT}$.

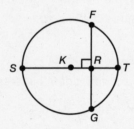

9.4 Using the Equidistant Chord Theorem and the Equidistant Chord Converse Theorem

The Equidistant Chord Theorem states: "If two chords of the same circle or congruent circles are congruent, then they are equidistant from the center of the circle."

The Equidistant Chord Converse Theorem states: "If two chords of the same circle or congruent circles are equidistant from the center of the circle, then the chords are congruent."

Example

In circle A, chord $\overline{CD}$ is congruent to chord $\overline{XY}$. So $PA = QA$.

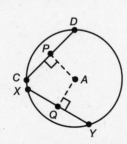

Using the Congruent Chord–Congruent Arc Theorem and the Congruent Chord–Congruent Arc Converse Theorem

The Congruent Chord–Congruent Arc Theorem states: "If two chords of the same circle or congruent circles are congruent, then their corresponding arcs are congruent."

The Congruent Chord–Congruent Arc Converse Theorem states: "If two arcs of the same circle or congruent circles are congruent, then their corresponding chords are congruent.

Example

In circle X, chord $\overline{JK}$ is congruent to chord $\overline{QR}$. So $m\overset{\frown}{JK} = m\overset{\frown}{QR}$.

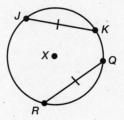

9.4 **Using the Segment-Chord Theorem**

Segments of a chord are the segments formed on a chord when two chords of a circle intersect.

The Segment-Chord Theorem states: "If two chords in a circle intersect, then the product of the lengths of the segments of one chord is equal to the product of the lengths of the segments of the second chord."

Example

In circle H, chords $\overline{LM}$ and $\overline{VW}$ intersect to form $\overline{LK}$ and $\overline{MK}$ of chord $\overline{LM}$ and $\overline{WK}$ and $\overline{VK}$ of chord $\overline{VW}$. So $LK \cdot MK = WK \cdot VK$.

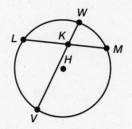

Using the Tangent Segment Theorem

A tangent segment is a segment formed from an exterior point of a circle to the point of tangency.

The Tangent Segment Theorem states: "If two tangent segments are drawn from the same point on the exterior of a circle, then the tangent segments are congruent."

Example

In circle Z, tangent segments $\overline{SR}$ and $\overline{ST}$ are both drawn from point S outside the circle. So, $SR = ST$.

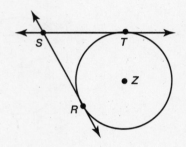

Using the Secant Segment Theorem

A secant segment is a segment formed when two secants intersect in the exterior of a circle. An external secant segment is the portion of a secant segment that lies on the outside of the circle.

The Secant Segment Theorem states: "If two secant segments intersect in the exterior of a circle, then the product of the lengths of one secant segment and its external secant segment is equal to the product of the lengths of the second secant segment and its external secant segment."

Example

In circle B, secant segments $\overline{GH}$ and $\overline{NP}$ intersect at point C outside the circle. So, $GC \cdot HC = NC \cdot PC$.

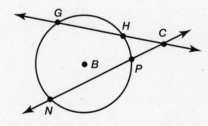

Using the Secant Tangent Theorem

The Secant Tangent Theorem states: "If a tangent and a secant intersect in the exterior of a circle, then the product of the lengths of the secant segment and its external secant segment is equal to the square of the length of the tangent segment."

Example

In circle F, tangent $\overline{QR}$ and secant $\overline{YZ}$ intersect at point Q outside the circle. So, $QY \cdot QZ = QR^2$.

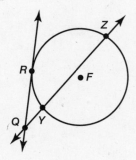

Arcs and Sectors of Circles

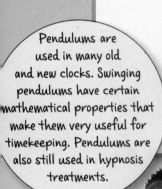

Replacement for a Carpenter's Square

Inscribed and Circumscribed Triangles and Quadrilaterals

A carpenter's square is a tool that is used to create right angles. These "squares" are usually made of a strong material such as metal so that the right angle is not easily bent or broken. It is a useful tool for stair and roof framing, especially to ensure that all building codes are being maintained.

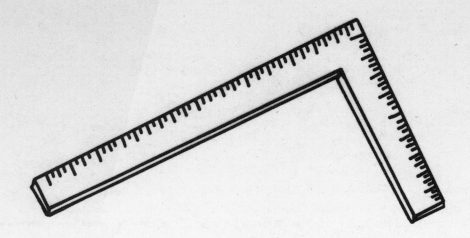

PROBLEM 1 In Need of a New Tool

 A carpenter is working on building a children's playhouse. She accidentally drops her carpenter's square, and the right angle gets bent. She still needs to cut out a piece of plywood that is in the shape of a right triangle. So, the carpenter gets out her compass and her straightedge to get the job done.

1. Use the steps to re-create how the carpenter created the right triangle.

   a. The hypotenuse of the triangle needs to be 6 centimeters. Use your ruler and open your compass to 3 centimeters. In the space provided, draw a circle with a diameter of 6 centimeters. Use the given point as the center.

   b. Use your straightedge to draw a diameter on the circle.

   c. One of the legs of the triangle is to be 4 centimeters long. Open your compass to 4 centimeters. Place the point of your compass on one of the endpoints of the diameter and draw an arc that passes through the circle.

   d. Use your straightedge to draw segments from the endpoints of the diameter to the intersection of the circle and the arc.

   e. Use your protractor to verify that this triangle is a right triangle.

•

An **inscribed polygon** is a polygon drawn inside a circle such that each vertex of the polygon touches the circle.

10

2. Consider △ABC that is inscribed in circle P.

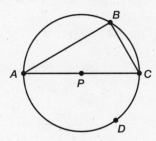

a. What do you know about $\overline{AC}$?

b. What do you know about $m\overset{\frown}{ADC}$? Explain your reasoning.

c. What does this tell you about $m\angle ABC$? Explain your reasoning.

d. What kind of triangle is △ABC? How do you know?

3. Write an Inscribed Right Triangle–Diameter Conjecture about the kind of triangle inscribed in a circle when one side of the triangle is a diameter.

4. Write the converse of the conjecture you wrote in Question 3. Do you think this statement is also true?

It would appear that △ABC is a right triangle and that ∠B is a right angle. This observation can be stated as a theorem and then proved.

5. Create a proof of the Inscribed Right Triangle–Diameter Conjecture.

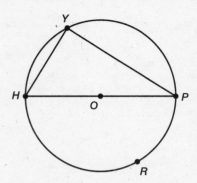

Given: △HYP is inscribed in circle O such that $\overline{HP}$ is the diameter of the circle.

Prove: △HYP is a right triangle.

Nice work! You have just proved the Inscribed Right Triangle–Diameter Theorem.

The **Inscribed Right Triangle–Diameter Theorem** states: "If a triangle is inscribed in a circle such that one side of the triangle is a diameter of the circle, then the triangle is a right triangle."

The converse of the Inscribed Right Triangle–Diameter Theorem can also be proved as a separate theorem. The converse is used in a situation when you are given an inscribed right triangle and want to conclude that one side of the inscribed triangle is a diameter of the circle.

6. Create a proof of the Inscribed Right Triangle–Diameter Converse Conjecture.

Given: Right △HYP is inscribed in circle O.

Prove: $\overline{HP}$ is the diameter of circle O.

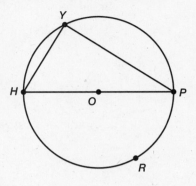

Oops, we did it again! We proved the Right Triangle–Diameter Converse Conjecture. And now it's a theorem.

 The **Inscribed Right Triangle–Diameter Converse Theorem** states: "If a right triangle is inscribed in a circle, then the hypotenuse is a diameter of the circle."

A **circumscribed polygon** is a polygon drawn outside a circle such that each side of the polygon is tangent to a circle.

7. Mr. Scalene asks his geometry class to draw a triangle and to use a compass to draw a circle inside the triangle such that the circle was tangent to each side of the triangle. See if you can do this.

   a. Use a straightedge to draw a triangle.

   b. Use your compass to construct a circle inside the triangle such that each side of the triangle is tangent to the circle.

This has something to do with points of concurrency!

Quadrilaterals and Circles

1. Consider the relationship between opposite angles of an inscribed quadrilateral.

   a. Use your compass to draw a circle.

   b. Use your straightedge to draw an inscribed quadrilateral that is not a parallelogram in your circle. Label the vertices of your quadrilateral.

   c. Use your protractor to determine the measures of the angles of the quadrilateral. What is the relationship between the measures of each pair of opposite angles?

   d. Write an Inscribed Quadrilateral–Opposite Angles Conjecture about the opposite angles of an inscribed quadrilateral.

It would appear that opposite angles of the inscribed quadrilateral are supplementary. This observation can be stated as a theorem and then proved.

2. Create a proof of the Inscribed Quadrilateral–Opposite Angles Conjecture.

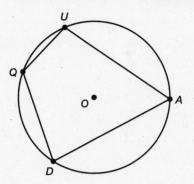

Given: Quadrilateral *QUAD* is inscribed in circle *O*.

Prove: ∠*Q* and ∠*A* are supplementary angles.
∠*U* and ∠*D* are supplementary angles.

The **Inscribed Quadrilateral–Opposite Angles Theorem** states:

"If a quadrilateral is inscribed in a circle, then the opposite angles are supplementary."

Way to go! You have just proved the Inscribed Quadrilateral–Opposite Angles Theorem.

PROBLEM Circumscribed Quadrilaterals

 Ms. Rhombi asks her geometry class to draw a quadrilateral and to use a compass to draw a circle inside the quadrilateral such that the circle was tangent to each side of the quadrilateral.

Most of her students use a straightedge and a compass, draw a quadrilateral, and try to draw a circle inside the quadrilateral as shown.

Well, THAT doesn't look right. I bet there's a better way to do this.

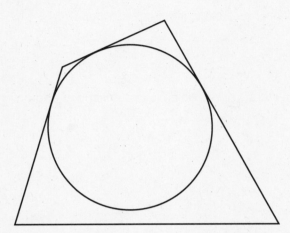

One of her students has talked to a friend who happens to be in Mr. Scalene's class, so she knows exactly what to do if it was a triangle. Let's see if you are able to circumscribe the quadrilateral the same way you circumscribed the triangle.

 1. Construct a circle inscribed in the quadrilateral shown. Explain your process.

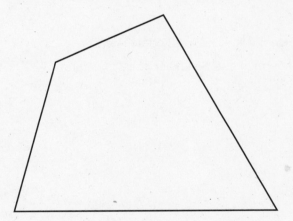

2. Ms. Rhombi then writes a theorem on the blackboard:

A circle can be inscribed in a quadrilateral if and only if the angle bisectors of the four angles of the quadrilateral are concurrent.

Using this theorem, how can you tell if it is possible to inscribe a circle in the quadrilateral in Question 1?

Is it possible to inscribe a circle in this quadrilateral?

3. Consider quadrilateral *WXYZ*, which is circumscribed about circle *C* as shown.

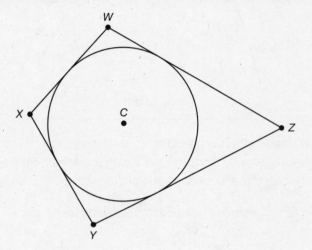

Given: *WX* + *YZ* = 23 centimeters

Determine the perimeter of quadrilateral *WXYZ*.

4. Karl raises his hand and informs Ms. Rhombi that he has discovered another property related to the angles of an inscribed quadrilateral. Karl shows his teacher the diagram shown.

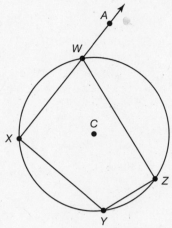

He claims that the measure of any exterior angle of the quadrilateral is equal to the measure of the opposite interior angle in the quadrilateral. In other words, $m\angle AWZ = m\angle Y$.

Explain Karl's reasoning.

 Be prepared to share your solutions and methods.

10

Gears
Arc Length

LEARNING GOALS

In this lesson, you will:

- Distinguish between arc measure and arc length.
- Use a formula to solve for arc length in degree measures.
- Distinguish between degree measure and radian measure.
- Use a formula to solve for arc length in radian measures.

KEY TERMS

- arc length
- radian

Gears are used in many mechanical devices to provide torque, or the force that causes rotation. For instance, an electric screwdriver contains gears. The motor of an electric screwdriver can make the spinning components spin very fast, but the gears are needed to provide the force to push a screw into place. Gears can be very large or very small, depending on their application.

PROBLEM 1 Large and Small Gears

1. Consider the large gear represented by circle O, containing a central angle; $\angle AOB$, whose measure is equal to 60°; a minor arc, $\overset{\frown}{AB}$; and a major arc, $\overset{\frown}{ACB}$, as shown.

   Consider the small gear represented by circle E, containing a central angle; $\angle FEG$, whose measure is equal to 60°; a minor arc, $\overset{\frown}{FG}$; and a major arc, $\overset{\frown}{FDG}$, as shown.

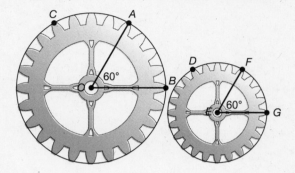

   a. Is the large gear similar to the small gear? Explain your reasoning.

   b. Is the length of the radii in the large gear proportional to the length of the radii in the small gear? Explain your reasoning.

   c. Determine the degree measure of the minor arc in each circle.

   d. What is the ratio of the degree measure of the minor arc to the degree measure of the entire circle for each of the two gears?

   e. The degree measure of the intercepted arc in the large gear is equal to the degree measure of the intercepted arc in the small gear, but do the two intercepted arcs appear to be the same length?

2. Explain why Casey is incorrect.

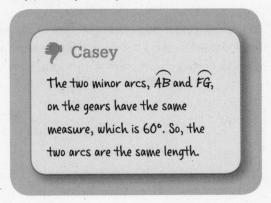

> 👎 **Casey**
>
> The two minor arcs, $\overset{\frown}{AB}$ and $\overset{\frown}{FG}$, on the gears have the same measure, which is 60°. So, the two arcs are the same length.

Arc length is a portion of the circumference of a circle. The *length* of an arc is different from the *degree measure* of the arc. Arcs are measured in degrees whereas arc lengths are linear measurements.

To determine the arc length of the minor arc, you need to work with the circumference of the circle, which requires knowing the radius of the circle.

3. If the length of the radius of the large gear, or line segment *OB* is equal to 4 centimeters, determine the circumference of circle *O*.

4. Use the circumference of circle *O* determined in Question 3 and the ratio determined in Question 1, part (d) to solve for the length of the minor arc.

5. If the length of the radius of the small gear, or line segment *EF*, is equal to 2 centimeters, determine the circumference of circle *E*.

6. Use the circumference of circle *E* determined in Question 5 and the ratio determined in Question 1, part (d) to solve for the length of the minor arc.

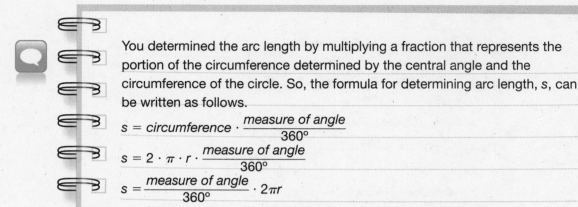

You determined the arc length by multiplying a fraction that represents the portion of the circumference determined by the central angle and the circumference of the circle. So, the formula for determining arc length, s, can be written as follows.

$$s = \text{circumference} \cdot \frac{\text{measure of angle}}{360°}$$

$$s = 2 \cdot \pi \cdot r \cdot \frac{\text{measure of angle}}{360°}$$

$$s = \frac{\text{measure of angle}}{360°} \cdot 2\pi r$$

It is important to notice that this formula implies

- $\frac{s}{r} = m \cdot \frac{\pi}{180°}$, where m is the measure of the angle.

- $\frac{s}{r}$ is directly proportional to the measure of the central angle, m.

7. Calculate the arc length of each circle. Express your answer in terms of π.

a.

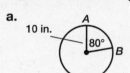

10 in.

80°

b.

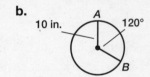

10 in.

120°

c.

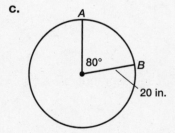

80°

20 in.

d.

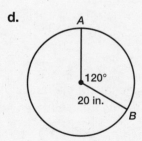

120°

20 in.

8. Look at Question 7, parts (a) and (c) as well as Question 7, parts (b) and (d). In each pair, the central angle is the same but the radius has been doubled. What effect does doubling the radius have on the length of the arc? Justify why this relationship exist?

9. Two semicircular cuts were taken from the rectangular region shown. Determine the perimeter of the shaded region. Do not express your answer in terms of π.

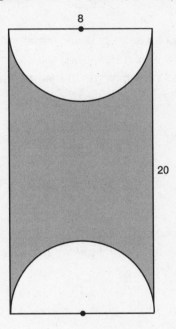

10. Use the diagram shown to answer each question.

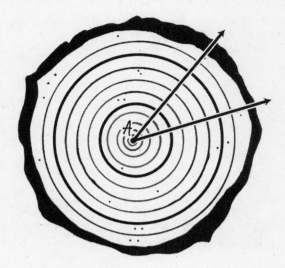

a. The radius of a small tree ring (small circle) is *r*, and the radius of a larger tree ring (large circle) is 10*r*. How does the arc length of the minor arc in the small tree ring compare to the arc length of the minor arc in the large tree ring?

b. If the arc length of the minor arc in the small tree ring is equal to 3 inches, what is the arc length of the minor arc in the large tree ring?

c. If $m\angle A = 20°$, the length of the radius of the small tree ring is *r*, the length of the radius of the large tree ring is 10*r*, and the length of the minor arc of the small tree ring is 3 inches, determine the circumference of the large tree ring.

Amy is a summer intern at a manufacturing plant. One of the machines at the plant consists of two wheels with a belt connecting the two wheels. The radius of the smaller wheel is 3 centimeters. The radius of the larger wheel is 5 centimeters. The centers of the wheels are 14 centimeters apart.

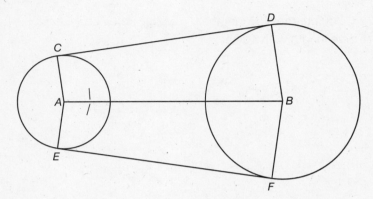

Amy's first task for her new internship is to calculate the length of the belt that will fit snugly around the two wheels. She notices that the belt can be divided into four sections. Help Amy calculate the length of the belt.

1. Describe the four sections that Amy noticed.

2. Draw a segment from point *A* perpendicular to radius $\overline{DB}$. Label the point of intersection point *G*. Draw a segment from point *A* perpendicular to radius $\overline{BF}$. Label the point of intersection point *H*.

3. Classify quadrilateral *ACDG*. Explain your reasoning.

4. Classify triangle *AGB*. Explain your reasoning.

5. Calculate the side lengths of triangle *ABG*. Label each side length in the diagram.

Some side lengths involve radicals. Simplify the radical for now instead of using a decimal approximation. This will help to minimize rounding errors in calculations.

6. Calculate the length of $\overline{CD}$.

Good job, now you've got two of the four pieces you need!

7. The length of the belt along each circle is an arc length. Describe what information is needed to calculate an arc length.

8. Calculate the measure of major arc *DF* by first calculating the measure of the central angle for major arc *DF*.

9. Calculate the length of major arc *DF*.

10. Calculate the length of minor arc *CE*.

11. Calculate the total length of the belt.

So far you have described the measures of angles and arcs using degrees. A *radian* is another unit that can be used to measure angles and arcs.

One **radian** is defined as the measure of a central angle whose arc length is the same as the radius of the circle.

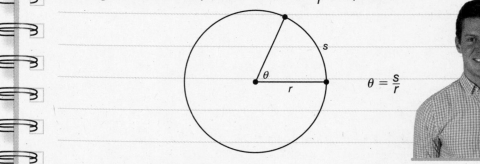

Let r represent the length of the radius of the circle, θ represent the measure of the central angle in radians, and s represent the length of the intercepted arc. Note that $\frac{s}{r}$ is equal to θ.

You read the symbol θ as "theta."

$$\theta = \frac{s}{r}$$

The circle has a radius of length r. The circumference of the circle is $2\pi r$. There are 360° in a circle.

Because 360° is equivalent to $\frac{2\pi r}{r} = 2\pi$ radians, it follows that 180° is equivalent to π radians.

Therefore, $\dfrac{radian\ measure}{degree\ measure} = \dfrac{\pi}{180°}$ and $\dfrac{degree\ measure}{radian\ measure} = \dfrac{180°}{\pi}$

When converting degrees to radians, multiply a degree measure by $\dfrac{\pi}{180°}$.

When converting radians to degrees, multiply a degree measure by $\dfrac{180°}{\pi}$.

1. If $\theta = \frac{\pi}{2}$ and $r = 4$, solve for the length of the intercepted arc.

2. If $r = 2$ and the intercepted arc length is 5, what is the measure of the central angle?

3. At the same central angle θ, if the radius is 6 centimeters, what is the arc length of the intercepted arc?

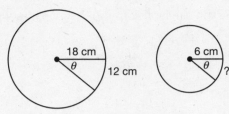

4. The measure of a central angle is 120°. The length of the radius is 20 centimeters.

   a. Determine the arc length using the formula:
$$\frac{measure\ of\ angle}{360°} \cdot 2\pi r$$

   b. Determine the arc length using the formula:
$$\theta = \frac{s}{r}$$

   c. Compare your answers in part (a) and part (b).

Talk the Talk

1. Describe the similarities and differences between radians and degrees.

Most mathematicians, physicists, and other scientists use radians to describe degree measures.

2. Which unit do you prefer to use? Explain your reasoning.

Be prepared to share your solutions and methods.

10

Playing Darts
Sectors and Segments of a Circle

The game of darts has a lot of interesting language associated with it. Players have given special names to certain types of scores. For example, a "Bed and Breakfast" happens when a player scores a 20, a 5, and a 1 on his or her turn. When a player lands on a triple score, a double score, and a single score all in the same sector of the dartboard, that's called a "Shanghai." And trying to end a game by getting a double score of 2 is apparently so frustrating that it has been called the "Madhouse."

The term "hat trick" is also used in darts. Can you guess what a hat trick is?

A standard dartboard is shown. Each section of the board is surrounded by wire, and the numbers indicate scoring for the game. For a single throw, the highest possible score can be achieved by landing a dart at the very center or the bull's-eye, of the dartboard.

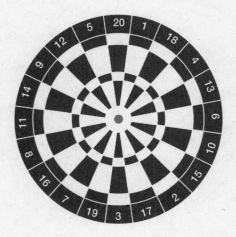

Concentric circles are circles that share the same center point.

 1. How many concentric circles do you see in the dartboard shown, not including the dartboard itself? Draw these circles.

2. The diameter of the outermost circle is 170 millimeters. Calculate its area. Express your answer in terms of π.

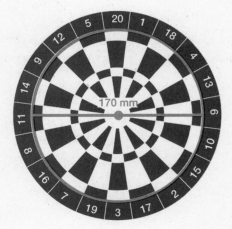

170 mm

A **sector of a circle** is a region of the circle bounded by two radii and the included arc.

3. The dartboard can be divided into congruent sectors.

Each sector looks like a piece of pizza.

a. Determine the number of sectors contained in the outermost circle.

b. Determine the measure of the central angle and the measure of the intercepted arc formed by each sector.

c. Determine the ratio of the length of each intercepted arc to the circumference.

d. Determine the ratio of the area of each section to the area of the circle.

e. Determine the area contained by each of these sectors of the circle. Express your answer in terms of π. Explain how you determined the area.

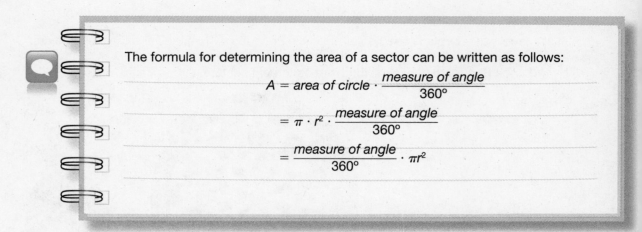

The formula for determining the area of a sector can be written as follows:

$$A = \text{area of circle} \cdot \frac{\text{measure of angle}}{360°}$$

$$= \pi \cdot r^2 \cdot \frac{\text{measure of angle}}{360°}$$

$$= \frac{\text{measure of angle}}{360°} \cdot \pi r^2$$

4. How does the formula for determining the area of a sector compare to the formula for determining the arc length.

The innermost circle of the dartboard has a diameter of 108 millimeters and is divided into 20 congruent sectors as shown.

5. Darcy and Mike notice that half of the sectors of the innermost circle on the dartboard are the same color. Mike says that to calculate the total area of all the sectors of the same color, he could calculate the area of half the circle. Darcy says to, instead, calculate the area of one sector and multiply that area by 10.

Who's correct? Explain your reasoning.

PROBLEM 2 Segment of a Circle

A **segment of a circle** is a region of the circle bounded by a chord and the included arc.

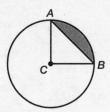

1. Name the chord and the arc that bound the shaded segment of the circle.

Maybe the area of the segment is the area of something minus the area of something else . . .

2. Describe a method to calculate the area of the segment of the circle.

3. If the length of the radius of circle *C* is 8 centimeters and $m\angle ACB = 90°$, use your method to determine the area of the shaded segment of the circle. Express your answer in terms of π. Then, rewrite your answer rounded to the nearest hundredth.

4. The area of the segment shown is $9\pi - 18$ square feet. Calculate the radius of circle O.

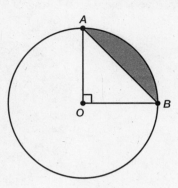

5. The area of the segment is 10.26 square feet. Calculate the radius of circle O.

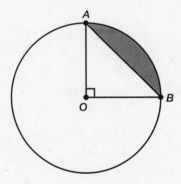

6. The length of the radius is 10 inches. Calculate the area of the shaded region of circle O. Express your answer in terms of π.

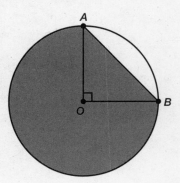

James covers the entire top of his piece of pie with whipped cream, but he doesn't like to eat the upper portion of the pie crust where it is thickest.

$\overline{EP}$ and $\overline{EI}$ are radii of a circle.

$m\overline{EP} = 4''$

$m\angle PEI = 60°$

Upper crust

1. What in this situation relates to a sector of a circle?

2. What in this situation relates to a segment of a circle?

3. If each piece of pie is the same size, how many pieces are in the pie?

4. Determine the area to be covered with whipped cream before James removes the upper crust.

5. Determine the area to be covered with whipped cream on only the upper crust.

6. Determine the length of the upper crust.

Be prepared to share your solutions and methods.

Circle K. Excellent!
Circle Problems

In this lesson, you will:

- Use formulas associated with circles to solve problems.
- Use theorems associated with circles to solve problems.
- Use angular velocity and linear velocity to solve problems.

- linear velocity
- angular velocity

A pendulum is a freely swinging weight, usually attached to a string or wire which is fixed at one of its ends. You can discover something really interesting about a pendulum by conducting a simple experiment:

While keeping the string or wire tight and fixed, move the weight to an angle of about 10 degrees to vertical. Let go, and time how long it takes for the weight to make 10 swings up and back. Then, repeat this process with the weight starting at about 20 degrees to vertical.

What you should find is that the times are almost exact! This is why pendulums are so useful for keeping time.

PROBLEM 1 Ferris Wheel

 This Ferris wheel is 50 meters tall. The actual wheel is constructed with steel arcs that connect one passenger car to the next passenger car.

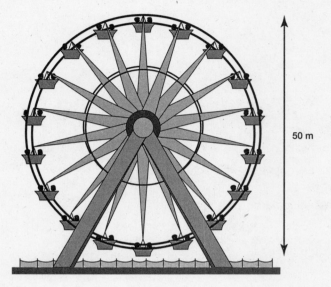

50 m

 Determine the length of each steel arc connecting one passenger car to the next passenger car.

Abraj Al Bait Towers clock in Mecca, Saudi Arabia, has a clock face with a diameter of 43 meters.

1. Determine the length of an arc connecting any two numbers on the clock face.

2. Determine the area of the sector formed by the minute hand and the hour hand when the time is 1:00.

3. Determine the area of the sector formed by the minute hand and the hour hand when the time is 3:00.

4. Determine the area of the sector formed by the minute hand and the hour hand when the time is 4:00.

Two types of circular velocity are *linear velocity* and *angular velocity*.

Linear velocity can be described as an amount of distance over a specified amount of time.

Linear velocity can be expressed as $v = \frac{s}{t}$ where

   v = velocity (mph, ft/s)

   s = arc length (m, ft)

   t = time (s, min, hr)

   1. Use the formula to determine the linear velocity of a point on a circle that travels 24 centimeters in 8 seconds.

Angular velocity can be described as an amount of angle movement (in radians) over a specified amount of time.

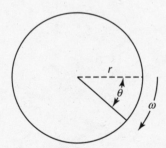

Angular velocity can be expressed as $\omega = \frac{\theta}{t}$ where

   ω = angular velocity (radians/s, radians/min)

   θ = angular measurement (radians)

   t = time (s, min, hr)

2. Use the formula to determine the angular velocity of a point that rotates through $\frac{3\pi}{4}$ radians in 6 seconds.

3. A car tire with a diameter of 60 centimeters turns with an angular velocity of 6 radians per second. Determine the distance traveled by the tire in 5 minutes.

The following situation contains an element of linear velocity and an element of angular velocity.

1. A square is inscribed in a circle. The length of each side of the square is 2 centimeters. Determine the area of the shaded region.

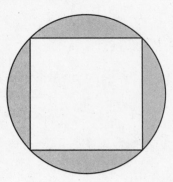

2. A circle is inscribed in a square. The length of the diameter of the circle is $2\sqrt{2}$ centimeters. Determine the area of the shaded region.

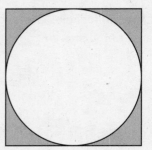

Angela owns a lawn care business. One client has a rectangular lawn that is 9 meters by 12 meters. He wants to install sprinklers to water the lawn. He is willing to pay for two sprinklers and suggests the following placements for the sprinklers. Each sprinkler rotates in quarter circles and sprays water 8.4 meters.

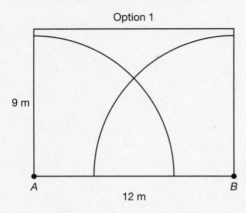

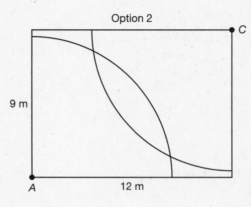

Angela must prepare a report for the client that includes her recommendation for how to best water his lawn.

1. Angela begins by analyzing the suggestions made by the client. She begins by drawing some additional lines to decompose the area of the lawn that is covered by the sprinklers. Describe the shapes that make up each composed area.

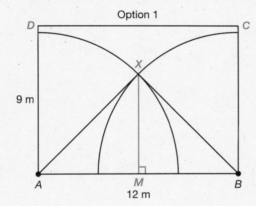

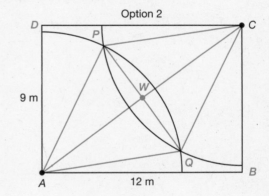

2. Angela then calculates the area of the lawn covered by the sprinklers in the first option.

   a. Determine the lengths of $\overline{AX}$, $\overline{BX}$, $\overline{MX}$, $\overline{AM}$, and $\overline{BM}$.

   b. Calculate the area of triangle AXB.

   c. Calculate the measures of $\angle DAX$, $\angle BAX$, $\angle CBX$, and $\angle ABX$.

   d. Calculate the area of the two sectors.

   e. Calculate the total area of the lawn covered by the sprinklers in the first option.

3. Angela then calculates the area of the lawn covered by the sprinklers in the second option.

   a. Calculate the lengths of $\overline{AC}$ and $\overline{PQ}$.

   b. Calculate the area of rhombus $APCQ$.

c. Calculate $m\angle DAP + m\angle BAQ$ and $m\angle DCP + m\angle BCQ$.

d. Calculate the area of the two sectors for each sprinkler.

e. Calculate the total area of the lawn covered by the sprinklers in the second option.

4. Which option covered a larger percentage of the lawn?

5. Angela is disappointed that neither option waters the entire lawn. She wonders if she can water the entire lawn if she positions the sprinklers differently, perhaps in the interior of the lawn. Draw a recommendation that includes where to position the sprinklers and a justification that the entire lawn will be watered. If it is not possible to water the entire lawn using two sprinklers, explain why not.

6. Write a letter to the client with your recommendation for the best option to water his entire lawn.

 Be prepared to share your solutions and methods.

Chapter 10 Summary

KEY TERMS

- inscribed polygon (10.1)
- circumscribed polygon (10.1)
- arc length (10.2)
- radian (10.2)
- concentric circles (10.3)
- sector of a circle (10.3)
- segment of a circle (10.3)
- linear velocity (10.4)
- angular velocity (10.4)

POSTULATES AND THEOREMS

- Inscribed Right Triangle–Diameter Theorem (10.1)
- Inscribed Right Triangle–Diameter Converse Theorem (10.1)
- Inscribed Quadrilateral–Opposite Angles Theorem (10.1)

10.1 Using the Inscribed Right Triangle–Diameter Theorem and the Inscribed Right Triangle–Diameter Converse Theorem

The Inscribed Right Triangle–Diameter Theorem states: "If a triangle is inscribed in a circle such that one side of the triangle is a diameter of the circle, then the triangle is a right triangle."

The Inscribed Right Triangle–Diameter Converse Theorem states: "If a triangle is inscribed in a circle then the hypotenuse is a diameter of the circle."

Examples

Triangle RST is inscribed in circle Q. Because $\overline{RT}$ of $\triangle RST$ is a diameter of circle Q, $\triangle RST$ is a right triangle.

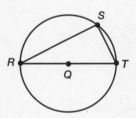

Triangle ABC is inscribed in circle D. Because $\triangle ABC$ is a right triangle, the hypotenuse of $\triangle ABC$, $\overline{BC}$, is a diameter of circle D.

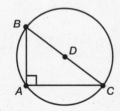

10.1 Using the Inscribed Quadrilateral–Opposite Angles Theorem

The Inscribed Quadrilateral–Opposite Angles Theorem states: "If a quadrilateral is inscribed in a circle, then the opposite angles are supplementary."

Example

Quadrilateral *PRST* is inscribed in circle *M*.

So, $m\angle P + m\angle S = 180°$ and $m\angle T + m\angle R = 180°$.

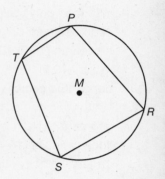

10.2 Determining Arc Length using Degrees

Arc length is a portion of the circumference of a circle. The length of an arc is different from the degree measure of the arc. Arcs are measured in degrees while arc lengths are measured in linear measurements. To determine arc length, *s*, using degrees, use the following formula:

$$s = \frac{\text{measure of angle}}{360} \cdot 2\pi r$$

Example

In circle *W*, the length of the radius is 3 inches and $\overline{GH}$ has a measure of 80°. So, the arc length of *GH* is $\dfrac{80}{360} \cdot 2\pi(3) = \dfrac{2}{9} \cdot 6\pi = \dfrac{4}{3}\pi$.

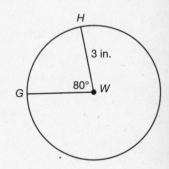

10.2 Determining Arc Length using Radians

A radian is another unit of measure for lengths of arcs. One radian is the measure of a central angle whose arc length is the same as the radius of the circle. To determine arc length using radians, use the following formula: $\theta = \dfrac{s}{r}$ where θ is the measure of the central angle in radians, *s* is the length of the intercepted arc, and *r* is the length of the radius.

Example

In circle *P*, $\theta = \dfrac{\pi}{4}$, and $r = 8$ m. So, $\dfrac{\pi}{4} = \dfrac{s}{8}$, and $8\pi = 2s$, or $s = 2\pi$.

10.3 Determining the Area of a Sector Using the Formula

The sector of a circle is a region of the circle bounded by two radii and the included arc. To determine the area of a sector, use the following formula:

Area of a sector $= \dfrac{\text{measure of angle}}{360} \cdot \pi r^2$ where r is the length of the radius of the circle.

Example

Determine the area of a sector bounded by a 40° inscribed angle in a circle with a radius of 5 cm.

Area of sector $= \dfrac{40}{360} \cdot \pi(5)^2 = \dfrac{1}{9} \cdot 25\pi = \dfrac{25}{9}\pi$ cm.

10

10.3 Determining the Area of a Segment

The segment of a circle is a region of the circle bounded by a chord and the included arc.

Example

Determine the area of the segment in circle K.

Area of sector $= \dfrac{40}{360} \cdot \pi(5)^2 = \dfrac{1}{9} \cdot 25\pi = \dfrac{25}{9}\pi$ cm.

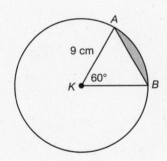

10.4 Determining Linear Velocity

Linear velocity is the amount of distance an object travels over a specified amount of time. Linear velocity is expressed using the formula $v = \dfrac{s}{t}$, where v is the velocity, s is the arc length, and t is time.

Example

A point on a circle travels 38 inches in 10 seconds. So, the velocity of the point is

$v = \dfrac{24 \text{ in.}}{10 \text{ sec}} = 2.4$ in./sec.

Determining Angular Velocity

Linear velocity is the amount of angle movement in radians an object travels over a specified amount of time. Linear velocity is expressed using the formula: $\omega = \frac{\theta}{t}$, where ω is the angular velocity, θ is the angular measurement in radians, and t is time.

Example

A point on a circle rotates through $\frac{\pi}{4}$ radians in 8 seconds. So, the angular velocity of the point is $\omega = \dfrac{\frac{\pi}{4}}{8} = \frac{\pi}{32}$ rad/sec.

Glossary

A

Addition Property of Equality

The addition property of equality states:
"If $a = b$, then $a + c = b + c$."

Example

If $x = 2$, then $x + 5 = 2 + 5$, or $x + 5 = 7$ is an example of the Addition Property of Equality.

Addition Rule for Probability

The Addition Rule for Probability states: "The probability that Event A occurs or Event B occurs is the probability that Event A occurs plus the probability that Event B occurs minus the probability that both A and B occur."

$$P(A \text{ or } B) = P(A) + P(B) = P(A \text{ and } B)$$

Example

You flip a coin two times. Calculate the probability of flipping a heads on the first flip or flipping a heads on the second flip.

Let A represent the event of flipping a heads on the first flip. Let B represent the event of flipping a heads on the second flip.

$P(A \text{ or } B) = P(A) + P(B) - P(A \text{ and } B)$

$P(A \text{ or } B) = \frac{1}{2} + \frac{1}{2} - \frac{1}{4}$

$P(A \text{ or } B) = \frac{3}{4}$

So, the probability of flipping a heads on the first flip or flipping a heads on the second flip is $\frac{3}{4}$.

adjacent angles

Adjacent angles are angles that share a common side and a common vertex, and lie on opposite sides of their common side.

Example

Angle *BAC* and angle *CAD* are adjacent angles. Angle *FEG* and angle *GEH* are adjacent angles.

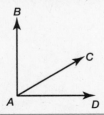
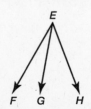

adjacent arcs

Adjacent arcs are two arcs of the same circle sharing a common endpoint.

Example

Arcs *ZA* and *AB* are adjacent arcs.

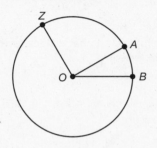

adjacent side

The adjacent side of a triangle is the side adjacent to the reference angle that is not the hypotenuse.

Example

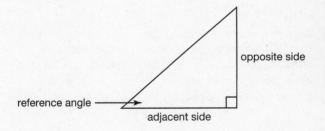

altitude

An altitude is a line segment drawn from a vertex of a triangle perpendicular to the line containing the opposite side.

Example

Segment *EG* is an altitude of triangle *FED*.

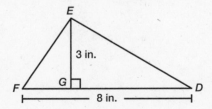

angle

An angle is a figure that is formed by two rays that extend from a common point called the vertex.

Example

Angles *A* and *B* are shown.

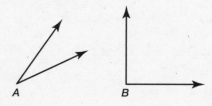

angle bisector

An angle bisector is a ray that divides an angle into two angles of equal measure.

Example

Ray *AT* is the angle bisector of angle *MAH*.

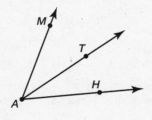

angular velocity

Angular velocity is a type of circular velocity described as an amount of angle movement in radians over a specified amount of time. Angular velocity can be expressed as $\omega = \frac{\theta}{t}$, where ω = angular velocity, θ = angular measurement in radians, and *t* = time.

annulus

An annulus is the region bounded by two concentric circles.

Example

The annulus is the shaded region shown.

arc

An arc is the curve between two points on a circle. An arc is named using its two endpoints.

Example

The symbol used to describe arc *BC* is $\overset{\frown}{BC}$.

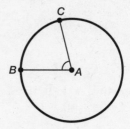

arc length

An arc length is a portion of the circumference of a circle. The length of an arc of a circle can be calculated by multiplying the circumference of the circle by the ratio of the measure of the arc to 360°.

$$\text{arc length} = 2\pi r \cdot \frac{x°}{360°}$$

Example

In circle *A*, the radius $\overline{AB}$ is 3 centimeters and the measure of arc *BC* is 83 degrees.

$$(2\pi r)\left(\frac{m\overset{\frown}{BC}}{360°}\right) = 2\pi(3)\left(\frac{83°}{360°}\right)$$
$$\approx 4.35$$

So, the length of arc *BC* is approximately 4.35 centimeters.

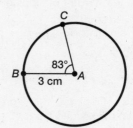

Glossary

axis of symmetry

An axis of symmetry is a line that passes through a figure and divides the figure into two symmetrical parts that are mirror images of each other.

Example

Line *k* is the axis of symmetry of the parabola.

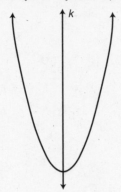

B

base angles of a trapezoid

The base angles of a trapezoid are either pair of angles that share a base as a common side.

Example

Angle *T* and angle *R* are one pair of base angles of trapezoid *PART*. Angle *P* and angle *A* are another pair of base angles.

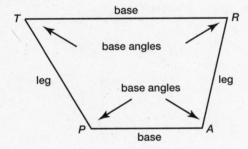

biconditional statement

A biconditional statement is a statement written in the form "if and only if *p*, then *q*." It is a combination of both a conditional statement and the converse of that conditional statement. A biconditional statement is true only when the conditional statement and the converse of the statement are both true.

Example

Consider the property of an isosceles trapezoid: "The diagonals of an isosceles trapezoid are congruent." The property states that if a trapezoid is isosceles, then the diagonals are congruent. The converse of this statement is true: "If the diagonals of a trapezoid are congruent, then the trapezoid is an isosceles trapezoid." So, this property can be written as a biconditional statement: "A trapezoid is isosceles if and only if its diagonals are congruent."

binomial

Polynomials with exactly two terms are binomials.

Example

The polynomial $3x + 5$ is a binomial.

C

categorical data (qualitative data)

Categorical data are data that each fit into exactly one of several different groups, or categories. Categorical data are also called "qualitative data."

Example

Animals: lions, tigers, bears, etc.
U.S. Cities: Los Angeles, Atlanta, New York City, Dodge City, etc.

The set of animals and the set of U.S. cities are two examples of categorical data sets.

Cavalieri's principle

Cavalieri's principle states that if all one-dimensional slices of two-dimensional figures have the same lengths, then the two-dimensional figures have the same area. The principle also states that given two solid figures included between parallel planes, if every plane cross section parallel to the given planes has the same area in both solids, then the volumes of the solids are equal.

center of a circle

The center of a circle is a fixed point in the plane that is at an equal distance from every point on the circle.

Example

Point *H* is the center of the circle.

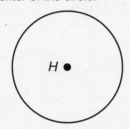

central angle

A central angle of a circle is an angle whose sides are radii. The measure of a central angle is equal to the measure of its intercepted arc.

Example

In circle *O*, ∠*AOC* is a central angle and $\widehat{AC}$ is its intercepted arc. If $m\angle AOC = 45°$, then $m\widehat{AC} = 45°$.

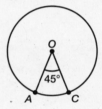

centroid

The centroid of a triangle is the point at which the medians of the triangle intersect.

Example

Point *X* is the centroid of triangle *ABC*.

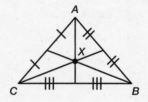

chord

A chord is a line segment whose endpoints are points on a circle. A chord is formed by the intersection of the circle and a secant line.

Example

Segment *CD* is a chord of circle *O*.

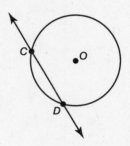

circular permutation

A circular permutation is a permutation in which there is no starting point and no ending point. The circular permutation of *n* objects is $(n - 1)!$.

Example

A club consists of four officers: a president (P), a vice-president (VP), a secretary (S), and a treasurer (T). There are $(4 - 1)!$, or 6 ways for the officers to sit around a round table.

circumcenter

The circumcenter of a triangle is the point at which the perpendicular bisectors intersect.

Example

Point *X* is the circumcenter of triangle *ABC*.

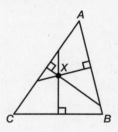

circumscribed polygon

A circumscribed polygon is a polygon drawn outside a circle such that each side of the polygon is tangent to the circle.

Example

Triangle ABC is a circumscribed triangle.

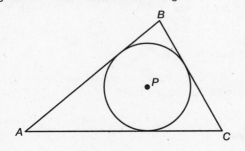

closed (closure)

When an operation is performed on any of the numbers in a set and the result is a number that is also in the same set, the set is said to be closed (or to have closure) under that operation.

Example

The set of whole numbers is closed under addition. The sum of any two whole numbers is always another whole number.

closed interval

A closed interval $[a, b]$ describes the set of all numbers between a and b, including a and b.

Example

The interval $[3, 7]$ is the set of all numbers greater than or equal to 3 and less than or equal to 7.

coefficient

Within a polynomial, a coefficient is a number multiplied by a power.

Example

The term $3x^5$ has a coefficient of 3.

coefficient of determination

The coefficient of determination measures the "strength" of the relationship between the original data and its quadratic regression equation.

collinear points

Collinear points are points that are located on the same line.

Example

Points A, B, and C are collinear.

combination

A combination is an unordered collection of items. One notation for the combinations of r elements taken from a collection of n elements is:

$$_nC_r = C(n, r) = C^n_r$$

Example

The two-letter combinations of the letters A, B, and C are: AB, AC, BC.

compass

A compass is a tool used to create arcs and circles.

Example

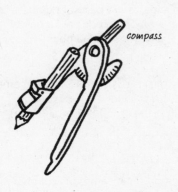

compass

complement of an event

The complement of an event is an event that contains all the outcomes in the sample space that are not outcomes in the event. In mathematical notation, if E is an event, then the complement of E is often denoted as $\bar{E}$ or E^c.

Example

A number cube contains the numbers 1 though 6. Let E represent the event of rolling an even number. The complement of Event E is rolling an odd number.

Glossary

complementary angles

Two angles are complementary if the sum of their measures is 90°.

Example

Angle 1 and angle 2 are complementary angles.
$m\angle 1 + m\angle 2 = 90°$

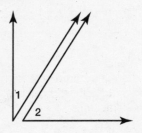

completing the square

Completing the square is a process for writing a quadratic expression in vertex form which then allows you to solve for the zeros.

complex conjugates

Complex conjugates are pairs of numbers of the form $a + bi$ and $a - bi$. The product of a pair of complex conjugates is always a real number.

Example

The expressions $(1 + i)$ and $(1 - i)$ are complex conjugates. The product of $(1 + i)$ and $(1 - i)$ is a real number: $(1 + i)(1 - i) = 1 - i^2 = 1 - (-1) = 2$.

complex numbers

The set of complex numbers is the set of all numbers written in the form $a + bi$, where a and b are real numbers.

composition of functions

A composition of functions is the combination of functions such that the output from one function becomes the input for the next function.

Example

The composition of function $f(x)$ composed with $g(x)$ is denoted $(f \circ g)(x)$ or $f(g(x))$. It is read as "f composed with $g(x)$" or "f of $g(x)$."

compound event

A compound event combines two or more events, using the word "and" or the word "or."

Example

You roll a number cube twice. Rolling a six on the first roll and rolling an odd number on the second roll are compound events.

concavity

The concavity of a parabola describes the orientation of the curvature of the parabola.

Example

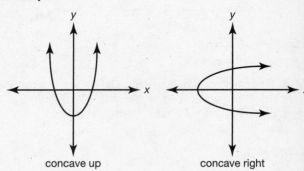

concave up   concave right

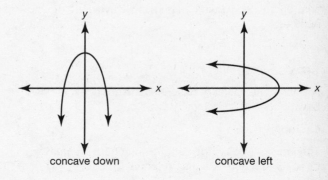

concave down   concave left

concentric circles

Concentric circles are circles in the same plane that have a common center.

Example

The circles shown are concentric because they are in the same plane and have a common center H.

conclusion

Conditional statements are made up of two parts. The conclusion is the result that follows from the given information.

Example

In the conditional statement "If two positive numbers are added, then the sum is positive," the conclusion is "the sum is positive."

concurrent

Concurrent lines, rays, or line segments are three or more lines, rays, or line segments intersecting at a single point.

Example

Lines ℓ, m, and n are concurrent lines.

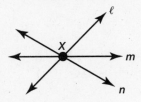

conditional probability

A conditional probability is the probability of event B, given that event A has already occurred. The notation for conditional probability is $P(B|A)$, which reads, "the probability of event B, given event A."

Example

The probability of rolling a 4 or less on the second roll of a number cube, given that a 5 is rolled first, is an example of a conditional probability.

conditional statement

A conditional statement is a statement that can be written in the form "If p, then q."

Example

The statement "If I close my eyes, then I will fall asleep" is a conditional statement.

congruent line segments

Congruent line segments are two or more line segments that have equal measures.

Example

Line segment AB is congruent to line segment CD.

conjecture

A conjecture is a hypothesis that something is true. The hypothesis can later be proved or disproved.

construct

A constructed geometric figure is created using only a compass and a straightedge.

construction proof

A construction proof is a proof that results from creating a figure with specific properties using only a compass and straightedge.

Example

A construction proof is shown of the conditional statement: If $\overline{AB} \cong \overline{CD}$, then $\overline{AC} \cong \overline{BD}$.

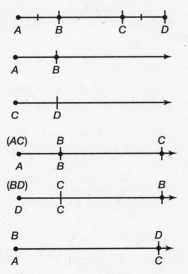

contrapositive

To state the contrapositive of a conditional statement, negate both the hypothesis and the conclusion and then interchange them.

Conditional Statement: If p, then q.
Contrapositive: If not q, then not p.

Example

Conditional Statement: If a triangle is equilateral, then it is isosceles.

Contrapositive: If a triangle is not isosceles, then it is not equilateral.

converse

To state the converse of a conditional statement, interchange the hypothesis and the conclusion.

Conditional Statement: If p, then q.
Converse: If q, then p.

Example

Conditional Statement: If $a = 0$ or $b = 0$, then $ab = 0$.
Converse: If $ab = 0$, then $a = 0$ or $b = 0$.

Converse of Multiplication Property of Zero

The Converse of Multiplication Property of Zero states that if the product of two or more factors is equal to zero, then at least one factor must be equal to zero. This is also called the Zero Product Property.

Example

If $(x - 2)(x + 3) = 0$, then $x - 2 = 0$ or $x + 3 = 0$.

coplanar lines

Coplanar lines are lines that lie in the same plane.

Example

Line A and line B are coplanar lines. Line C and line D are not coplanar lines.

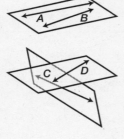

corresponding parts of congruent triangles are congruent (CPCTC)

CPCTC states that if two triangles are congruent, then each part of one triangle is congruent to the corresponding part of the other triangle.

Example

In the triangles shown, $\triangle XYZ \cong \triangle LMN$. Because corresponding parts of congruent triangles are congruent (CPCTC), the following corresponding parts are congruent.

- $\angle X \cong \angle L$
- $\angle Y \cong \angle M$
- $\angle Z \cong \angle N$
- $\overline{XY} \cong \overline{LM}$
- $\overline{YZ} \cong \overline{MN}$
- $\overline{XZ} \cong \overline{LN}$

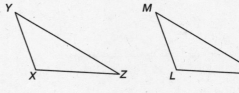

cosecant (csc)

The cosecant (csc) of an acute angle in a right triangle is the ratio of the length of the hypotenuse to the length of the side opposite the angle.

Example

In triangle ABC, the cosecant of angle A is:

$$\csc A = \frac{\text{length of hypotenuse}}{\text{length of side opposite } \angle A} = \frac{AB}{BC}$$

The expression "csc A" means "the cosecant of angle A."

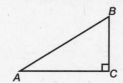

cosine (cos)

The cosine (cos) of an acute angle in a right triangle is the ratio of the length of the side adjacent to the angle to the length of the hypotenuse.

Example

In triangle ABC, the cosine of angle A is:

$$\cos A = \frac{\text{length of side adjacent to } \angle A}{\text{length of hypotenuse}} = \frac{AC}{AB}$$

The expression "cos A" means "the cosine of angle A."

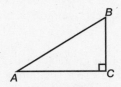

cotangent (cot)

The cotangent (cot) of an acute angle in a right triangle is the ratio of the length of the side adjacent to the angle to the length of the side opposite the angle.

Example

In triangle ABC, the cotangent of angle A is:

$$\cot A = \frac{\text{length of side adjacent to } \angle A}{\text{length of side opposite } \angle A} = \frac{AC}{BC}$$

The expression "cot A" means "the cotangent of angle A."

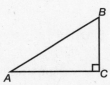

counterexample

A counterexample is a single example that shows that a statement is not true.

Example

Your friend claims that you add fractions by adding the numerators and then adding the denominators. A counterexample is $\frac{1}{2} + \frac{1}{2}$. The sum of these two fractions is 1. Your friend's method results in $\frac{1+1}{2+2}$, or $\frac{1}{2}$. Your friend's method is incorrect.

Counting Principle

The Counting Principle states that if action A can occur in m ways and for each of these m ways action B can occur in n ways, then actions A and B can occur in $m \cdot n$ ways.

Example

In the school cafeteria, there are 3 different main entrées and 4 different sides. So, there are $3 \cdot 4$, or 12 different lunches that can be created.

D

deduction

Deduction is reasoning that involves using a general rule to make a conclusion.

Example

Sandy learned the rule that the sum of the measures of the three interior angles of a triangle is 180 degrees. When presented with a triangle, she concludes that the sum of the measures of the three interior angles is 180 degrees. Sandy reached the conclusion using deduction.

degree measure of an arc

The degree measure of a minor arc is equal to the degree measure of its central angle. The degree measure of a major arc is determined by subtracting the degree measure of the minor arc from 360°.

Example

The measure of minor arc AB is 30°. The measure of major arc BZA is $360° - 30° = 330°$.

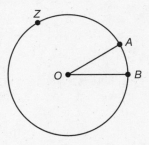

degree of a polynomial

The greatest exponent in a polynomial determines the degree of the polynomial.

Example

The polynomial $2x^3 + 5x^2 - 6x + 1$ has a degree of 3.

degree of a term

The degree of a term in a polynomial is the exponent of the term.

Example

In the polynomial $5x^2 - 6x + 9$, the degree of the term $6x$ is 1.

dependent events

Dependent events are events for which the occurrence of one event has an impact on the occurrence of subsequent events.

Example

A jar contains 1 blue marble, 1 green marble, and 2 yellow marbles. You randomly choose a yellow marble without replacing the marble in the jar, and then randomly choose a yellow marble again. The events of randomly choosing a yellow marble first and randomly choosing a yellow marble second are dependent events because the 1st yellow marble was not replaced in the jar.

diameter

The diameter of a circle is a line segment with each endpoint on the circle that passes through the center of the circle.

Example

In circle O, $\overline{AB}$ is a diameter.

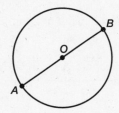

diameter of a sphere

The diameter of a sphere is a line segment with each endpoint on the sphere that passes through the center of the sphere.

Example

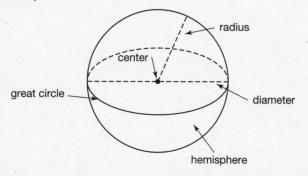

difference of two cubes

The difference of two cubes is an expression in the form $a^3 - b^3$ that can be factored as $(a - b)(a^2 + ab + b^2)$.

Example

The expression $x^3 - 8$ is a difference of two cubes because it can be written in the form $x^3 - 2^3$. The expression can be factored as $(x - 2)(x^2 + 2x + 4)$.

difference of two squares

The difference of two squares is an expression in the form $a^2 - b^2$ that can be factored as $(a + b)(a - b)$.

Example

The expression $x^2 - 4$ is a difference of two squares because it can be written in the form $x^2 - 2^2$. The expression can be factored as $(x + 2)(x - 2)$.

dilation factor

The dilation factor is the common factor which every y-coordinate of a graph is multiplied by to produce a vertical dilation.

direct proof

A direct proof begins with the given information and works to the desired conclusion directly through the use of givens, definitions, properties, postulates, and theorems.

directrix of a parabola

The directrix of a parabola is a line such that all points on the parabola are equidistant from the focus and the directrix.

Example

The focus of the parabola shown is the point $(0, 2)$. The directrix of the parabola shown is the line $y = -2$. All points on the parabola are equidistant from the focus and the directrix.

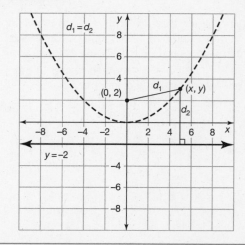

disc

A disc is the set of all points on a circle and in the interior of a circle.

discriminant

The discriminant is the radicand expression in the Quadratic Formula which "discriminates" the number of roots of a quadratic equation.

Example

The discriminant in the Quadratic Formula is the expression $b^2 - 4ac$.

disjoint sets

Two or more sets are disjoint sets if they do not have any common elements.

Example

Let N represent the set of 9th grade students. Let T represent the set of 10th grade students. The sets N and T are disjoint sets because the two sets do not have any common elements. Any student can be in one grade only.

Distance Formula

The Distance Formula can be used to calculate the distance between two points.

The distance between points (x_1, y_1) and (x_2, y_2) is $d = \sqrt{(x_2 - x_1)^2 + (y_2 - y_1)^2}$.

Example

To calculate the distance between the points $(-1, 4)$ and $(2, -5)$, substitute the coordinates into the Distance Formula.

$d = \sqrt{(x_2 - x_1)^2 + (y_2 - y_1)^2}$

$d = \sqrt{(2 + 1)^2 + (-5 - 4)^2}$

$d = \sqrt{3^2 + (-9)^2}$

$d = \sqrt{9 + 81}$

$d = \sqrt{90}$

$d \approx 9.49$

So, the distance between the points $(-1, 4)$ and $(2, -5)$ is approximately 9.49 units.

draw

To draw is to create a geometric figure using tools such as a ruler, straightedge, compass, or protractor. A drawing is more accurate than a sketch.

E

element

A member of a set is called an element of that set.

Example

Set B contains the elements a, b, and c.

$B = \{a, b, c\}$

endpoint of a ray

An endpoint of a ray is a point at which a ray begins.

Example

Point C is the endpoint of ray CD.

endpoints of a line segment

An endpoint of a line segment is a point at which a segment begins or ends.

Examples

Points A and B are endpoints of segment AB.

Glossary

Euclidean geometry

Euclidean geometry is a complete system of geometry developed from the work of the Greek mathematician Euclid. He used a small number of undefined terms and postulates to systematically prove many theorems.

Euclid's first five postulates are:

1. A straight line segment can be drawn joining any two points.
2. Any straight line segment can be extended indefinitely in a straight line.
3. Given any straight line segment, a circle can be drawn having the segment as radius and one endpoint as center.
4. All right angles are congruent.
5. If two lines are drawn that intersect a third line in such a way that the sum of the inner angles on one side is less than two right angles, then the two lines inevitably must intersect each other on that side if extended far enough. (This postulate is equivalent to what is known as the parallel postulate.)

Example

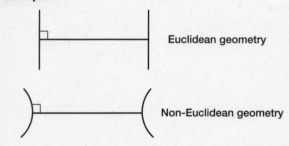

Euclidean geometry

Non-Euclidean geometry

event

An event is an outcome or a set of outcomes in a sample space.

Example

A number cube contains the numbers 1 through 6. Rolling a 6 is one event. Rolling an even number is another event.

expected value

The expected value is the average value when the number of trials in a probability experiment is large.

experimental probability

Experimental probability is the ratio of the number of times an event occurs to the total number of trials performed.

Example

You flip a coin 100 times. Heads comes up 53 times. The experimental probability of getting heads is $\frac{53}{100}$.

exponentiation

Exponentiation means to raise a quantity to a power.

exterior angle of a polygon

An exterior angle of a polygon is an angle that is adjacent to an interior angle of a polygon.

Examples

Angle *JHI* is an exterior angle of quadrilateral *FGHI*.

Angle *EDA* is an exterior angle of quadrilateral *ABCD*.

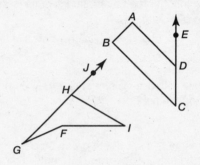

external secant segment

An external secant segment is the portion of each secant segment that lies outside of the circle. It begins at the point at which the two secants intersect and ends at the point where the secant enters the circle.

Example

Segment *HC* and segment *PC* are external secant segments.

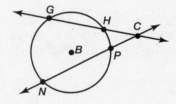

extract the square root

To extract a square root, solve an equation of the form $a^2 = b$ for a.

Example

To extract the square root for the equation $x^2 = 9$, solve for x.

$x^2 = 9$
$x = \pm\sqrt{9}$
$x = \pm 3$

factor an expression

To factor an expression means to use the Distributive Property in reverse to rewrite the expression as a product of factors.

Example

The expression $2x + 4$ can be factored as $2(x + 2)$.

factored form

A quadratic function written in factored form is in the form $f(x) = a(x - r1)(x - r_2)$, where $a \neq 0$.

Example

The function $h(x) = x^2 - 8x + 12$ written in factored form is $(x - 6)(x - 2)$.

factorial

The factorial of n, written as $n!$, is the product of all non-negative integers less than or equal to n.

Example

$3! = 3 \times 2 \times 1 = 6$

flow chart proof

A flow chart proof is a proof in which the steps and corresponding reasons are written in boxes. Arrows connect the boxes and indicate how each step and reason is generated from one or more other steps and reasons.

Example

A flow chart proof is shown for the conditional statement: If $\overline{AB} \cong \overline{CD}$, then $\overline{AC} \cong \overline{BD}$.

Given: $\overline{AB} \cong \overline{CD}$

Prove: $\overline{AC} \cong \overline{BD}$

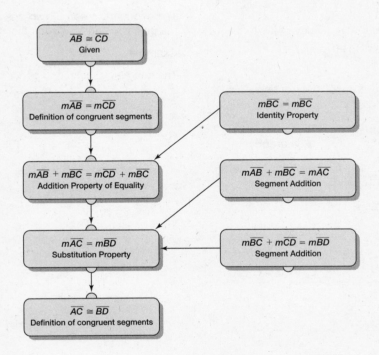

focus of a parabola

The focus of a parabola is a point such that all points on the parabola are equidistant from the focus and the directrix.

Example

The focus of the parabola shown is the point (0, 2). The directrix of the parabola shown is the line $y = -2$. All points on the parabola are equidistant from the focus and the directrix.

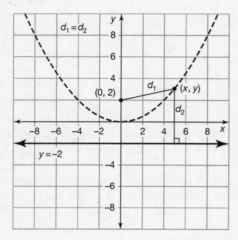

general form of a parabola

The general form of a parabola centered at the origin is an equation of the form $Ax^2 + Dy = 0$ or $By^2 + Cx = 0$.

Example

The equation for the parabola shown can be written in general form as $x^2 - 2y = 0$.

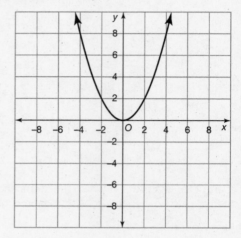

frequency table

A frequency table shows the frequency of an item, number, or event appearing in a sample space.

Example

The frequency table shows the number of times a sum of two number cubes occurred.

Sum of Two Number Cubes	Frequency
2	1
3	2
4	3
5	4
6	5
7	6
8	5
9	4
10	3
11	2
12	1

geometric mean

The geometric mean of two positive numbers a and b is the positive number x such that $\frac{a}{x} = \frac{x}{b}$.

Example

The geometric mean of 3 and 12 is 6.

$\frac{3}{x} = \frac{x}{12}$

$x^2 = 36$

$x = 6$

Glossary

geometric probability

Geometric probability is probability that involves a geometric measure, such as length, area, volume, and so on.

Example

A dartboard has the size and shape shown. The gray shaded area represents a scoring section of the dartboard. Calculate the probability that a dart that lands on a random part of the target will land in a gray scoring section.

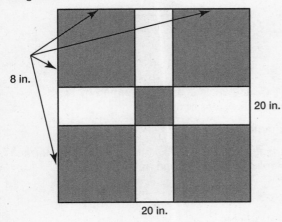

Calculate the area of the dartboard: $20(20) = 400$ in.²

There are 4 gray scoring squares with 8-in. sides and a gray scoring square with $20 - 8 - 8 = 4$-in. sides. Calculate the area of the gray scoring sections: $4(8)(8) + 4(4) = 272$ in.²

Calculate the probability that a dart will hit a gray scoring section: $\frac{272}{400} = 0.68 = 68\%$.

great circle of a sphere

The great circle of a sphere is a cross section of a sphere when a plane passes through the center of the sphere.

Example

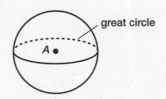

greatest integer function (floor function)

The greatest integer function, also known as a floor function, is defined as the greatest integer less than or equal to x.

Example

The greatest integer function is defined as $G(x) = \lfloor x \rfloor$. If $x = 3.75$ then $G(x) = 3$.

H

half-closed (half-open) interval

A half-closed or half-open interval $(a, b]$ describes the set of all numbers between a and b, including b but not including a. The half-closed interval $[a, b)$ describes the set of all numbers between a and b, including a but not including b.

Example

The interval $(3, 7]$ is the set of all numbers greater than 3 and less than or equal to 7.

The interval $[3, 7)$ is the set of all numbers greater than or equal to 3 and less than 7.

hemisphere

A hemisphere is half of a sphere bounded by a great circle.

Example

A hemisphere is shown.

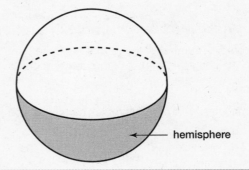

hypothesis

A hypothesis is the "if" part of an "if-then" statement.

Example

In the statement, "If the last digit of a number is a 5, then the number is divisible by 5," the hypothesis is "If the last digit of a number is a 5."

I

image

An image is a new figure formed by a transformation.

Example

The figure on the right is the image that has been created by translating the original figure 3 units to the right horizontally.

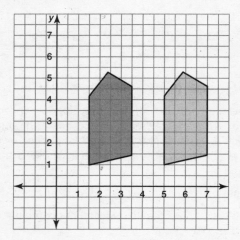

the imaginary number *i*

The number *i* is a number such that $i^2 = -1$.

imaginary numbers

The set of imaginary numbers is the set of all numbers written in the form $a + bi$, where a and b are real numbers and b is not equal to 0.

imaginary part of a complex number

In a complex number of the form $a + bi$, the term bi is called the imaginary part of a complex number.

Example

The imaginary part of the complex number $3 + 2i$ is $2i$.

imaginary roots/imaginary zeros

Imaginary roots are imaginary solutions to equations.

Example

The quadratic equation $x^2 - 2x + 2$ has two imaginary roots: $1 + i$ and $1 - i$.

incenter

The incenter of a triangle is the point at which the angle bisectors of the triangle intersect.

Example

Point X is the incenter of triangle ABC.

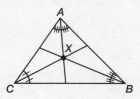

included angle

An included angle is an angle formed by two consecutive sides of a figure.

Example

In triangle ABC, angle A is the included angle formed by consecutive sides $\overline{AB}$ and $\overline{AC}$.

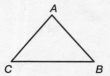

included side

An included side is a line segment between two consecutive angles of a figure.

Example

In triangle ABC, $\overline{AB}$ is the included side formed by consecutive angles A and B.

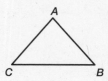

independent events

Independent events are events for which the occurrence of one event has no impact on the occurrence of the other event.

Example

You randomly choose a yellow marble, replace the marble in the jar, and then randomly choose a yellow marble again. The events of randomly choosing a yellow marble first and randomly choosing a yellow marble second are independent events because the 1st yellow marble was replaced in the jar.

Glossary

indirect measurement

Indirect measurement is a technique that uses proportions to determine a measurement when direct measurement is not possible.

Example

You can use a proportion to solve for the height x of the flagpole.

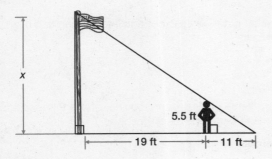

$$\frac{x}{5.5} = \frac{19 + 11}{11}$$

$$\frac{x}{5.5} = \frac{30}{11}$$

$$11x = 165$$

$$x = 15$$

The flagpole is 15 feet tall.

indirect proof or proof by contradiction

An indirect proof, or proof by contradiction, uses the contrapositive. By proving that the contrapositive is true, you prove that the statement is true.

Example

Given: Triangle DEF

Prove: A triangle cannot have more than one obtuse angle.

Given $\triangle DEF$, assume that $\triangle DEF$ has two obtuse angles. So, assume $m\angle D = 91°$ and $m\angle E = 91°$. By the Triangle Sum Theorem, $m\angle D + m\angle E + m\angle F = 180°$. By substitution, $91° + 91° + m\angle F = 180°$, and by subtraction, $m\angle F = -2°$. But, it is not possible for a triangle to have a negative angle, so this is a contradiction. This proves that a triangle cannot have more than one obtuse angle.

induction

induction is reasoning that involves using specific examples to make a conclusion.

Example

Sandy draws several triangles, measures the interior angles, and calculates the sum of the measures of the three interior angles. She concludes that the sum of the measures of the three interior angles of a triangle is 180°. Sandy reached the conclusion using induction.

inscribed angle

An inscribed angle is an angle whose vertex is on a circle and whose sides contain chords of the circle.

Example

Angle BAC is an inscribed angle. The vertex of angle BAC is on the circle and the sides of angle BAC contain the chords $\overline{AB}$ and $\overline{AC}$.

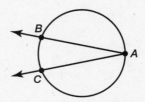

inscribed polygon

An inscribed polygon is a polygon drawn inside a circle such that each vertex of the polygon is on the circle.

Example

Quadrilateral $KLMN$ is inscribed in circle J.

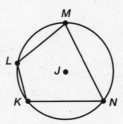

integers

The set of integers consists of the set of whole numbers and their opposites.

Example

The numbers -12, 0, and 30 are integers.

intercepted arc

An intercepted arc is formed by the intersections of the sides of an inscribed angle with a circle.

Example

$\overline{PR}$ is an intercepted arc of inscribed angle *PSR*.

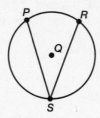

interior angle of a polygon

An interior angle of a polygon is an angle which is formed by consecutive sides of the polygon or shape.

Example

The interior angles of $\triangle ABC$ are $\angle ABC$, $\angle BCA$, and $\angle CAB$.

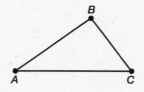

intersecting sets

Two or more sets are intersecting sets if they have common elements.

Example

Let *V* represent the set of students who are on the girls' volleyball team. Let *M* represent the set of students who are in the math club. Julia is on the volleyball team and belongs to the math club. The sets *V* and *M* are intersecting sets because the two sets have at least one common element, Julia.

interval

An interval is defined as the set of real numbers between two given numbers.

Example

The interval (3, 7) is the set of all numbers between 3 and 7, not including 3 or 7.

inverse

To state the inverse of a conditional statement, negate both the hypothesis and the conclusion.
Conditional Statement: If *p*, then *q*.
Inverse: If not *p*, then not *q*.

Example

Conditional Statement: If a triangle is equilateral, then it is isosceles.

Inverse: If a triangle is not equilateral, then it is not isosceles.

inverse cosine

The inverse cosine, or arc cosine, of *x* is the measure of an acute angle whose cosine is *x*.

Example

In right triangle *ABC*, if $\cos A = x$, then $\cos^{-1} x = m\angle A$.

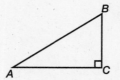

inverse function

An inverse function takes the output value, performs some operation(s) on this value, and arrives back at the original function's input value.

Example

The inverse of the function $y = 2x$ is the function $x = 2y$, or $y = \frac{x}{2}$.

inverse operation

"Undoing," working backward, or retracing steps to return to an original value or position is referred to as using the inverse operation.

Example

The operations of addition and subtraction are inverse operations.

inverse sine

The inverse sine, or arc sine, of x is the measure of an acute angle whose sine is x.

Example

In right triangle ABC, if $\sin A = x$, then $\sin^{-1} x = m\angle A$.

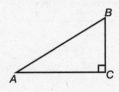

inverse tangent

The inverse tangent (or arc tangent) of x is the measure of an acute angle whose tangent is x.

Example

In right triangle ABC, if $\tan A = x$, then $\tan^{-1} x = m\angle A$.

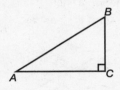

irrational numbers

The set of irrational numbers consists of all numbers that cannot be written as $\frac{a}{b}$ where a and b are integers.

Example

The number π is an irrational number.

isometric paper

Isometric paper is often used by artists and engineers to create three-dimensional views of objects in two dimensions.

Example

The rectangular prism is shown on isometric paper.

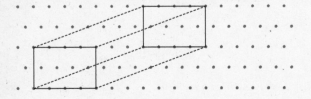

isosceles trapezoid

An isosceles trapezoid is a trapezoid whose nonparallel sides are congruent.

Example

In trapezoid $JKLM$, side $\overline{KL}$ is parallel to side $\overline{JM}$, and the length of side $\overline{JK}$ is equal to the length of side $\overline{LM}$, so trapezoid $JKLM$ is an isosceles trapezoid.

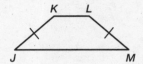

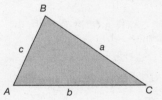

Law of Cosines

The Law of Cosines, or

$$a^2 = c^2 + b^2 - 2bc \cdot \cos A$$
$$b^2 = a^2 + c^2 - 2ac \cdot \cos B$$
$$c^2 = a^2 + b^2 - 2ab \cdot \cos C$$

can be used to determine the unknown lengths of sides or the unknown measures of angles in *any* triangle.

Example

In triangle ABC, the measure of angle A is 65°, the length of side b is 4.4301 feet, and the length of side c is 7.6063 feet. Use the Law of Cosines to calculate the length of side a.

$$a^2 = 4.4301^2 + 7.6063^2 - 2(4.4301)(7.6063) \cos 65°$$

The length of side a is 7 feet.

Law of Sines

The Law of Sines, or $\frac{\sin A}{a} = \frac{\sin B}{b} = \frac{\sin C}{c}$, can be used to determine the unknown side lengths or the unknown angle measures in *any* triangle.

Example

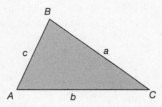

In triangle *ABC*, the measure of angle *A* is 65°, the measure of angle *B* is 80°, and the length of side *a* is 7 feet. Use the Law of Sines to calculate the length of side *b*.

$$\frac{7}{\sin 65°} = \frac{b}{\sin 80°}$$

The length of side *b* is 7.6063 feet.

leading coefficient

The leading coefficient of a function is the numerical coefficient of the term with the greatest power.

Example

In the function $h(x) = -7x^2 + x + 25$, the value -7 is the leading coefficient.

least integer function (ceiling function)

The least integer function, also known as the ceiling function, is defined as the least integer greater than or equal to *x*.

Example

The least integer function is defined as $L(x) = \lceil x \rceil$. If $x = 3.75$ then $L(x) = 4$.

line

A line is made up of an infinite number of points that extend infinitely in two opposite directions. A line is straight and has only one dimension.

Example

The line below can be called line *k* or line *AB*.

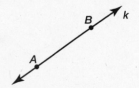

line segment

A line segment is a portion of a line that includes two points and all of the collinear points between the two points.

Example

The line segment shown is named $\overline{AB}$ or $\overline{BA}$.

linear pair

A linear pair of angles are two adjacent angles that have noncommon sides that form a line.

Example

The diagram shown has four pairs of angles that form a linear pair.

- Angles 1 and 2 form a linear pair.
- Angles 2 and 3 form a linear pair.
- Angles 3 and 4 form a linear pair.
- Angles 4 and 1 form a linear pair.

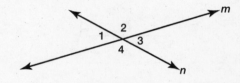

linear velocity

Linear velocity is a type of circular velocity described as an amount of distance over a specified amount of time. Linear velocity can be expressed as $v = \frac{s}{t}$, where v = velocity, s = arc length, and t = time.

locus of points

A locus of points is a set of points that satisfy one or more conditions.

Example

A circle is defined as a locus of points that are a fixed distance, called the radius, from a given point, called the center.

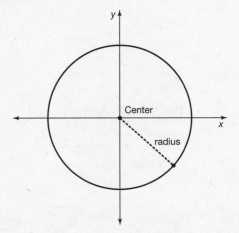

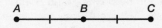

major arc

Two points on a circle determine a major arc and a minor arc. The arc with the greater measure is the major arc. The other arc is the minor arc.

Example

Circle Q is divided by points A and B into two arcs, arc ACB and arc AB. Arc ACB has the greater measure, so it is the major arc. Arc AB has the lesser measure, so it is the minor arc.

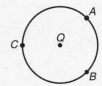

median

The median of a triangle is a line segment drawn from a vertex to the midpoint of the opposite side.

Example

The 3 medians are drawn on the triangle shown.

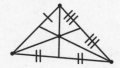

midpoint

The midpoint of a line segment is the point that divides the line segment into two congruent segments.

Example

Because point B is the midpoint of $\overline{AC}$, $\overline{AB} \cong \overline{BC}$.

$$\underset{A}{\bullet} \quad | \quad \underset{B}{} \quad | \quad \underset{C}{\bullet}$$

Midpoint Formula

The Midpoint Formula can be used to calculate the midpoint between two points. The midpoint between (x_1, y_1) and (x_2, y_2) is $\left(\dfrac{x_1 + x_2}{2}, \dfrac{y_1 + y_2}{2}\right)$.

Example

To calculate the midpoint between the points $(-1, 4)$ and $(2, -5)$, substitute the coordinates into the Midpoint Formula.

$$\left(\frac{x_1 + x_2}{2}, \frac{y_1 + y_2}{2}\right) = \left(\frac{-1 + 2}{2}, \frac{4 - 5}{2}\right)$$

$$= \left(\frac{1}{2}, \frac{-1}{2}\right)$$

So, the midpoint between the points $(-1, 4)$ and $(2, -5)$ is $\left(\dfrac{1}{2}, -\dfrac{1}{2}\right)$.

midsegment of a trapezoid

The midsegment of a trapezoid is a line segment formed by connecting the midpoints of the legs of the trapezoid.

Example

Segment XY is the midsegment of trapezoid $ABCD$.

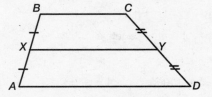

midsegment of a triangle

A midsegment of a triangle is a line segment formed by connecting the midpoints of two sides of a triangle.

Example

Segment AB is a midsegment.

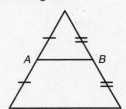

minor arc

Two points on a circle determine a minor arc and a major arc. The arc with the lesser measure is the minor arc. The other arc is the major arc.

Example

Circle Q is divided by points A and B into two arcs, arc ACB and arc AB. Arc AB has the lesser measure, so it is the minor arc. Arc ACB has the greater measure, so it is the major arc.

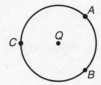

monomial

Polynomials with only one term are monomials.

Example

The expressions $5x$, 7, $-2xy$, and $13x^3$ are monomials.

N

natural numbers

The set of natural numbers consists of the numbers that you use to count objects.

Example

The numbers 1, 2, 3, 4, . . . are natural numbers.

negative square root

A square root that is negative.

Example

The negative square root of 9 is -3.

non-uniform probability model

When all probabilities in a probability model are not equivalent to each other, it is called a non-uniform probability model.

Example

Spinning the spinner shown represents a non-uniform probability model because the probability of landing on a shaded space is not equal to the probability of landing on a non-shaded space.

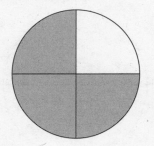

O

oblique cylinder

When a circle is translated through space in a direction that is not perpendicular to the plane containing the circle, the solid formed is an oblique cylinder.

Example

The prism shown is an oblique cylinder.

Glossary

oblique rectangular prism

When a rectangle is translated through space in a direction that is not perpendicular to the plane containing the rectangle, the solid formed is an oblique rectangular prism.

Example

The prism shown is an oblique rectangular prism.

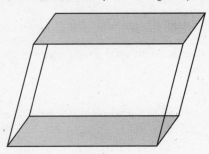

oblique triangular prism

When a triangle is translated through space in a direction that is not perpendicular to the plane containing the triangle, the solid formed is an oblique triangular prism.

Example

The prism shown is an oblique triangular prism.

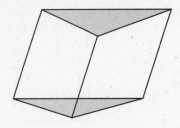

one-to-one function

A function is a one-to-one function if both the function and its inverse are functions.

Example

The equation $y = x^3$ is a one-to-one function because its inverse, $\sqrt[3]{x} = y$, is a function. The equation $y = x^2$ is not a one-to-one function because its inverse, $\pm \sqrt{x} = y$, is not a function.

open interval

An open interval (a, b) describes the set of all numbers between a and b, but not including a or b.

Example

The interval $(3, 7)$ is the set of all numbers greater than 3 and less than 7.

opposite side

The opposite side of a triangle is the side opposite the reference angle.

Example

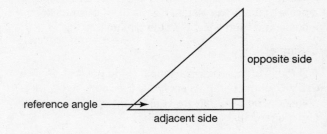

organized list

An organized list is a visual model for determining the sample space of events.

Example

The sample space for flipping a coin 3 times can be represented as an organized list.

HHH	THH
HHT	THT
HTH	TTH
HTT	TTT

orthocenter

The orthocenter of a triangle is the point at which the altitudes of the triangle intersect.

Example

Point X is the orthocenter of triangle ABC.

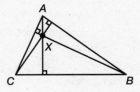

outcome

An outcome is the result of a single trial of an experiment.

Example

Flipping a coin has two outcomes: heads or tails.

Glossary

parabola

The shape that a quadratic function forms when graphed is called a parabola. A parabola is the set of all points in a plane that are equidistant from a fixed point called the focus and a fixed line called the directrix.

Example

The focus of the parabola shown is the point (0, 2). The directrix of the parabola shown is the line $y = -2$. All points on the parabola are equidistant from the focus and the directrix.

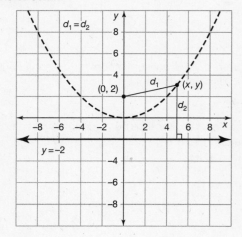

paragraph proof

A paragraph proof is a proof that is written in paragraph form. Each sentence includes mathematical statements that are organized in logical steps with reasons.

Example

The proof shown is a paragraph proof that vertical angles 1 and 3 are congruent.

Angle 1 and angle 3 are vertical angles. By the definition of linear pair, angle 1 and angle 2 form a linear pair. Angle 2 and angle 3 also form a linear pair. By the Linear Pair Postulate, angle 1 and angle 2 are supplementary. Angle 2 and angle 3 are also supplementary. Angle 1 is congruent to angle 3 by the Congruent Supplements Theorem.

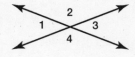

perfect square trinomial

A perfect square trinomial is an expression in the form $a^2 + 2ab + b^2$ or in the form $a^2 - 2ab + b^2$.

Example

The trinomial $x^2 + 6x + 9$ is a perfect square trinomial because it can be written as $x^2 + 2(3)x + 3^2$.

permutation

A permutation is an ordered arrangement of items without repetition.

Example

The permutations of the letters A, B, and C are:

ABC	ACB
BAC	BCA
CAB	CBA

perpendicular bisector

A perpendicular bisector is a line, line segment, or ray that intersects the midpoint of a line segment at a 90-degree angle.

Example

Line k is the perpendicular bisector of $\overline{AB}$. It is perpendicular to $\overline{AB}$, and intersects $\overline{AB}$ at midpoint M so that $AM = MB$.

plane

A plane is a flat surface with infinite length and width, but no depth. A plane extends infinitely in all directions.

Example

Plane A is shown.

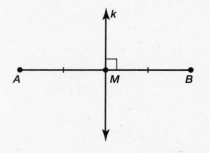

Glossary

point

A point has no dimension, but can be visualized as a specific position in space, and is usually represented by a small dot.

Example

point *A* is shown.

point of concurrency

A point of concurrency is the point at which three or more lines intersect.

Example

Point *X* is the point of concurrency for lines ℓ, *m*, and *n*.

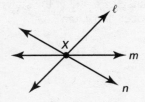

point of tangency

A tangent to a circle is a line that intersects the circle at exactly one point, called the point of tangency.

Example

Line *RQ* is tangent to circle *P*. Point *Q* is the point of tangency.

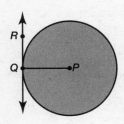

point-slope form

The point-slope form of a linear equation that passes through the point (x_1, y_1) and has slope *m* is $y - y_1 = m(x - x_1)$.

Example

A line passing through the point (1, 2) with a slope of $\frac{1}{2}$ can be written in point-slope form as

$$y - 2 = \frac{1}{2}(x + 1).$$

polynomial

A polynomial is a mathematical expression involving the sum of powers in one or more variables multiplied by coefficients.

Example

The expression $3x^3 + 5x - 6x + 1$ is a polynomial.

positive square root

A square root that is positive.

Example

The positive square root of 9 is 3.

postulate

A postulate is a statement that is accepted to be true without proof.

Example

The following statement is a postulate: A straight line may be drawn between any two points.

pre-image

A pre-image is the figure that is being transformed.

Example

The figure on the right is the image that has been formed by translating the pre-image 3 units to the right horizontally.

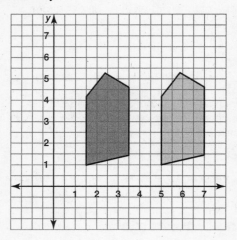

principal square root

A positive square root of a number.

Example

The principal square root of 9 is 3.

principal square root of a negative number

For any positive real number n, the principal square root of a negative number, $-n$, is defined by $\sqrt{-n} = i\sqrt{n}$.

Example

The principal square root of -5 is $\sqrt{-5} = i\sqrt{5}$.

probability

The probability of an event is the ratio of the number of desired outcomes to the total number of possible outcomes, $P(A) = \dfrac{\text{desired outcomes}}{\text{possible outcomes}}$.

Example

When flipping a coin, there are 2 possible outcomes: heads or tails. The probability of flipping a heads is $\frac{1}{2}$.

probability model

A probability model lists the possible outcomes and the probability for each outcome. In a probability model, the sum of the probabilities must equal 1.

Example

The table shows a probability model for flipping a fair coin once.

Outcomes	Heads (H)	Tails (T)
Probability	$\frac{1}{2}$	$\frac{1}{2}$

propositional form

When a conditional statement is written using the propositional variables p and q, the statement is said to be written in propositional form.

Example

Propositional form:
"If p, then q."
$p \rightarrow q$

propositional variables

When a conditional statement is written in propositional form as "If p, then q," the variables p and q are called propositional variables.

pure imaginary number

A pure imaginary number is a number of the form bi, where b is not equal to 0.

Example

The imaginary numbers $24i$ and $15i$ are pure imaginary numbers.

Q

Quadratic Formula

The Quadratic Formula is $x = \dfrac{-b \pm \sqrt{b^2 - 4ac}}{2a}$.

Glossary

quadratic regression

A quadratic regression is a mathematical method to determine the equation of a "parabola of best fit" for a data set.

Example

The graph of the quadratic regression for these data is shown.

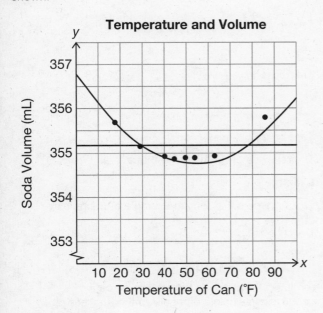

Temperature and Volume

radius

The radius of a circle is a line segment with one endpoint on the circle and one endpoint at the center.

Example

In circle O, $\overline{OA}$ is a radius.

radius of a sphere

The radius of a sphere is a line segment with one endpoint on the sphere and one endpoint at the center.

Example

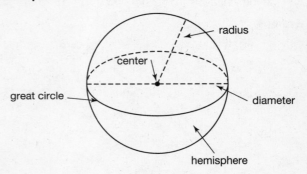

R

---

radian

One radian is defined as the measure of a central angle whose arc length is the same as the radius of the circle.

radical expression

A radical expression is an expression that involves a radical symbol ($\sqrt{}$).

radicand

The value that is inside a radical is called the radicand.

Example

In the radical expression $\sqrt{25}$, the number 25 is the radicand.

rational numbers

The set of rational numbers consists of all numbers that can be written as $\frac{a}{b}$ where a and b are integers, but b is not equal to 0.

Example

The number 0.5 is a rational number because it can be written as the fraction $\frac{1}{2}$.

rationalizing the denominator

Rationalizing the denominator is the process of eliminating a radical from the denominator of an expression. To rationalize the denominator, multiply by a form of one so that the radicand of the radical in the denominator is a perfect square.

Example

Rationalize the denominator of the expression $\frac{5}{\sqrt{3}}$.

$$\frac{5}{\sqrt{3}} = \frac{5}{\sqrt{3}} \cdot \frac{\sqrt{3}}{\sqrt{3}}$$
$$= \frac{5\sqrt{3}}{\sqrt{9}}$$
$$= \frac{5\sqrt{3}}{3}$$

ray

A ray is a portion of a line that begins with a single point and extends infinitely in one direction.

Example

The ray shown is ray *AB*.

real numbers

The set of real numbers consists of the set of rational numbers and the set of irrational numbers.

Examples

The numbers -3, 11.4, $\frac{1}{2}$, and $\sqrt{5}$ are real numbers.

real part of a complex number

In a complex number of the form $a + bi$, the term a is called the real part of a complex number.

Example

The real part of the complex number $3 + 2i$ is 3.

reference angle

A reference angle is the angle of the right triangle being considered. The opposite side and adjacent side are named based on the reference angle.

Example

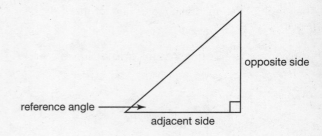

Reflexive Property

The reflexive property states that $a = a$.

Example

The statement $2 = 2$ is an example of the reflexive property.

relative frequency

A relative frequency is the ratio or percent of occurrences within a category to the total of the category.

Example

John surveys 100 students in his school about their favorite school subject. Of the 100 students, 37 chose math as their favorite subject. The relative frequency of students show selected math as their favorite subject is $\frac{37}{100}$, or 37%.

remote interior angles of a triangle

The remote interior angles of a triangle are the two angles that are not adjacent to the specified exterior angles.

Example

The remote interior angles with respect to exterior angles 4 are angles 1 and 2.

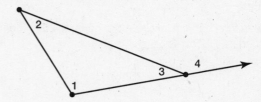

Glossary

restrict the domain

To restrict the domain of a function means to define a new domain for the function that is a subset of the original domain.

right cylinder

A disc translated through space in a direction perpendicular to the plane containing the disc forms a right cylinder.

Example

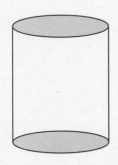

right rectangular prism

A rectangle translated through space in a direction perpendicular to the plane containing the rectangle forms a right rectangular prism.

Example

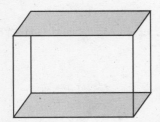

right triangular prism

A triangle translated through space in a direction perpendicular to the plane containing the triangle forms a right triangular prism.

Example

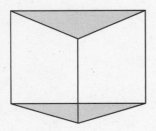

rigid motion

A rigid motion is a transformation of points in space. Translations, reflections, and rotations are examples of rigid motion.

roots

The roots of a quadratic equation indicate where the graph of the equation crosses the x-axis.

Example

The roots of the quadratic equation $x^2 - 4x = -3$ are $x = 3$ and $x = 1$.

Rule of Compound Probability involving "and"

The Rule of Compound Probability involving "and" states: "If Event A and Event B are independent, then the probability that Event A happens *and* Event B happens is the product of the probability that Event A happens and the probability that Event B happens, given that Event A has happened."

$$P(A \text{ and } B) = P(A) \cdot P(B)$$

Example

You flip a coin two times. Calculate the probability of flipping a heads on the first flip and flipping a heads on the second flip.

Let A represent the event of flipping a heads on the first flip. Let B represent the event of flipping a heads on the second flip.

$P(A \text{ and } B) = P(A) \cdot P(B)$

$P(A \text{ and } B) = \frac{1}{2} \cdot \frac{1}{2}$

$P(A \text{ or } B) = \frac{1}{4}$

So, the probability of flipping a heads on the first flip and flipping a heads on the second flip is $\frac{1}{4}$.

S

sample space

A list of all possible outcomes of an experiment is called a sample space.

Example

Flipping a coin two times consists of four outcomes: HH, HT, TH, and TT.

secant (sec)

The secant (sec) of an acute angle in a right triangle is the ratio of the length of the hypotenuse to the length of the side adjacent to the angle.

Example

In triangle *ABC*, the secant of angle *A* is:

$$\sec A = \frac{\text{length of hypotenuse}}{\text{length of side adjacent to } \angle A} = \frac{AB}{AC}$$

The expression "sec *A*" means "the secant of angle *A*."

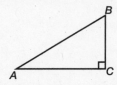

secant of a circle

A secant of a circle is a line that intersects the circle at two points.

Example

The line intersecting the circle through points *A* and *B* is a secant.

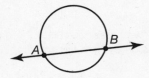

secant segment

A secant segment is formed when two secants intersect outside of a circle. A secant segment begins at the point at which the two secants intersect, continues into the circle, and ends at the point at which the secant exits the circle.

Example

Segment *GC* and segment *NC* are secant segments.

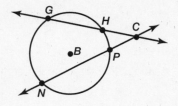

second differences

Second differences are the differences between consecutive values of the first differences.

Example

x	y	First Differences	Second Differences
−3	−5		
		5	
−2	0		−2
		3	
−1	3		−2
		1	
0	4		−2
		−1	
1	3		−2
		−3	
2	0		−2
		−5	
3	−5		

sector of a circle

A sector of a circle is a region of the circle bounded by two radii and the included arc.

Example

In circle *Y*, arc *XZ*, radius *XY*, and radius *YZ* form a sector.

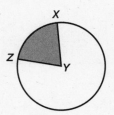

segment bisector

A segment bisector is a line, line segment, or ray that intersects a line segment so that the line segment is divided into two segments of equal length.

Example

Line *k* is a segment bisector of segment *AC*. The lengths of segments *AB* and *BC* are equal.

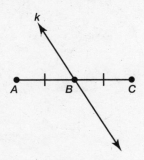

segment of a circle

A segment of a circle is a region bounded by a chord and the included arc.

Example

In circle *A,* chord $\overline{BC}$ and arc *BC* are the boundaries of a segment of the circle.

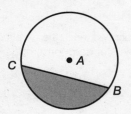

segments of a chord

Segments of a chord are the segments formed on a chord if two chords of a circle intersect.

Example

The segments of chord $\overline{HD}$ are $\overline{EH}$ and $\overline{ED}$.
The segments of chord $\overline{RC}$ are $\overline{ER}$ and $\overline{EC}$.

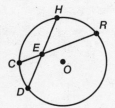

semicircle

A semicircle is an arc whose endpoints form the endpoints of a diameter of the circle.

Example

Arc *XYZ* and arc *ZWX* are semicircles of circle *P*.

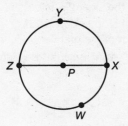

set

A set is a collection of items. If *x* is a member of set *B*, then *x* is an element of set *B*.

Example

Let *E* represent the set of even whole numbers.
$E = \{2, 4, 6, 8, \ldots\}$

similar triangles

Similar triangles are triangles that have all pairs of corresponding angles congruent and all corresponding sides are proportional.

Example

Triangle *ABC* is similar to triangle *DEF*.

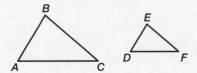

simulation

A simulation is an experiment that models a real-life situation.

Example

You can simulate the selection of raffle numbers by using the random number generator on a graphing calculator.

sine (sin)

The sine (sin) of an acute angle in a right triangle is the ratio of the length of the side opposite the angle to the length of the hypotenuse.

Example

In triangle ABC, the sine of angle A is:

$$\sin A = \frac{\text{length of side opposite } \angle A}{\text{length of hypotenuse}} = \frac{BC}{AB}$$

The expression "sin A" means "the sine of angle A."

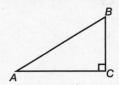

sketch

To sketch is to create a geometric figure without using tools such as a ruler, straightedge, compass, or protractor. A drawing is more accurate than a sketch.

skew lines

Skew lines are two lines that do not intersect and are not parallel. Skew lines do not lie in the same plane.

Example

Line m and line p are skew lines.

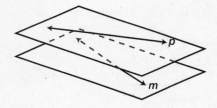

sphere

A sphere is the set of all points in space that are a given distance from a fixed point called the center of the sphere.

Example

A sphere is shown.

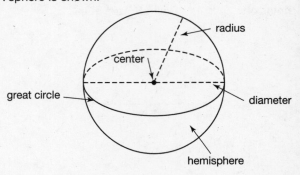

square root

A number b is a square root of a if $b^2 = a$.

Example

The number 3 is a square root of 9 because $3^2 = 9$.

standard form (general form) of a quadratic function

A quadratic function written in the form $f(x) = ax^2 + bx + c$, where $a \neq 0$, is in standard form, or general form.

Example

The function $f(x) = -5x^2 - 10x + 1$ is written in standard form.

Glossary

standard form of a parabola

The standard form of a parabola centered at the origin is an equation of the form $x^2 = 4py$ or $y^2 = 4px$, where p represents the distance from the vertex to the focus.

Example

The equation for the parabola shown can be written in standard form as $x^2 = 2y$.

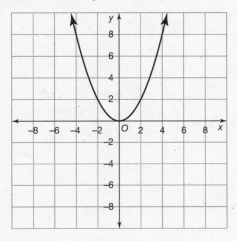

step function

A step function is a piecewise function whose pieces are disjoint constant functions.

Example

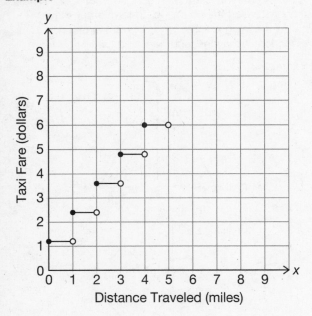

straightedge

A straightedge is a ruler with no numbers.

Substitution Property of Equality

The Substitution Property of Equality states: "If a and b are real numbers and $a = b$, then a can be substituted for b."

Example

If $AB = 12$ ft and $CD = 12$ ft, then $AB = CD$.

Subtraction Property of Equality

The Subtraction Property of Equality states: "If $a = b$, then $a - c = b - c$."

Example

If $x + 5 = 7$, then $x + 5 - 5 = 7 - 5$, or $x = 2$ is an example of the subtraction property of equality.

sum of two cubes

The sum of two cubes is an expression in the form $a^3 + b^3$ that can be factored as $(a + b)(a^2 - ab + b^2)$.

Example

The expression $x^3 + 8$ is a sum of two cubes because it can be written in the form $x^3 + 2^3$. The expression can be factored as $(x + 2)(x^2 - 2x + 4)$.

supplementary angles

Two angles are supplementary if the sum of their measures is 180°.

Example

Angle 1 and angle 2 are supplementary angles.
If $m\angle 1 = 75°$, then $m\angle 2 = 180° - 75° = 105°$.

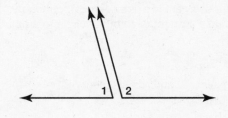

Glossary

tangent (tan)

The tangent (tan) of an acute angle in a right triangle is the ratio of the length of the side opposite the angle to the length of the side adjacent to the angle.

Example

In triangle ABC, the tangent of angle A is:

$$\tan A = \frac{\text{length of side opposite } \angle A}{\text{length of side adjacent to } \angle A} = \frac{BC}{AC}$$

The expression "tan A" means "the tangent of angle A."

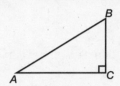

tangent of a circle

A tangent of a circle is a line that intersects the circle at exactly one point, called the point of tangency.

Example

Line RQ is tangent to circle P.

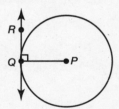

tangent segment

A tangent segment is a line segment formed by connecting a point outside of the circle to a point of tangency.

Example

Line segment AB and line segment AC are tangent segments.

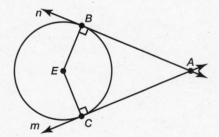

term

Within a polynomial, each product is a term.

Example

The polynomial $2x + 3y + 5$ has three terms: $2x$, $3y$, and 5.

theorem

A theorem is a statement that has been proven to be true.

Example

The Pythagorean Theorem states that if a right triangle has legs of lengths a and b and hypotenuse of length c, then $a^2 + b^2 = c^2$.

theoretical probability

Theoretical probability is the mathematical calculation that an event will happen in theory.

Example

The theoretical probability of rolling a 1 on a number cube is $\frac{1}{6}$.

transformation

A transformation is an operation that maps, or moves, a figure, called the preimage, to form a new figure called the image. Three types of transformations are reflections, rotations, and translations.

Example

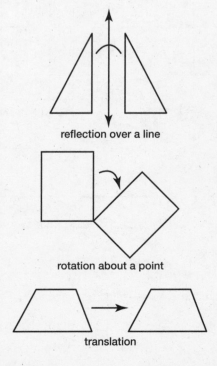

reflection over a line

rotation about a point

translation

Glossary

Transitive Property of Equality

The Transitive Property of Equality states: "If $a = b$ and $b = c$, then $a = c$."

Example

If $x = y$ and $y = 2$, then $x = 2$ is an example of the Transitive Property of Equality.

translation

A translation is a transformation in which a figure is shifted so that each point of the figure moves the same distance in the same direction. The shift can be in a horizontal direction, a vertical direction, or both.

Example

The top trapezoid is a vertical translation of the bottom trapezoid by 5 units.

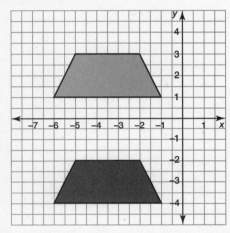

tree diagram

A tree diagram is a diagram that illustrates sequentially the possible outcomes of a given situation.

Example

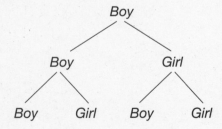

trinomial

Polynomials with exactly three terms are trinomials.

Example

The polynomial $5x^2 - 6x + 9$ is a trinomial.

truth table

A truth table is a table that summarizes all possible truth values for a conditional statement $p \rightarrow q$. The first two columns of a truth table represent all possible truth values for the propositional variables p and q. The last column represents the truth value of the conditional statement $p \rightarrow q$.

Example

The truth value of the conditional statement $p \rightarrow q$ is determined by the truth value of p and the truth value of q.

- If p is true and q is true, then $p \rightarrow q$ is true.
- If p is true and q is false, then $p \rightarrow q$ is false.
- If p is false and q is true, then $p \rightarrow q$ is true.
- If p is false and q is false, then $p \rightarrow q$ is true.

p	q	$p \rightarrow q$
T	T	T
T	F	F
F	T	T
F	F	T

truth value

The truth value of a conditional statement is whether the statement is true or false. If a conditional statement could be true, then the truth value of the statement is considered true. The truth value of a conditional statement is either true or false, but not both.

Example

The truth value of the conditional statement "If a quadrilateral is a rectangle, then it is a square" is false.

two-column proof

A two-column proof is a proof consisting of two columns. In the left column are mathematical statements that are organized in logical steps. In the right column are the reasons for each mathematical statement.

Example

The proof shown is a two-column proof.

Statements	Reasons
1. $\angle 1$ and $\angle 3$ are vertical angles.	**1.** Given
2. $\angle 1$ and $\angle 2$ form a linear pair. $\angle 2$ and $\angle 3$ form a linear pair.	**2.** Definition of linear pair
3. $\angle 1$ and $\angle 2$ are supplementary. $\angle 2$ and $\angle 3$ are supplementary.	**3.** Linear Pair Postulate
4. $\angle 1 \cong \angle 3$	**4.** Congruent Supplements Theorem

two-way frequency table (contingency table)

A two-way frequency table, also called a contingency table, shows the number of data points and their frequencies for two variables. One variable is divided into rows, and the other is divided into columns.

Example

The two-way frequency table shows the hand(s) favored by people who do and do not participate in individual or team sports.

Sports Participation

Favored Hand		Individual	Team	Does Not Play	Total
	Left	3	13	8	24
	Right	6	23	4	33
	Mixed	1	3	2	6
	Total	10	39	14	63

two-way relative frequency table

A two-way relative frequency table displays the relative frequencies for two categories of data.

Example

The two-way relative frequency table shows the hand(s) favored by people who do and do not participate in individual or team sports.

	Individual	Team	Does Not Play	Total
Left	$\frac{3}{63} \approx 4.8\%$	$\frac{13}{63} \approx 20.6\%$	$\frac{8}{63} \approx 12.7\%$	$\frac{24}{63} \approx 38.1\%$
Right	$\frac{6}{63} \approx 9.5\%$	$\frac{23}{63} \approx 36.5\%$	$\frac{4}{63} \approx 6.3\%$	$\frac{33}{63} \approx 52.4\%$
Mixed	$\frac{1}{63} \approx 1.6\%$	$\frac{3}{63} \approx 4.8\%$	$\frac{2}{63} \approx 3.2\%$	$\frac{6}{63} \approx 9.5\%$
Total	$\frac{10}{63} \approx 15.9\%$	$\frac{39}{63} \approx 61.9\%$	$\frac{14}{63} \approx 22.2\%$	$\frac{63}{63} = 100\%$

Glossary

two-way table

A two-way table shows the relationship between two data sets, one data set is organized in rows and the other data set is organized in columns.

Example

The two-way table shows all the possible sums that result from rolling two number cubes once.

2nd Number Cube

1st Number Cube		1	2	3	4	5	6
	1	2	3	4	5	6	7
	2	3	4	5	6	7	8
	3	4	5	6	7	8	9
	4	5	6	7	8	9	10
	5	6	7	8	9	10	11
	6	7	8	9	10	11	12

U

uniform probability model

A uniform probability model occurs when all the probabilities in a probability model are equally likely to occur.

Example

Rolling a number cube represents a uniform probability model because the probability of rolling each number is equal.

V

Venn diagram

A Venn diagram uses circles to show how elements among sets of numbers or objects are related.

Example

Whole numbers 1–10

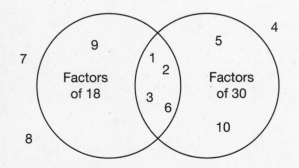

vertex angle of an isosceles triangle

The vertex angle of an isosceles triangle is the angle formed by the two congruent legs.

Example

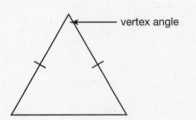

vertex form

A quadratic function written in vertex form is in the form $f(x) = a(x - h)^2 + k$, where $a \neq 0$.

Example

The quadratic equation $y = 2(x - 5)^2 + 10$ is written in vertex form. The vertex of the graph is the point (5, 10).

vertex of a parabola

The vertex of a parabola, which lies on the axis of symmetry, is the highest or lowest point on the parabola.

Example

The vertex of the parabola is the point $(1, -4)$, the minimum point on the parabola.

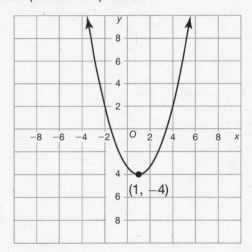

vertical angles

Vertical angles are two nonadjacent angles that are formed by two intersecting lines.

Examples

Angles 1 and 3 are vertical angles.
Angles 2 and 4 are vertical angles.

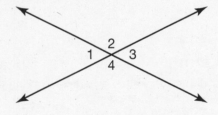

vertical dilation

A vertical dilation of a function is a transformation in which the y-coordinate of every point on the graph of the function is multiplied by a common factor.

Example

The coordinate notation $(x, y) \rightarrow (x, ay)$, where a is the dilation factor, indicates a vertical dilation.

vertical motion model

A vertical motion model is a quadratic equation that models the height of an object at a given time. The equation is of the form $g(t) = -16t^2 + v0t + h0$, where $g(t)$ represents the height of the object in feet, t represents the time in seconds that the object has been moving, $v0$ represents the initial velocity (speed) of the object in feet per second, and $h0$ represents the initial height of the object in feet.

Example

A rock is thrown in the air at a velocity of 10 feet per second from a cliff that is 100 feet high. The height of the rock is modeled by the equation $y = -16t^2 + 10t + 100$.

W

whole numbers

The set of whole numbers consists of the set of natural numbers and the number 0.

Example

The numbers 0, 1, 2, 3, . . . are whole numbers.

Z

Zero Product Property

The Zero Product Property states that if the product of two or more factors is equal to zero, then at least one factor must be equal to zero. This is also called the Converse of Multiplication Property of Zero.

Example

If $(x - 2)(x + 3) = 0$, then $x - 2 = 0$ or $x + 3 = 0$.

zeros

The x-intercepts of a graph of a quadratic function are also called the zeros of the quadratic function.

Example

The zeros of the quadratic function $f(x) = -2x^2 + 4x$ are $(0, 0)$ and $(2, 0)$.

Glossary

Index

A

Absolute maximum
  determining, from graph, 861, 864,
    879, 895
  and form of quadratic function, 894
  interpreting meaning of, 888, 895
  and interval of function, 881
  and range of function, 880
  See also Vertex(–ices)
Absolute minimum
  determining, 863, 864, 895
  interpreting meaning of, 888
  and interval of function, 881
  and range of function, 880
  See also Vertex(–ices)
Acute scalene triangle, 1208
Acute triangles
  altitudes of, 92
  angle bisectors of, 82
  on coordinate plane, 1202
  identifying, 1207
  medians of, 87
  perpendicular bisectors of, 77
  points of concurrency for, 97
  scalene, 1208
Addition
  of arguments vs. functions, 916, 917
  Associative Property of Addition
    for polynomials, 952
    set notation for, 1086, 1089
  closure under, 1078–1081
  Commutative Property of Addition,
    1088, 1089
  with complex numbers, 1106–1110
  Distributive Property of Division over
    Addition, 1087, 1089
  Distributive Property of Multiplication
    over Addition, 1087, 1089
  of polynomials, 951–952, 954–956
Addition Property of Equality, 154
Addition Rule for Probability, 1351
Additive identity, for real numbers,
  1087, 1089
Additive inverse, of real numbers,
  1087, 1089
Adjacent angles, 140–141
Adjacent arcs, 664
Adjacent side
  defined, 569
  of 45°–45°–90° triangles, 569–574
  of 30°–60°–90° triangles, 574–577
Algebra
  for equation of a circle
    to determine center and radius,
      1237–1247
    in standard form vs. in general
      form, 1237–1239

using Pythagorean Theorem,
  1234–1236
with points of concurrency, 98–103
proving Hypotenuse-Leg Congruence
  Theorem with, 425
proving Side-Angle-Side Theorem
  with, 376
Algebraic expressions, simplifying with
  i, 1095
Algebraic method
  of completing the square, 1015
  of determining inverses for linear
    functions, 1155–1156
Algebraic reasoning
  angles of right triangles, 588–589
  proving Pythagorean Theorem
    with, 314
Algebraic solutions
  of polynomials, 950–951
  of systems of equations, 1062–1068
Algebra tiles, modeling multiplication of
  binomials with, 958–963, 968
Alternate Exterior Angle Converse
  Theorem, 186, 189
Alternate Exterior Angle Theorem, 180
Alternate Interior Angle Converse
  Theorem, 186, 188
Alternate Interior Angle Theorem,
  178–179, 269
Altitude, 92–96
  defined, 92
  drawn to hypotenuse of right
    triangles, 304–310
  geometric mean, 307–310
  Right Triangle Altitude/Hypotenuse
    Theorem, 307
  Right Triangle Altitude/Leg
    Theorem, 307
  Right Triangle/Altitude Similarity
    Theorem, 304–306
Angle
  adjacent, 140–141
  bisecting, 57–59
  of circles
    central angle, 656, 662, 663, 665
    inscribed angle, 665–670
    measuring, 676–688
    radian measure, 744–745
  complementary, 137–139
  copying/duplicating, 54–56
  cosecant of, 599
  cosine of, 606
  cotangent of, 589–591
  defined, 52
  included, 280
  inverse cosine of, 612
  inverse sine of, 600

inverse tangent of, 591–593
linear pairs, 142–143
of perpendicular lines, 1192
reference, 569–574
right, 422
of rotation, 340
secant of, 610
sine of, 597
supplementary, 136, 138–139
symbol ($\angle$), 52
tangent of, 584–589
translating on coordinate plane,
  52–54
of triangles
  of congruent triangles, 360
  exterior, 217–223
  interior, remote, 218–219
  interior, side length and,
    213–217
  remote, 218–219
  similar triangles, 264, 268,
    274–281, 283
  spherical triangles, 447
  See also specific types of triangles
vertex, 448
vertical, 144–145
Angle Addition Postulate, 152, 173
Angle-Angle-Angle (AAA), 404
Angle-Angle-Side (AAS) Congruence
  Theorem, 390–399, 406, 408
  congruence statement for,
    397–398
  congruent triangles on coordinate
    plane, 393–395
  constructing congruent triangles,
    390–392
  defined, 390
  proof of, 396
Angle-Angle (AA) Similarity
  Theorem, 283
  defined, 275
  in indirect height measurement, 321
  in indirect width measurement,
    322–324
  similar triangles, 274–276
Angle Bisector/Proportional Side
  Theorem, 286–290
  applying, 288–290
  defined, 286
  proving, 287
Angle bisectors, 57–59, 82–86
Angle of rotation, 340
Angle postulates
  Corresponding Angle Converse
    Postulate, 186–187
  Corresponding Angle Postulate,
    176–178

Cross sections
    area of
        for cylinders, 817–818
        for hemispheres, 819–820
    determining shapes of, 830–836
        cones, 834
        cubes, 832–833
        cylinders, 830
        hexagons, 835
        pentagons, 835
        pyramids, 833
        spheres, 831
Cubes
    cross-section shapes for, 832–833
    difference of two cubes,
        995–996, 998
    sum of two cubes, 997–998
c value
    and graphical behavior of
        function, 1118
    and y-intercept of parabola, 903
Cycles, 1002
Cylinders
    annulus of, 818
    building, 804–806
    cross-section shapes for, 830
    height of, 778, 822, 823
    oblique, 787, 801
    radius of, 822, 823
    right, 787, 789, 801
    as rotation of rectangles, 778
    tranformations for, 792
    from two-dimensional figures
        by stacking, 788
        by translation, 786–787
    volume of, 791, 792, 804–806,
        812–813, 822–823

D

Data, median of, 805
Decimals, repeating, 1083–1084
Deduction
    defined, 121
    identifying, 122–126
Degree
    of polynomials, 945, 947–949
    of products from multiplication of
        binomials, 964
    of terms for polynomials, 944–945,
        947–949
Degree measures
    converting to radian measures, 744
    defined, 662
    of intercepted arcs, 736
    of minor arcs, 736–737
Dependent events, 1320–1323, 1357
    compound probability of
        with "and," 1339
        with "or," 1352–1356
    conditional probability of,
        1422–1426
    on two-way tables, 1397–1398
Dependent quantities
    from problem situations, 1174
    in standard form of quadratic
        functions, 859, 863
    in tables of values, 1154

Diagonals
    of kites, 510, 556
    of parallelograms, 496, 556
    of quadrilaterals, 556
    of rectangles, 486, 488
    of rhombi, 500, 556
    of squares, 484–485
    of three-dimensional solids, 838–844
    two-dimensional, 838
Diagonal translation, of three-
        dimensional figures, 783, 785
Diameter
    of circles, 758
        and chords, 690–694
        as longest chord, 654
        and radius, 653
    of concentric circles, 748–749
    of cones, 780
    of spheres, 816
Diameter–Chord Theorem, 691
Difference of two cubes, 995–996, 998
Difference of two squares, 992–994
Dilation factor, 922
Dilations
    proving similar triangles, 279, 281
    of quadratic functions, 921–924
    of rectangles, 265
    of similar triangles, 260–264,
        266–267
Direct proof, 460
Directrix of a parabola, 1258, 1268,
        1270–1273
Discriminant(s)
    of quadratic equations, 1122
    of Quadratic Formula, 1037–1041, 1118
Discs
    of cylinders, 804
    defined, 779
Disjoint sets, 1319, 1351
Distance
    Angle Bisector/Proportional Side
        Theorem for, 288–290
    on coordinate plane, 18–20, 24
    Distance Formula, 21–23, 1197
    on a graph, 20
    to horizon, 686
    between lines and points not on lines,
        1197–1199
    between points, 18–23
    from three or more points. See Points
        of concurrency
    using Pythagorean Theorem, 21
Distance Formula, 21–23, 1197
Distributive Property, 818
    factoring with, 886
    and greatest common factor, 972, 973
    and imaginary numbers, 1120
    and multiplication of polynomials,
        963, 965–966, 968
    and subtraction of polynomials,
        954–956
    to write quadratic equation in
        standard form, 859
Distributive Property of Division over
        Addition, 1087, 1089
Distributive Property of Division over
        Subtraction, 1087, 1089

Distributive Property of Multiplication
        over Addition, 1087, 1089
Distributive Property of Multiplication
        over Subtraction, 1087, 1089
Division
    and associative properties, 1086
    closure under, 1079–1081
    and commutative properties, 1086
    with complex numbers,
        1111–1112
    Distributive Property of Division over
        Addition, 1087, 1089
    Distributive Property of Division over
        Subtraction, 1087, 1089
Domain
    describing, 880, 882–883
    determining, from inverse functions,
        1172
    of functions vs. other relations, 1152
    and inverse of quadratic function,
        1170, 1171
    in linear piecewise functions, 1135,
        1136, 1139, 1143
    restricting the, 1172–1176
Dot paper, 782
Double roots, 1040, 1122
Draw (geometric figures), 8
Duplicating
    an angle, 55–56
    a line segment
        with an exact copy, 31–33
        with circles, 27–31

E

Element (of a set), 1319
    combinations of, 1442–1445
    repeated, permutations with,
        1435–1439
Elliptic geometry, 149
Endpoint(s)
    of angles, 52, 54
    and graphing inequalities, 1143
    in greatest and least integer
        functions, 1149, 1150
    inclusion of, in step functions,
        1145, 1148
    of a line segment, 11, 26
    of a ray, 10
Equality
    Addition Property of, 154
    Subtraction Property of, 155
Equal symbol (=), 12
Equidistant Chord Converse Theorem,
        694
Equidistant Chord Theorem, 693
Equilateral triangles
    altitudes of, 95
    angle bisectors of, 85
    constructing, 68
    on coordinate plane, 1203
    defined, 13
    exterior angles of polygons, 544
    medians of, 90
    perpendicular bisectors of, 80
Equivalent functions, graphs of, 961
Error, in indirect measurement, 319
Euclid, 148

Index

entering inequality symbols in, 1147
factoring with, 973
graphing step functions with,
    1147–1148, 1150
multiplying binomials with, 960
selecting CBR data for analysis
    on, 1049
setting up CBR with, 1045
table function on, 951
value function on, 951
See also Calculator-based ranger
    (CBR)
Graphs
decreasing, 861
determining inverses of non-linear
    functions with, 1166–1169
of equivalent functions, 961
increasing, 861
linear functions
    piecewise, 1134–1135, 1138–1139,
      1143
    quadratic function graphs vs.,
      871–872, 874–875
    polynomials, and algebraic solutions,
      950–951
    quadratic equations, and solutions,
      1039, 1117
    quadratic functions
      analyzing, 860–861, 863
      and *a*-value, 890–891
      comparing, 864
      determining *x*-intercepts from,
        879–880, 882–883
      determining *y*-intercept from,
        882–883
      functions with multiple
        transformations, 923–925
      linear function graphs vs., 871–872,
        874–875
      and solutions, 1039
      zeros and *x*-intercepts of
        graph, 880
    quadratic motion
      identifying inequalities with, 1055
      predicting features of, 1044
      quadratic regression, 1048–1050,
        1052
      replicating trajectory similar
        to, 1051
    step functions
      analyzing, 1147, 1148
      of greatest and least integer
        functions, 1148–1150
    verifying products of binomials with,
      961–962
Great circle of a sphere, 816
Greatest common factor
factoring polynomials with,
    972–973, 981
of quadratic functions, 886–887
Greatest integer function (floor function),
    1148, 1150

H

Half-closed intervals, 881
Half-open intervals, 881
Height

of cones, 780, 817
of cylinders, 778, 822, 823
of hemispheres, 819, 820
indirect measurement of, 318–321
linear functions for, 866–867
of prisms, 813
of solid figures, 812
Hemispheres, 819
defined, 816
height of, 819, 820
Hertz (unit), 1002
Hexagons
cross-section shapes for, 835
exterior angles of, 542, 544, 548
interior angles of, 535–538
Hinge Converse Theorem, 464–467
Hinge Theorem, 462–463
Horizontal lines, 1195–1196
identifying, 1195–1196
reflections over, 919, 920
writing equations for, 1196
Horizontal translation, 25, 26
of angles, 53
of quadratic functions, 917–918, 920,
    923, 925
of three-dimensional figures, 783
h variable, in vertex form, 907
Hyperbolic geometry, 149
Hypotenuse
of 45°–45°–90° triangles, 237, 569–574
of right triangles, altitudes drawn to,
    304–310
of 30°–60°–90° triangles, 246,
    574–577
Hypotenuse-Angle (HA) Congruence
    Theorem, 429–430
Hypotenuse-Leg (HL) Congruence
    Theorem, 422–426
Hypotheses
of conditional statement, 128
conjectures as, 176
defined, 128
rewriting, 132–133

I

i. See Imaginary numbers
Image
of angles, 54
defined, 24–26
of line segments, 25–26
pre-image same as, 54
Imaginary double roots, 1122
Imaginary numbers *(i)*, 1091–1095
defined, 1093, 1100
numbers and expressions in set
    of, 1097
polynomials with, 1107–1110
powers of, 1092–1094, 1100–1103
pure, 1096, 1104
and real numbers, 1096
set of, 1104
simplifying expressions involving,
    1094–1095
Imaginary part of a complex number,
    1096, 1104
Imaginary roots, 1117
Imaginary zeros

calculating, 1119–1120
defined, 1117
Incenter
algebra used to locate, 99
constructing, 82–86
defined, 86
Included angle, 280
Included side, 280
Independent events, 1320–1323, 1357
compound probability of
    with "and," 1339
    with "or," 1346–1351
conditional probability of,
    1422–1426
multiple trials of two, 1453–1465
    using combinations, 1455–1462
    using formula for, 1463–1465
Rule of Compound Probability
    involving "and," 1336
two trials of two, 1450–1452
on two-way tables, 1397, 1398
Independent quantities
from problem situations, 1174
in standard form of quadratic
    functions, 859, 863
in tables of values, 1154
Indirect measurement, 318–324
defined, 318
of height, 318–321
of width, 322–324
Indirect proof (proof by contradiction),
    460–461
Hinge Converse Theorem,
    464–467
Hinge Theorem, 462–463
Tangent to a Circle Theorem, 684
Indivisibles, method of, 799
Induction
defined, 121
identifying, 122–126
Inequalities
graphing, 1143
linear piecewise functions with,
    1142–1145
quadratic
    identifying, on graphs, 1055
    intervals as solutions to,
      1056–1057
    solving, with number line,
      1056, 1057
    solving, with Quadratic Formula,
      1053–1060
symbols for, in graphing
    calculator, 1147
Inscribed angles (circles), 656,
    665–670
Inscribed Angle Theorem, 667–670
Inscribed figures
parallelograms, 1229
polygons, 724–727, 765–770
quadrilaterals, 729–730
squares, 763, 1228
triangles, 724–727
Inscribed Right Triangle–Diameter
    Converse Theorem, 727
Inscribed Right Triangle–Diameter
    Theorem, 725–726

Index

Index

Index

Index

Index